The Farmer, the Plough and the Devil

The Story of Fordhall Farm

ARTHUR HOLLINS

The Farmer, the Plough and the Devil

The Story of Fordhall Farm

ILLUSTRATED BY
BARBARA VINCENT

ASHGROVE PRESS, BATH

The author offers his sincere thanks to
Graham Rose for his invaluable help
in the writing of this book

Published in Great Britain by
ASHGROVE PRESS LTD
19 Circus Place
Bath, Avon BA1 2PW

©Arthur Hollins 1984, 1986

ISBN 0 906798 69 8

First published 1984
First paperback edition 1986

British Library Cataloguing in Publication Data:
Hollins, Arthur
The farmer, the plough and the devil:
the story of Fordhall Farm.
I. Country life- England- Shropshire- History-
20th century   2. Shropshire- Social life
and customs
I. Title
942.4'5082'0924   S522.G7

Typeset in Garamond by
Ann Buchan (Typesetters)
Walton-on-Thames, Surrey
Printed by Redwood Burn Ltd
Trowbridge, Wiltshire

Dedicated to my wife May,
whose love and enthusiasm
made all our achievements possible

CONTENTS

CHAPTER ONE

The Spoils of War

I can still hear the ring of Betty's elated 'They're here, they're here', as she shouted through the kitchen door and then disappeared again. Joan, the other maid, had been making beds. The thud of her feet, as she pounded down the stairs upset baby Margaret who was slowly stirring her mess of bread and milk on the table in front of her high chair. She had barely begun to scream by the time Joan, too, had disappeared through the back door. Aunt Edith, tutting her disapproval, moved to comfort Margaret and nearly tripped over Gladys and me as we slid down from our seats at the table and scurried after them.

By the time we reached the yard, the gently wheezing Foden had come to a halt and Joan was confirming to a sergeant, with a moustache which made him look more severe than Kitchener, that it was indeed Fordhall Farm.

While the maids regarded the sergeant with evident admiration, Gladys and I stared at the lorry. Lorries were rare in Shropshire at the time and usually meant the military. To Betty and Joan, who were still in their teens, soldiers meant excitement and a different, more worldly brand of teasing that they suffered from the men about the farm.

'Right lads, out,' the sergeant barked. The response was a deep groan as twenty reluctant looking Tommies began to clamber over the tailboard. They'd been potato picking in the district every day for weeks. Their hands were cracked and worn from groping in the soil. Their backs still ached from the previous day's arduous bending to lift the tubers into baskets. One of them said to Joan that he'd joined the army to fight the Hun in France and all he'd done was fire ten rounds of rifle ammunition on a practice range and pick potatoes.

However, the presence of the girls stimulated them and they began to joke as they took off their hard caps, greatcoats and khaki tunics. Being female, Gladys captured her share of attention and was soon shrieking with delight and straddling one of the Tommy's shoulders.

I was more timid and slunk behind the lorry to examine its strange spoked wheels and solid tyres. My hope was that I'd escape the notice of the stern sergeant. But, marching imperiously round to put his greatcoat in the lorry cab, he brushed roughly against me and knocked me over. Before I began to cry, he'd picked me up and brushed the litter from my clothes. Through drying tears I saw something sparkling in the giant palm of his out-stretched hand. Since I was hesitant he thrust it towards me saying, 'Go on then, lad, it's a souvenir'. For years afterwards I thought all souvenirs resembled the bright brass regimental button which he'd given me.

Stripped for work, with their short cropped hair and flannel collarless shirts, the soldiers looked strangely buccolic. Even Joan and Betty clearly found that they'd lost some of their glamour, and yielded to Aunt Edith's command to return to housework.

My father, who'd been busy round the stables when the soldiers arrived, looked at them doubtfully when he came to announce that all was ready. But he was happier when he saw how quickly they responded to the sergeant's order to mount the waggons and move off to the field.

Remembering the soldiers at Fordhall, Aunt Edith told me much later how tall they had seemed in comparison with my father. According to Aunt Edith, he responded to the challenge to his authority which their size and numbers seemed to represent by an initial curtness. This soon turned into a patronizing attitude towards both the sergeant and his men as he discovered their unfamiliarity with rural life. However, not even the sergeant seemed to resent my father's adoption of command, because he swung Gladys and me from each hand with great gaiety as we tried to keep pace with him when he stalked from the farmyard and climbed the steep hill of Villa Field to meet the men in the carts who had come round by the road along our farm boundary.

When father saw how well the men worked, he became much more friendly. They picked in the wake of our foreman, Jack, who split the furrows in which the potatoes had been grown with a digging plough. I was fascinated by the way the soil was thrown laterally from the large double-sided ploughshare like water from the prow of a ship. Progress, as the mammoth Clydesdale horse tugged the implement through the ground, was accompanied by a faint hissing as it smashed its way through the dried relics of the potato stems.

Once it had passed, the still, slightly sharp October air became impregnated with the musky odour of freshly turned soil. It must be one of the most poignant of all smells to anyone who has ever worked on the land; with a quality which no chemist would ever be able to capture. Whenever I smell it now, I see again the eager hands plunging earthwards to clutch the newly exposed potatoes, as though plundering the eggs in an underground nest of some strange reptile. Then, I just delighted in the surprising brilliance of the tubers as they lay revealed on the dark freshly turned soil. And, for a while, I joined the men starting to flick them into enormous wicker-work baskets which creaked and chuckled as they settled and filled.

Doubtless to divert my attention and prevent me from being crushed beneath his soldiers' boots, the sergeant, who still wore cap and tunic and issued directions with his stub of Malacca cane, sat me on the shaft of one of the high sided carts. Even today, when I see one of those carts stuck away in the nettles behind a farm shed, it impresses me more than almost anything I've ever seen on a farm. I'm a small man, and the sheer scale of their wheels is over-awing. Some of them were over eight feet in diameter, to make traction easy on soft land.

The iron gadgetry used for the attachment of harness, tail-boards, etc. provided endless tackle for imaginative games. Its rapid metalic jingling as the carts were tugged ponderously across the field contrasted brightly with the slower rhythmic groans as they lurched from side to side. Perhaps time has distorted memory, but the groans from the carts always seemed to grow louder as their load increased. And when father was about that was always accomplished rapidly.

Aunt Edith said that even the sergeant had been amazed by the speed with which my father seemed to move about the field or from the field to the farmyard and back. He made certain that picking was never held up for want of empty baskets. And even I remember that I could tell where he was the moment I saw a ten foot high cylinder of stacked baskets staggering in front of a group of picking soldiers.

There were no sophisticated, air-conditioned potato stores at that time. Potatoes from baskets were tipped into the cart and then trundled to a clamp at the top of the field near a gate. High land was always chosen for the clamp site to ensure good drainage in winter. When a long, shallow, trough had been dug out it was thickly carpeted with straw. Potatoes from the carts were tipped onto this base and built into a high, triangular-sectioned mound. When a clamp was full, the potatoes were covered with a thick cladding of straw to protect them from the frost and the clamp itself was sealed with soil. Well built, a clamp resembled the tumulus of an ancient and important prince. Certainly a relic, which I'd already begun to treasure, was buried in the 1918 Fordhall clamp. For most of the first morning of picking I'd carried the regimental button in my trouser pocket. I'd shown it to no-one. But from time to time I'd secretly fondled it. After Gladys and I had become bored with watching the picking, we had rolled about in the straw of the clamp bottom. Clearly the button must have been lost during the game. Because by lunchtime it had gone.

I was afraid to mention it in case the fierce sergeant became angry. But I couldn't muster much appetite for the crusty fresh bread or great hunks of our cheese which Joan and Betty happily carried out to the field for the joy of seeing the soldiers again.

I suppose that, someday, that button might be ploughed up again in Villa field. However, it won't be in my time because I'll never have the field ploughed so deeply. It's a pity, because it shone so brightly and I can't even remember what it depicted.

I do, however, remember that to Joan and Betty's delight the soldiers returned for several days until the picking was completed. For them it must have been a period of endless titillation. I remember not understanding why, when Aunt Edith was out of the kitchen, they giggled so convulsively together and discreetly showed each other the marks on their buttocks where they'd been pinched. It seemed that the sergeant, who by retaining his uniform had kept his allure, was capable of offering many sorts of souvenir.

When he drove away with his men for the last time the girls became very subdued. But my father was quite jubilant. It had been his record harvest and the crop had all been put safely in the clamp without the usual breaks for bad weather. I was lurking about the stable watching Jack quietly rub down the horses with a handful of straw to wipe away the sweat and dirt of the day when my father came whistling chirpily through the door. When he saw Jack, he stopped and grinned: 'There must be more than seventy tons in that clamp, Jack.' Jack, the foreman, just grunted and, dropping the straw, began to work on the horses with a hard brush. 'I told you that extra fertiliser would pay dividends.'

Jack remained silent but I noticed him frowning. Father laughed tauntingly and, taking the fork he'd come to fetch, went out again. Jack turned and looked as though he was about to shout something. But seeing me he just tutted and continued with his work.

CHAPTER TWO

The Master Bedroom

I remember little but conflict between my father and Jack. Temperamentally, they were so ill-adjusted that anything closer than a master/servant relationship would hardly have been possible.

I have no doubt that my father had the profoundest respect for Jack's abilities as a country craftsman. But, from the first moment that I was conscious, it was clear that Jack disapproved of my father's farming methods, which he always considered slipshod and too opportunist.

However, there was more to divide them than Jack's intuitive respect for the land on which he had been born. Before my father arrived at Fordhall, my ailing grandfather had relied daily more upon Jack for the running of the farm. He had become the master as far as the men were concerned. But, when my father appeared, he lost that authority.

My widowed maternal grandfather was considered unblessed. His wife had born him no sons – a farming tragedy when boys were always required to continue working the land. Instead, he had two daughters – my mother, the eldest, and Aunt Edith.

So that when Alfred Hollins, from over the county boundary near Nantwich in Cheshire, came courting to Fordhall, he received a grateful and effusive welcome. As a younger son in a farming family, he'd have had to play a subservient role at home. That wouldn't have pleased a man dissatisfied with anything second rate – someone quite confident that his talents merited the master's place.

However, my grandfather was grateful that young Hollins was free and had sufficient experience on a dairy farm to be able to take over the running of Fordhall shortly after marrying my mother in 1912.

The 1915-1918 war was clearly the epoch of my father's greatest activity at Fordhall. Three children in just over three years, and bumper crops harvested and sold, must have kept him at home most of the time. Certainly, the records show that he responded well to the government's call for increased farm output to beat the German U-boat blockade. Too well, it became obvious later.

Just before the Kaiser's war, Fordhall had been a typical Welsh Marches' mixed dairy farm. Much of the land was in permanent pasture to provide winter hay and summer grazing for a dozen cows, a small flock of sheep, some young stock and the few bullocks which were fattened for beef. The lowland by the river could only be used for grazing and some haymaking in summer, when it had dried out sufficiently to carry the stock.

Most of the higher land was also devoted to meadows, but, from time to time, it was ploughed and sown in a rotation of crops — barley (for the cows), oats (for the horses), turnips (for the cows in winter) — in succeeding years, before being sown in grass again.

In good seasons, more oats and barley were produced than were required to feed the stock and they were sold to supplement income. The principle earner was the cheese made by my mother in the dairy. Exquisite mellow, tangy, fifty-six pound barrels of Cheshire cheese, when matured at Fordhall, found a good market in the nearby town of Market Drayton. A few breeding sows in the stys thrived on whey and skimmed milk from the dairy.

Potatoes grow well in light sandy soils and occasionally a few acres of the highland were planted with this crop. Since they store well and can be consumed directly by man, they were the crop which Fordhall could most easily expand to help in Britain's food production drive. Therefore, during the war, many more acres of the higher land than normal were ploughed for potatoes.

Although it might seem strange now, no one then would have questioned my father's obligation to continue supporting Aunt Edith or allowing her to continue living at home until she was married. Of course she realised she must pay for that support by helping with all the work. Happily, Aunt Edith's presence at Fordhall caused little friction. A plump, boisterous and extrovert person, she had a good sense of humour and a mammoth capacity for work. She acted as a perfect foil to my mother.

Mother was slighter and more thoughtful — the planner and thinker in the family. The good taste and the delicacy which was reflected in her dress, exquisite needlework and sense of refinement in decoration, became invaluable assets in her dairy activities. She knew intuitively when to cease churning butter or just how to manipulate the complex processes during which milk is converted into cheese; processes which change subtly with the season and the quality of the milk. That made her one of Shropshire's finest cheesemakers.

While she was fostering this reputation, Aunt Edith swept Fordhall along with the gusto she employed when wielding a broom. Too feckless a personality to schedule her tasks, she was never happier than when faced with an immediate challenge. A mountain of dough to knead when breadmaking, acres of floor tiles to mop or a gigantic heap of dirty dishes to wash were, for Aunt Edith, a chance to bustle her power-packed muscles into activity. The noisy effort often made a quiff of hair fall irritatingly across her eyes which she repeatedly tried to replace by extending her lower lip and puffing — a gesture which comically contorted her normally placid round face. Almost as part of her other household chores, she coped ably with her ailing father, who died quite soon after my parents married.

So, with someone so dependable about the house, there was nothing to prevent my parents from starting a family quickly. The arrival of Gladys, born in May 1914, must have made my father wonder whether Fordhall induced the exclusive conception of girls. To reassure himself, he tried again and I was born just over a year later. Like a harbinger of peace, Margaret arrived in late 1917 and was barely walking when the armistice was announced.

We were all born in this master bedroom where I write. My mother's grandparents first occupied it. Their descendants, whom I knew, mother and Aunt Edith, my two sisters, myself and my children were born in the four-poster bed which I can reach if I turn round. From it, all of them have gazed at the simple but refined stucco frieze round the edge of the ceiling. Its thread of rose foliage, thickened by years of whitening and thought to be contemporary with the brick-and-timber Tudor section of the house, has garlanded our joy in health or wreathed our sorrow in sickness and death.

In and out of that low-lintelled, skull-thudding, oak-panelled door beyond the bed people have rushed in sadness or pleasure to make announcements which have punctuated our family saga; oak boards, thick enough to tolerate generations of angry slamming, but too ill-fitting to completely muffle the turbulent words of parents in argument or prevent distress in frightened, prying children.

I find it mysteriously comforting to shut myself in a room containing objects which have been known to my ancestors. In it I feel intimately bound to tradition. And since the master bedroom at Fordhall has been a second womb to my family, it's here that I have always come to make the important decisions.

There are certainly less draughty and more convenient rooms at Fordhall. But none of them is really better placed for the Master of the farm because, with the exception of two flat fields behind the house, much of the land can be seen from its window. It's a view which I still find as beautiful and appealing as any I have known. I'm as uncritical about it as any ardent lover about the woman he worships.

And certainly no lover could bestow more affection or attention upon his mistress than I have upon the foreground, which is the land I farm. It's been in turn ungrateful, capricious, unyielding — almost taunting, frequently infuriating, never easy or servile. But, like all worthwhile women, when ultimately seduced, wonderfully rewarding.

There is something about its shape which suggests husbandry. Reminiscent of the iron shoes of oxen which I often kick up when walking ploughed fields, the arc of light, high land surrounds low, damp meadows beside the idling Tern river. Quite early I recognised the shoes' message. Men didn't plough land with oxen unless they believed in its fertility. One of the earliest of them must have been the Romano-British squire who liked the view and sited his house nearby in Villa field where such a fine crop of potatoes was harvested.

However, when my turn came to farm Fordhall, a lot had happened to the land which I had to understand before I could benefit by its ultimate promise. My father must have been responsible for most of the changes which would have baffled the retired centurion.

While the bumper wartime harvests lead to prosperity at Fordhall, my parents became increasingly worried about my health. I'd turned out to be a disappointing boy; something of a runt. As a baby, I took copious milk from my mother and often rejected it. At times I would hardly feed at all.

Soon after I was born my parents had little hope that I'd survive. And this anxiety continued when I'd been weaned onto cow's milk from a bottle and was starting to take some solid food. For a period during my second and third years I began to improve. But shortly after the 1918 potato harvest I became sickly again.

This pattern of bursts of healthy energy alternating with periods of being a semi-invalid persisted throughout my childhood.

I don't suppose that I'll ever know what confined me so often to this bedroom at Fordhall during those years. As a dairy farmer, I find it hard to accept that I might have been unable to digest certain products in fresh whole milk. But, I'm obliged to admit the possibility.

Because I was born before herds were tested for the presence of brucellosis (which can also attack and lead to death in men), it is possible that while still a baby I contracted a very mild infection of that disease. If I did, it hasn't produced the debilitating long-term symptoms suffered by many brucellosis victims.

Since my father was small I suppose that genetically I was preordained not to be a giant. Although now, in my sixties, I'm rather pleased to be small and very thin, my lack of stature was a dreadful handicap during childhood and youth. I'd probably never have been tall, but my extreme thinness must have stemmed from the slow growth rhythms imposed by my early illnesses. Later they meant that I was an easy target for bullying masters at school and that it was harder to command respect from the grown men I was destined to direct while still in my teens. As a young child they led to hours of confinement in this room.

Since I was frequently prevented from playing out of doors with my sisters, I was forced to rely more than most people on my own company. In consequence, I became more introverted than many children. That was something which developed into an excessive shyness with strangers, which took twenty years to overcome.

When I was fit enough to escape the sick room, instead of seeking companionship in the village, I roamed alone about our land and became fascinated by its abundant wild life. If I'd had the misfortune to have been born in a town, my early confinement could have been stultifying. But at Fordhall I was always surrounded by beauty and exciting prompts to the imagination. Much which I failed to learn from society or at school, I probably acquired in another way from the master bedroom and the landscape beyond its window.

Certainly the leather-bound 19th-century family bible, which stood upon the chest, introduced me to worlds remote from Shropshire. Its illustrations were wonderfully uncompromising. A frowning bearded Moses looked like the wrath of God as he pounded out his fateful message to the Israelites. The slightly pained expression on the face of a Victorian Jesus, the sort of face a stroke at Henley or a century maker at Lords might have possessed, suggested that no-one who wasn't prepared to accept the Gospel in its entirety could hope to be considered a good Englishman or a worthy servant of his monarch.

While discouraging questions on faith, my mother used the bible to stretch my mental and geographical horizons. When I was ill, as often as possible during her working days in the dairy, she'd slip quietly into my room. In contrast to the mild hysteria of a visit from my father, mother's visits seemed to induce a wonderful serenity. Pretending to have dashed in to see me, my father would in reality be searching for something he'd imagined he'd left in the wardrobe or the chest. While noisily slamming doors or closing drawers, he'd recount some comic incident which had taken place in the yard.

Mother didn't joke as often. If she teased a little, her pale blue eyes acquired an exceptional sparkle which was immediately reassuring. She probably felt that we children needed one parent whose reactions didn't vary. Perhaps even then she was beginning to worry about my father's unpredictable behaviour. For despite his normal cheeriness, he occasionally had bouts of seemingly unjustified irascibility. Mother's rare outbursts of impatience with him were usually answered by a laugh and didn't seem much different from the occasional tempers our own minor misbehaviour provoked. And her fine features soon returned to their usual composure.

Despite her thin face, she was one of those lucky people whose generous lips in repose always seemed to be smiling. As the invalid, I was the major beneficiary of that warmth.

A year older, Gladys needed far less support. She'd been a large baby and had progressed rapidly. By the time she was four, she was truly robust and with no malice, in boisterous play, she often sent me sprawling. In consequence, she was only allowed to remain in my sick room when accompanied by my mother, Aunt Edith or the maids. Weary of hours spent alone in bed, I welcomed her visits, but they usually had to be curtailed when the excitement made me flush and become feverish.

Margaret, although she grew well, was only recently weaned and was a much calmer child. She maintained the grave facade we all joked about later and which always remained an integral part of her character.

However, both Gladys and Margaret could dip into Mother's deep well of comfort when it was needed. And it is difficult to decide whether it was my good luck or misfortune which made me draw upon it most. Certainly it meant that I spent most time alone with her and came to know her best. In view of our need to make vital joint decisions in the future, it probably benefitted the family that I should have received the largest share of my mother's attention in childhood.

Since every time I glance at the family bible, I recapture a vision of my mother, it is not surprising that it's my most cherished heirloom. It's the weight which prompts the strongest memories. While I had to struggle to move it on and off my lap in bed, my mother handled it with the dexterity of a bookworm flipping through a paperback.

Each page, as it was turned, seemed to inject the room with a puff of the glue size and leather aroma which the bible still retains.

Sadly, I can't reproduce in this room the other element with which, in those days, the bible aroma became quickly mixed. It was the light, faintly sweet odour of whey which always clung to my mother's overall and nut brown hair when she returned from the dairy to brighten my days. As she turned the pages, reading the captions, she'd lean across to point out the characters or make me examine the animals and vegetation of strange lands. She introduced me then to my first camels, palm trees, sand dunes and mountain lions. Turbanned oriental men and mysterious veiled women, who lived in tents beside oases and resembled nothing I'd ever seen in Market Drayton, were all revealed to me as she elaborated the detail of their lives. I first became conscious of the courses of the Nile, the Tigris, and the Euphrates or the location of Niniveh,

Babylon or Nazareth, when she pointed them out on the decorative map of the Holy Lands. Of course, I was far too young fully to comprehend the significance of much of what she tried to impart, but at the time I was quite certain of one thing; all those animals, plants, places and people smelt deliciously of freshly separated whey.

However, confinement in the master bedroom wasn't restricted to periods of ill health. It served as a punishment cell as well as a clinic. Then, the window and everything beyond meant release. Staring at it now, I see that the putty which retains the glass is falling out again. I can never remember it being intact for more than a few months at a time. The problem is the ivy. It always wins in the end. Of course, it's supposed to be very bad for bricks and masonry. But it's undeniably pretty. And the family have always been reluctant to tear it down. So over the years it has spread over much of the facade and at times threatened to obliterate windows. Only constant pruning has allowed the view from the bedroom to remain.

Whenever the ivy was clipped, the putty would be replaced and for a while, on still days the room would cradle the aroma of linseed oil. The same smell sometimes dominated the stables when a horse had been unwell and linseed was included in the steaming hot 'tonic' mash which it was fed.

By the time the ivy had recovered from its trimming, the putty would have dried and cracked and, frequently helped by the idle fingers of brooding children, would have fallen away sufficiently to allow the young tendrils to begin their insidious invasion again.

I suspect that I was absent-mindedly trying to dig a fingernail beneath a fragment of dried putty when I first became aware of the whole micro world of the old trough. Rough hewn out of a block of local stone it still stands below the window. Someone, I think my uncle Tom in one of his few less gruff moments, told me that it was a coffin of an ancient warrior. If it's true, then as a small boy I must have imagined him as a giant. Because, what today appears as a pretty garden feature, then, when I could just peer over its worn edge, seemed like a gigantic lake.

There was always a cluster of kingcups at one end. Today their bright yellow flowers and gently swaying underwater stems remind me of the pre-Raphaelite garland and languid tresses of the drowned Ophelia. When a child, seen in profile from my low angle, they seemed like an exotic floating forest; a constant puzzle because other, more familiar plants, grew on land. I can still feel the slime of the green and brown algae on my hands and the ache of the muscles in my back and legs as I clung to the rim of the trough and strained to glance into its murky depths. The frustration of being confronted with masking reflections of clouds, the sun or my own face in the surface of the placid water, was constant. I remember vividly one day slapping at the water in indignation, messing up my clothes and being dragged away howling by Aunt Edith. However, even she, who was usually too busy to stop and answer infantile questions, paused from her eternal polishing and followed me out to the trough on the day I spotted movement in the water from the window and rushed downstairs to investigate. She held me aloft by the armpits to give me a better view of the tadpoles which had attracted my attention from above. Showing me the gelatinous spawn in a corner of the trough, she explained about frogs and in the following days she patiently lifted me up to follow the tadpoles' progress. It was my first biology lesson, the first introduction to the humbling mystery of nature.

For a while I was allowed to keep a tiny fully fledged frog in a jam jar of water and weed set on the ground next to the trough. My grief, when one morning I found that it had gone was almost inconsolable; worth at least the chocolate finger biscuit that Aunt Edith miraculously discovered in a tin. Having watched the progress from egg to adult and even seen a surprised frog leap down from the trough's rim and disappear into the vegetable garden, I understood how something developing in the pond could move away. What I still find somewhat remarkable is how the adult frogs, faced with a challenge of mountaineering more daunting than the North Face of the Eiger, ever managed to get into the trough to lay their spawn in the first place.

As a boy, I used to fight sleep at dusk trying to witness the ascent. And even today, when I stroll round the garden before bed, I still glance expectantly at the trough, hoping it will reveal the secret.

Once the frog had displayed the trough's potential for excitement and I was large enough to float sticks, to mimic boats, on its surface, it occupied much of my time on fine days when I was fit but still too young to be allowed to wander further.

I began dimly to realize that what appeared as a still pond was a seething mass of life, which changed perceptibly with the seasons. The slime wasn't just dirt earning me the title 'mucky pup'. It comprised a myriad variety of primitive organisms all flourishing and declining in harmony with the temperature of the water and the length and intensity of the daylight. Apart from the wriggling tadpoles there were, as the summer progressed, tiny bewhiskered mosquito larvae which either hung motionless from the surface of the water with their breathing tubes protruding or performed an erratic jackknifing ballet when disturbed by a prodding finger. But they were easier to catch than the darting pond skaters which skimmed the surface with more agility than any man on ice.

It wasn't long before trophies from the trough, safe from sisters and grumbling maids, in jars on my window ledge, lead me to realize that more of the murk in the water was alive. Just before the contents of the jars became totally foetid and it was hurled in disgust from the window by Aunt Edith, Joan or Betty, I'd be entranced by the slow motion on the wall of the jar. But it was only later that a toy microscope permitted me to see clearly the amorphous amoeba flowing round particles of organic matter in the thick water, or to appreciate the extraordinary beautiful forms of the filamentous spirogyra and the acrobatic hydra.

The trough didn't always provide only beauty and excitement. There was tragedy as well. Small toys fell from inattentive hands and disappeared in its turbid depths. Preoccupied adults often postponed their rescue until they'd been forgotten.

More bitter was the regret for Freddie. An almost albino carp, he'd been won one summer's evening, when Fred, the waggoner, and Bill, the cowman, took Joan and Betty to a fair which had arrived in Market Drayton. It was almost dark when they returned, jubilant. Fred's prowess in smashing clay pipes with .22 air rifle pellets had merited extra beer in celebration. The men were boisterous and loud voiced and the girls' giggles very shrill.

They must have awakened Aunt Edith and me simultaneously because I heard her shouting at them angrily. By the time I reached the window they were just realizing that their pride wasn't shared. Aunt Edith, always demure and reluctant to be seen in her nightdress and hair rollers, hadn't waited to examine the fish in the jam jar of water which Fred was holding aloft. Afraid of further trouble, the maids and Bill disappeared round the back of the house. Looking like a victim of gross ingratitude, Fred poured the contents of the jar into the trough and followed. By the time I crept down to the trough side next morning, 'Freddie', as the fish had been christened by one of the girls on the way home, seemed to have adapted well to his new habitat.

Although I agreed with Fred, who several times sought confirmation that he was a 'beauty', Freddie wasn't very big at first. However, through the rest of that summer, nourished I suppose on a banquet of mosquito larvae and weed, he thrived splendidly. Sadly, I was not alone in noticing this.

One late autumn afternoon – it must have been in 1920 because I'd started to attend Morton Saye village school – I was just arriving home with Gladys, when we were surprised to see a heron ponderously rising above the house. Jack, who'd been crossing the orchard, stood with us to watch as it climbed for a moment or two and then, holding its enormous wings rigid, it slid to the left in an accelerating glide towards its beat by the river. When it had disappeared behind the trees, Jack stood for a moment longer, clearly worried about how to make his announcement.

'Well, did you ever'. He paused and cleared his throat, realizing that I was unaware of what had happened. 'I'll fetch my shotgun to him if I see him hanging about here again. I suppose you saw he had that fish of yours in his beak?'

Regretting that he'd announced the upsetting news so tactlessly he grabbed my hand and dragged me round to the trough.

'We'd better see that he hasn't pinched that lead cow which you lost in there last week.'

He was obviously relieved when he found it trapped among the kingcup fronds. For he was right in presuming that its discovery would help me to forget 'Freddie's' fate.

It wasn't much of a dialogue really. I'd only registered my amazement, shock and sadness with my eyes and urged out a grateful 'thanks' when he found the cow from my farmyard set. But what he said to me probably amounted to his greatest verbal offering until I was well into my teens. Rarely voluble, unless roused, he was just as shy and self-contained as me. I think he knew that I found him quite a fearsome figure despite the fact that I was fascinated by his cap.

Like all good headgear it was very old and moulded both to his skull and by his work. A vital scrap of comfort in the wet and wind of winter (there were no heated tractor cabs then) and protection from the sun in summer, its peak was asymetrically flattened to his forehead. Its once speckled Donegal tweed had become a uniform greasy grey on the side where he'd leaned on the flank of a cow while working as a milker when he first began to work for my grandfather.

Instead of being round in plan like caps today, Jack's ancient Donegal was initially octagonal and originally very smart. But, by the time I first became aware of it most of the the initial form had gone. I was, however, conscious when it lost its final modish feature – a central covered button, the size of a florin, which was also octagonal. That came off in my presence as Jack was entering the stable carrying two buckets of water. He saw a rat creeping along the top rail of the hay rack above a horse's head. Quietly, posing the buckets, he snatched off his cap and hurled it at the rat. The only victim of the incident was the button. But its disappearance markedly changed Jack's allure.

It had seemed to balance the drop of moisture which habitually hovered on the end of his nose. Although it was broad and patrician, Jack always had trouble with that nose. As soon as he exerted himself at all, it began to dribble. Since for ten hours most days he was always actively engaged in something, it seemed as though he had a perpetual cold. It could, I suppose, have been an additional way of sweating out the gallons of ale which were his only indulgence outside his passion for gardening. Although later I found Jack's dew drop endearing, as a child it made him appear even more strange and frightening. Compelled to gaze at it and speculate upon whether it would fall free before he had time to brush it away with his sleeve, I always felt guilty when he caught me staring. His brooding brown eyes, which always seemed to be pondering matters of great moment, were to me his most daunting feature. He wasn't a very tall man, but he was as solid as the pillars in a Norman Church. A major feature of his face was a thick wedge of ill-groomed moustache. After particularly vigorous efforts at times like harvest, when he was hurling stooks of corn about, his nose leaked uncontrollably and his moustache became as wet as a mangrove swamp. One of my most distinct memories is of him further drenching the hair in cold tea gulped back after he'd climbed down from the top of a stack and was waiting for another load from the field. When he'd drunk his fill, he licked the whole of his upper lip dry with an immense tongue, wiped it with the back of his hand and then settled his pipe in the corner of his mouth.

CHAPTER THREE

A Country Childhood

Throughout my childhood many of our problems at Fordhall were common to our neighbours. Once their output no longer seemed vital to the Nation, most small farm families suffered the hardship of poor prices.

The Blockade and much greater dependence upon home food had made the 1914—18 war a bonanza epoch on the farm. Greater prosperity had begun to erase the memory of the hungry period in agriculture which began when, in the 1880s, the British market was opened to the competition of cheap grain and meat from America and the Commonwealth. But, once the war was over, this competition reappeared and was allowed to flourish regardless of the social consequences in the countryside. So that in my early years, well-patched breeches and well-darned pullover elbows — which then reflected poverty rather than today's nonchalance — were commonplace.

In retrospect, I see it as a period of corduroy shorts — brown corduroy shorts and grey flannel shirts. The shirts often had white rubber buttons which stood up well to their weekly pounding in the postub.

As uninterested in the fine detail of domestic activities as any boy, I couldn't help but be aware of the weekly wash. It remains in my memory like a vision of Hades. A house that was most often calm and smelt sweetly of the scent from flowers filtering through the windows overlaying the lactic odour of good diary products or the aroma of baking bread, each Monday reeked like a laundry. All the fine perfumes were belched out through open doors in great gusts of caustic, soapy steam every time Joan lifted the lid of the copper in which the wash was boiled. With her giant wooden forceps, looking like claws, she reminded me of a lobster as with much scalding drip and splash she flung clothes into a corrugated metal tub.

She became transformed into a leaping kitchen dervish when, grabbing the three-legged wooden dolly peg, she thrust it among the wet laundry and with a reciprocating twisting motion she agitated it violently to smash out the dirt. Since she was only five foot six, disengaging the legs and lifting the long peg to thrust it elsewhere involved a mini leap which I never ceased to find surprising. The final effort in heaving upwards with her stout, water-reddened arms provoked the sort of grunts made by champion tennis players as they serve. And if the stick came free more easily than expected, the jerk frequently sent her auburn hair spilling from the scarf she used to hold it in place. This always enraged her because, once free, it spread like a fan as she gyrated.

Since Mother insisted that a good wash required a full day, if everything was to be wind dried, flat ironed and stowed in a sweet airing cupboard by midnight, the ritual of a Monday began long before my sister or I were awake. This meant that I hated Monday breakfasts, which were taken from a kitchen table surface, clammy with moisture that clung unpleasantly to bare arms.

There were no early morning radio broadcasts to provide breakfast background noise in those days, so normally the meal was tranquil. But on Mondays, Joan's constant thudding, the bubbling of the copper and the shouts between Joan, her sister Betty and my aunt Edith rendered the whole atmosphere infernal. On Mondays, we left for school with relief.

Recalling wash days in our crowded kitchen, it seems strange that I should be referring to Joan and Betty, who acted as maids and also helped in the dairy, when I have previously mentioned the depression and increasing rural poverty. Not that sacking Joan and Betty would have been easy. In a less mechanized age their efforts were necessary. They were the daughters of our foreman, Jack and the sisters of his son and my best friend, Harry.

Since the middle ages, it had been a tradition that the daughters of farm workers acted as maids, either in the main farmhouse or in the dairy, and no-one would have considered them as anything but an obligatory charge on the holding. If we were to be poor, it had to be poor with Joan and Betty's job's intact. And even in our periods of greatest distress, I can't remember anyone ever suggesting that they should be sacked. They were as permanent a feature at Fordhall as the ripple of the Welsh mountains on the horizon which for many years were the perimeter of my known world and seemed as remote and turbulent as the strange men who have herded their black cattle and shepherded their sheep on them for centuries

On rare school holiday afternoons, when my father somehow managed to find time from his farming, he'd lift me over the side of his Morris Open Tourer, in which I'm sure he believed he was a Grand Prix driver, and take me racing off to a remote mountain farm. Our arrival always seemed to induce a feather shedding and explosive commotion of hens, geese and ducks. I'd try to regain their friendship while listening to the haggle over the price of a group of ewes between my deliberately offhand and slightly swaggering, gauntlet-waving father and the small dark man with fiery eyes and a sing-song voice.

Once the deal was done and we were driving back through our own truly English hills — the Long Mynde and the Wreakin, whose mushroom shaped top I can see clearly today — he'd snort out his contempt for the uncivilized Welsh whose temperaments, he clearly wanted to warn me, were as erratic as the violent earth movements which had accompanied the gestation of the bleak mountains in which they lived.

Father was obviously much happier nearer home among the Shropshire men he preferred, the men who supported his pretensions as a rural Gatsby at the golf club which flanks a low hill in the middleground beyond the obelisk to Clive of India.

Despite the rat incident, Jack's hat continued to survive. For many months more it served to wipe the sweat from his face and the dribble from his nose.

In cooler weather it became a useful beater. After a day's threshing in Autumn, when the whirring fans and vibrating sieves of the hired thresher had made our stackyard throb like a factory, he would use it to pound the scratchy dust from his clothes.

But, in the end, even its stout Donegal collapsed. And for a while Jack seemed like a displaced person. The other men guffawed irreverently when he appeared in the yard wearing the bright, clean checked cap he'd previously only worn on his stately progress to the pub on Sundays.

Sometimes, when returning from church, we'd see him heading towards the King's Head at Little Drayton. Unrecognisable as the weekday Jack, who tended to bustle and roll in movement like a sailor, on Sundays his formal serge suit and stiff while collar seemed to constrict his movements. He walked then with the dignity of a bishop in ritual procession.

Before its peak, too, became flattened, Jack's checked cap seemed to carry some of his portly Sunday aura onto the farm. To me, it gave him an alien facade and he became an even more forbidding figure.

By the time I began to go to school, Father had started to use the profits on the wartime potato crops to expand his social life. Golf had become an absorbing passion and he spent less time on the farm. Although he still devoted most mornings to Fordhall, he had often disappeared by the time Gladys and I reached home for lunch.

This left Jack in charge. So that for me he represented stern authority. He was the man most obliged to chastise me when my meddling play conflicted with daily farming activities. If I dragged a fork or brush away from the shippen or stable to pull it round like a lorry and then, tiring of the game, jettisoned it elsewhere, it always seemed to be Jack who found it and grunted out his displeasure. Unhappily, even at best, when I was young, our relationship was mutely hostile. Conflict was inevitable because he was such a wonderfully talented all-round, rural craftsman and cared so deeply about all his operations.

There was virtually no farm task which he couldn't tackle with great competence and extreme thoroughness. The work which probably demanded the greatest skill was the annual stint of hedging. A length of barbed wire or an electric fence will prevent cows and cattle from straying. But a tightly knit, well-laid hedge will provide wonderful shelter from wind as well. Beasts which are cold and miserable don't thrive. They consume more food and that's something which many modern farmers tend to forget. However, my father understood this well and relied upon Jack, who was an artist at providing outdoor cosy corners. Each year he would rejuvenate a new length of hedge.

As with many farms, our field boundaries had been demarcated during the epoch of eighteenth century land enclosure by planting hawthorn, ('May' or 'Quickthorn') hedges. Over the years other species of tree and shrub like willow, sycamore, crab-apple, ash and elderberry had become established, following the introduction of their seed by wind and birds.

Uncurbed, the vigorous leading stems of most trees and shrubs will thrust upwards to form high crowns, leaving bare trunks. So that instead of providing a mesh of twigs and foliage as a shield against the wind, a neglected hedge has little more protective value than a line of poles.

Wielding an axe or billhook with the dexterity of a surgeon, Jack would trim most of the lateral branches from a mainstem and then almost, but not quite, sever its base. Leaving clean wounds, which healed quickly, he'd bend the mainstem until it finally laid at twenty degrees from the ground. To hold the mainstem in place, he deftly made stakes from the tougher lateral branches, using the thinner, more pliable shoots as a binding.

This was Autumn and Winter work. By Spring, the shocked plants recovered. Thousands of new buds thrust through the top surface of the mainstem and, what for a few weeks had looked like a barren fence of unsawn timber, became rapidly transformed into a thick green hedge.

In the early 1920s many farms boasted a hedger. Since the quality of his work was apparent to everyone in the district, he was always galvanised by a sense of competition. Jack was no exception. And he relished a real challenge. A willow that had almost become a full sized tree since the hedge was last laid was the sort of monster he lusted to tame. Before the attack, he'd peer at it from all angles, moving slowly about while working at the edge of his hook or axe with the stone which honed it razor sharp. All the while he'd mutter audibly to himself. It was as though he was goading the plant.

'I could drive a horse and cart through there', he'd say. 'Maybe even loaded with hay. But, I'll have you, my beauty. Oh yes, I will. I'll have you soon as spit.'

When the incantation was over, he'd dart into the attack, wielding his hook like a Claymore. I marvelled at the way in which he made each cut count. He never hacked. One stroke was enough for a thick twig; two or three opposed thrusts for the stoutest branch. Even mainstems were sufficiently severed to lay with five or six strokes of an axe. They made the chips of fractured wood fly and frequently reduced the copious sap in a tree like willow to a plume of spray.

Once the onslaught had begun he wouldn't stop until the stem was staked and tied and the debris had been raked clear of the hedge bank. Then he'd stand back and admire his work thoughtfully, sharpening his tools again. 'There my beauty', he'd say, 'You look a mite tidier like that.'

I was always entranced by his skill and the speed at which he worked. So whenever possible I'd creep up and watch him hedging. Aware of my silent and fascinated presence, he'd occasionally dart a glance at me. It was those few rare acknowledgements of my existence, unadulterated by annoyance, which compensated for my otherwise almost perpetual fear of his wrath. But even our periods of brief truce were soon broken by his rabbiting activities. For hedging exposed the entrance to rabbit warrens and rabbits were my good friends.

Before he stopped work each day, Jack would mark these entrances with cut twigs which to me were as forbidding as tomb stones. I knew that after tea Jack and Bill would return with nets and a ferret in search of meat.

One evening I'd been permitted to go with them and was sickened by the spectacle. When all the outlets to the warren had been stopped by nets held down by pegs, the ferret was freed from its sack into the last open hole and began its turbulent underground marauding. Within minutes, fleeing, terrified rabbits were plunging and kicking at the nets in their efforts to escape. Grabbing them by the ears, Jack killed them with a rapid Karate blow, slashing the edge of his right hand across their necks. Although dead, they continued to shudder and kick for some moments in the pile on the ground where Jack hurled them.

I ran back to the house and can still remember vomitting on the way. Aunt Edith who met me thought I'd eaten too much for tea. But Jack, I'm sure, knew better. He was disappointed by what to him had seemed like cowardice in a country boy. Subconsciously, I suppose that he felt that my swift departure was a criticism of his pleasure.

Today, while a wild life protector myself, I'd be less critical of an activity which to farm workers of Jack's epoch was more than just a sport. Free milk, to take home in a can from the dairy, and the right to a rabbit or pigeon were in those days part of a farmworker's pay. The pursuit of rabbits in an age before easy transport, the cinema, radio or television also added some zest and variety to the unexciting life of a man like Jack who otherwise only spent his scarce free time on cultivating his magnificent garden or his visits to the King's Head.

I never heard him complain about the geographical constriction of his life or the limited entertainment opportunities in the district. He seldom went far into Market Drayton, our nearest town. Rare daytrips by train to Shrewsbury or Crewe were the extent of his travelling until he was over fifty. After that I'd sometimes take him to places like Wolverhampton or we'd pass through other Midlands towns on the way to an Agricultural Show. Although he'd enjoy the extra beer and the animation of the Showground, he made it clear that he didn't like the look of the towns. In fact he told me that he couldn't understand why anyone should want to live in 'such a midden of Bricks and Mortar'.

Life to Jack was incomprehensible without deep soil to till or horses and livestock to tend. By staying at Fordhall, he was expressing a strong preference for rural life, because the war provided him with opportunities to escape which he declined. He was too old for military service but could have earned much higher wages if, like some of his cronies at the pub, he'd gone to work in one of the giant Midlands munition or ordinance factories.

It was Jack's authoritative presence on the higher arable land and about the farmstead which drove me like the outlawed Hereward the Wake to those wild areas he avoided. When I was about four and could wriggle through the lower bars of gates, my world expanded greatly. I could take refuge in the wilderness of tall grass and weeds beneath the unkempt trees of the abandoned orchard. It was a jungle paradise for a child. The rabbits which Jack and Bill pursued so ardently elsewhere were safer and flourished in the orchard. I was still slight enough to tread their thin tracks through the high grass.

To anyone with the time for discovery, which only child-hood provides, they were highways packed with excitement. Even my most timorous stalking would flush hen pheasants from their nests along the margins. While I stopped to handle their warm speckled eggs, for a moment sylvan pandemonium reigned. The raucous, squawking departure of the pheasants prompted hens, roosting in the tangled briars, to cluck in chorus.

What seemed, in retrospect, to have been squadrons of chaffinches, bullfinches, blue tits, yellow hammers and a host of other small birds contributed their own particualr calls of alarm as they escaped the canopy of the gnarled old fruit trees. As they fled, their wings flashed bronze in the dappled light which in Summer, coupled with the strange resinous smell and the chill of the deep shadow, gave the orchard the mystical quality of a shrine. Although originally designed to provide

Fordhall with fruit, the aged trees in the orchard yielded sparsely. Mother always complained that the squirrels and her children harvested more of the fruit which she wanted to make jams, jellies and tarts with, than she did. As we began to grow and farm profits dwindled, she wanted the fruit to help feed us more cheaply. But every year the squirrels seemed to win.

One Autumn, my developing talents as a climber led me to discover a squirrel's cache in a hollow tree. But, by that time, I suppose my instincts for conservation had begun to develop and I didn't mention the neatly piled pears when I returned to the house.

My more formal interest in nature must have been sponsored by my first teacher at school, who encouraged me by awarding me prizes in wild flower competitions. The best of my blooms, the flags of wild iris or coronets of primroses, were discovered in the wet meadows which my improving health and growing liberty allowed me to reach. I mostly preferred to rove these marshes alone, acquiring the skill of a Fen man in discovering the few dry tracks between the man-high reeds. But occasionally, I'd introduce my sisters (after pledging them conspiratorially to silence) to the nests of moorhen, duck, snipe or even swan or heron which I had stumbled upon on the banks of our small pond or snugly hidden among the rushes and reeds of our blocked ditches. Sometimes, beneath the willows and alders which burgeoned on land which should have been pasture for cows, we'd spend hours watching an otter laboriously building its dam.

CHAPTER FOUR

Golf and Bag Muck

It became apparent later that most of my early wild life adventures were only possible because, despite the best efforts of Jack, the quality of my father's farming was deteriorating rapidly. The ditches, half choked with watercress in which we could capture shoals of red-bellied sticklebacks, ought to have been flowing fast to help drain the meadows. But, to Father, the work involved seemed less attractive than practising the approach shots which his golfing companions later confirmed made him devastating from less than seventy yards from the pin.

Sometimes Mother, who saw less and less of Father as he became mesmerised by his sport, would feel driven to catch a glimpse of his talents. She was trying, I suppose, to understand the increasing hold frivolity (as she saw it) had gained upon the man she loved. So she would take us to watch him play. The effort involved in providing what, to us children, was a wonderful picnic adventure must have been prodigious. To create the time, she'd try to advance her work in the dairy by working even later at night. And yet, before we were up, she'd have the pony harnessed and in the trap and she and Aunt Edith would have filled a hamper with sandwiches and extra delicious fruit pies and cakes.

I can remember being astonished by, and proud of, the allure of my mother on those occasions. Instead of her habitual white dairy overall, cap and wellingtons, she'd be wearing a plain, but smart, two-piece tweed suit acquired on one of her rare visits to Chester or Shrewsbury. A simple string of pearls appropriately decorated the neck of a plain thin woollen pullover. Most of all, I remember her shoes: sensibly low heeled brogues in tan leather, whose tiny tassels on the end of the thong laces fascinated me. As shoes, they seemed every bit as grand as those of the great ladies of our district whom I occasionally saw speeding their traps along the lanes.

In contrast, Aunt Edith's shoes were totally inappropriate. Though born and brought up on a farm, she'd always leaned towards urban dress. To picnic on rough heath land, she'd choose shoes reminiscent of those habitually worn by Mini Mouse. Their sky-scraper heels and long pointed toes she obviously found most becoming. Because, from time to time on her journey, she'd discreetly raise the skirt of her long floral cotton tea-dress and, slightly turning her stout ankle, she'd glance down and smile at them with pride. When we arrived at the position alongside one of the golf club fairways from which we'd see Father pass, almost inevitably Aunt Edith's heel would dig into the turf like the tooth of a harrow and then snap with a loud report. Restoring her equilibrium demanded much sympathetic sisterly clucking from Mother and an embarrassed manoeuvring behind bushes to remove precious silk stockings which would have laddered disastrously if she had continued to wear them without shoes.

The subsequent contrast between her bare feet and the floral tea-dress and straw hat with feather was ludicrous and upset us all. Mother looked distinguished, we were wearing our Sunday best to make Father proud of us in front of his sporting friends and even the pony was beautifully groomed. Only Aunt Edith's feet let us down. And when she was older, Gladys, who shared some of her Aunt's forthright temperament, didn't hesitate in letting her know. But Gladys needn't have worried because, not wanting to destroy the concentration of his playing companions, Father barely noticed us as his foursome passed by on the fairway. As he briefly smiled and nodded in our direction, I felt as if I were looking at a stranger.

He wore a startling white cotton cap and plus-fours with thick tartan socks. Strangest of all, his feet were clad in heavy liver and white shoes which looked as expensive as they were bizarre. The only easily recognisable feature of the man, who in the mornings I saw about our farmyard in ragged blue dungarees and big farm boots, was the quick bustling stride. Having played his shot, he dashed on up the fairway and had disappeared over the crest of a hill before we realised that one of the high points of our day was over. We had seen Father playing golf. There only remained our ritual visit to the nearby caves and lake before returning home.

I wonder now whether Mother, reflecting in the gloom of the caves, felt that watching Father indulge his passion had in any way helped her to understand it. My father's passion for golf might have been less destructive if the bonhomie at the club hadn't widened his social vistas. Loyally applauding successes marked by his proud arrival home with an annually increasing number of inscribed cups, goblets, spoons and tankards, my mother must have been secretly dismayed by the growing cost of obtaining them.

Reaching the club in his cob-drawn trap became irksome. So, following the example of some of his wealthier friends, he bought a car. Apart from allowing him more time to play and practise, the open tourer, which he couldn't afford, gave him much greater social flexibility. After drinks at the club he could ferry groups of cronies home for more drinks, food and cards. Dutifully conniving in this boundless generosity and taste for good living, after a heavy day in the dairy, my mother would grill half-inch slices of home cured ham and top them with eggs. Immense crumbling creamy cheeses were devoured by cheery men with appetites sharpened by the air on the golf course and large tots of my father's carefully chosen blends of whisky. Afterwards, when the lamps had been lit and the table cleared for cards, the whole atmosphere was made mellower and even more convivial by slowly circulating decanters of vintage port. Sometimes, before I crept off to bed, I would be allowed to help pass the decanter or simply stand silently behind my father's chair to watch his swift fingers dealing cards with a proud panache. Sadly, he was as impetuous a card player as he had become a farmer. And frequently I noticed my mother's pain as he laughingly passed silver coins and often notes across the table.

Once Fordhall had established its reputation as a foyer of late night entertainment, the cars of more casual acquaintances began to fill our yard. They would arrive in fanfares of hooting accompanied by gusts of laughter. Despite Mother's quiet protests that many of these people were merely worthless cadgers, my father would make them all welcome and dismiss her criticism with an angry shrug. Too young to be aware of their defects, my sisters and I found these new friends charming. They joked and occasionally gave us sixpences. Best of all they drove the wonderfully elegant cars of the early twenties. Upholstery garnished with silk fringes, horns like 'cor anglais' and fretted silver flutes to carry posies of violets made examining them a memorable experience.

Despite its grandeur, one car we didn't like belonged to my father's elder brother, Tom. It seemed as pompous as the man. Small like my father, he had all his loudness and none of his charm. If we were in the yard when he arrived he'd barely recognise our greeting and set off for the house door. I always felt that his threatening glance was aimed at me as he'd turn and say sharply, 'Don't you start climbing about in that motorcar. It's not a toy, you know.'

Although my mother protested that on the evenings that Uncle Tom joined the card game, there were often unpleasant arguments, my father continued to invite him. I suppose he wanted a family witness to his social success. While aware that there was some sense in Uncle Tom's uninvited comments about Father's inadequacies as a farmer, Mother couldn't tolerate his patronising attitude. He seemed almost pleased when he was the first to discover, in a walk before supper, that our potatoes were infected with Blight, the horrific disease which had destroyed crops in Southern Ireland in the 1840s, leading to mass starvation and the vast waves of emigrants, whose descendants today dominate the New York Police Force.

Despite our spraying the crops in an effort to control the disease, several times during the twenties it attacked our potatoes badly. One of my most vivid childhood memories remains the frightful stench of putrefaction as the foliage and stems in attacked areas of our fields turned black and rotted away. Perhaps such familiarity with crop failure, even at that age, gave me the courage to face it myself later. But it was certainly the reason for our family's early plight. For even bumper crops would barely have supported my father's excesses. And poor crops, further reduced by disease, hardly returned the cost of the seed.

While Father dissipated the cash ripped from the soil by his profitable wartime potato crops, our worked-out land yielded less every year. Trying to compensate for the loss of fertility, he applied more and more chemical fertiliser. But, by this time, years of ploughing and heavy cropping had deprived the soil of much of its vital organic matter. Instead of being held by the humus and slowly released to feed the crops, as soon as it rained most of the chemical fertiliser he applied was washed down the drains and lost into the river.

The crops he did manage to harvest yielded pitifully little when they were sold. Worried about feeding the growing number of unemployed in the towns, governments made no attempt to guarantee reasonable prices for home farmers and allowed cheap imports to depress market prices. Only the most ruthless and efficient farmers managed to survive.

The situation of rural workers was even worse. Men like Bert Hazell, later President of the National Union of Agricultural and Allied Workers, describe vividly the horrors of life for the East Anglian farm worker, when in 1922 farm losses were so great that workers were asked to accept an actual cut in the average wage from twenty-five shillings to eighteen shillings per week. They refused and almost starved during seven weeks on strike.

At least in our cow country we were a little better off because the sales of cheese for seven months of the year meant some regular, if small, income. If anything, in the towns the situation was worse. We found a ready demand for buttermilk left over from churning. Previously, we had merely fed it to pigs, but in the depression people were anxious to pay one penny per gallon for it as a source of human food. Thrifty housewives used to mash it into potatoes.

Stagnant industry was doing nothing to provide a land fit for war heroes to live and work in. Many of them, in despair, were wandering the country lanes calling from farm to farm, trying to obtain a share of the seasonal harvesting work. Others adopted new careers. Some joined religious movements like the Salvation Army and abandoned the search for personal material gain. Many sought survival in activities like the formation of itinerant 'Jazz Bands'.

Both groups helped to make life seem less desperate in the country. And for children like Gladys, Margaret and me their arrival in the district provided great excitement. We didn't understand the slump but our feet tapped gaily to the compulsive beat of a shaken tambourine or the drone of mock instruments into which the players hummed to make a sheet of tissue paper vibrate. It's odd to think now that in those days before radio and television we children in a remote corner of Shropshire were introduced to the tunes to which New York and London cafe society was dancing, by such ragged troupes of men.

Somehow we understood that we were expected to pay for our pleasure and soon became adept at disappearing behind hedges when the lady in the smart uniform or the man in a

shabby mackintosh came round with the collection bag or
outstretched cap.

We experienced our greatest proprietorial delight when, one
summer Sunday, my mother gave a band permission to hold a
concert after evening church in one of our fields alongside the
road. Looking back now, her face seemed as gaunt and haunted
as that of the leader of the band of Wolverhampton unemployed who had made the request. She doubtless wondered
how long it would be before we shared their fate.

We children were protected from her fears, but sometimes if
we woke late at night, we'd hear solemn murmerings between
my mother and Aunt Edith in the kitchen or, more frightening, violet arguments behind our parents' bedroom door.

Clearly, Father was adopting the common dizzy twenties'
attitude of trying to ignore the financial crisis. Instead of
economising, he was inviting larger and larger crowds of
friends to share our food and drink and Mother realised that
we'd soon be bankrupt.

Trying to avoid this disaster, she reared more hens to provide more eggs and chickens to market alongside her cheese
and an extra sow to make us more self-sufficient in pork, ham,
bacon and all the wonderful by-products like brawn, sausages,
black puddings and lard which those extraordinarily useful
animals provide. Extra weaned piglets could be sold, too, to
other farmers for cash.

These attempts to increase income meant aching backs for
Gladys and me. Already, by the time we'd reached eight, like
all farm children of the epoch we were expected to help with
small duties around the house. My first tasks were to fill the oil
lamps before leaving for school or when I returned in the
evening. When Gladys thought I was competent, she allowed
me regularly to trim and occasionally replace the wicks and
also to burnish the brass oil tanks with metal polish or make
the glass chimneys gleam by washing them in soapy water. In
those days, my hands seemed always to be grimy with soot,
greasy with oil or scrupulously clean, pink and deeply wrink-
led as the result of immersion in water. But more fowl and pigs
meant impregnantion with more natural and frequently
malodorous dirt.

Both Gladys and I were excited when Mother returned from
Market Drayton with Carouso, a Rhode Island Red cock of
magnificent plumage, a highly strident call and the disdain of

a great opera singer when he strutted about on the cowshed roof or crowned the vast midden which grew like Vesuvius in our yard each winter. He'd been bought to replace the previous old cock which had provided a tough supper for a marauding fox some weeks earlier. His role was to fertilise eggs, increasing the number of chickens we'd have for sale or poulets to lay more eggs.

While he accomplished his task with an evident, clucking delight, the fertilised eggs provided even more work for Mother. They were too precious to consign to us children and Father found poultry absurd. So it was Mother who had to find time, in an already packed day, to collect the eggs when they had been laid and place them in an incubator. It was she who worked late, checking the temperature and gently turning the eggs to ensure they were warmed equally on all sides. Once hatched, she confined the chicks under a warm brooder lamp. Of course, the mother hens would have undertaken this work in the nesting boxes provided in our chicken coops. But an emerging chick will make a tasty snack for a hungry rat and Mother preferred to guard them much more closely during the first weeks of their life.

She was equally solicitous about the baby piglets when our sows littered. Pigs are notoriously careless mothers but Victoria, one of our best sows at the time, was extra casual. In fact, she was casual about everything except eating and being scratched, about which she was very enthusiastic. While some sows affect a maidenly diffidence when introduced to a boar and only succumb to his advances in squealing panic, Victoria barely noticed his presence. When the time was right, Mother would ask Bill to pop her in the cart and drive her to meet her mate at a nearby farm. Bill enjoyed this break in routine particularly as Victoria created no fuss and the farmer who owned the boar was an expert producer of home brewed beer. For us children it was an adventure too.

When he'd finished the morning milking and let the cows out into their pasture, Bill would harness a horse to a cart and back it up to a loading ramp. Then he'd open the door of Victoria's sty and show her some delicious pig swill in a bucket. Her snout would immediately begin oscillating like a radar scanner as her sharp eye saw the swill and then, very quietly and deliberately, with the affected dignity of a brothel madame, (she never moved quickly) she would rise to her feet and begin to move towards the bucket. All Bill had to do was walk casually up the ramp and into the cart and she would follow. And then, while she plunged her snout into the swill, he'd close the tail gate and go off for his breakfast. Since taking the sow to the boar was a minor social event for Bill, he'd return with his normally rough skin shining from the extra scrubbing and his auburn hair plastered down with aromatic violet oil, in his best sports jacket and trousers. Meanwhile, replete with swill, Victoria would be snoring profoundly on the cart bottom.

Like an affectionate grandma, she tolerated with a grunting good humour the teasing of the children and the jogging of the cart on our two mile journey. To rouse more interest in the world at large, Bill would occasionally turn round from driving and scratch her back vigorously with his free hand. Bill never needed to prod Victoria with the stick he'd brought along to get her into the mating area of the boar owner's yard. The enticement of the bucket was enough. She hardly noticed either the arrival of the boar or the click as the gate closed confining her with her empassioned lover. For an instant, she'd lift her head and look round and then plunge her snout back into the swill.

On the way home, Victoria always sprawled inelegantly on the cart floor, sleeping deeply. From time to time, obviously dreaming about mountains of delicious swill, she'd stir and grunt and then relax again. Even the much brisker pace of the return journey, conducted by a delighted Bill whose face was flushed with home brew, failed to disturb her. And she'd be left to her dreams in the cart for a couple of hours before being returned to her sty.

She never became as cantankerous as most sows in developing pregnancy and even to the moment of farrowing she remained good humoured when either Gladys or I entered her sty to muck it out and spread clean straw. The young piglets, invariably a large litter of eight or nine, were born almost without a pause between munching. And later she hardly seemed to notice their squeaks as they struggled in a vibrant pink mass to push their baby snouts onto her teats.

This lack of maternal interest my mother found frustrating. It meant she had to spend hours helping the least fortunate piglets to obtain their share of milk. Some sows will deliberately kill piglets in what seems to be an attempt to select only the

strongest to survive. But Victoria clearly couldn't rouse herself to such conscious discrimination. Instead, in her pauses for slumber between meals, she'd simply sprawl out, sometimes crushing the life out of several of them with her massive carcass. Only the quickest, most perceptive piglets survived. Trying to prevent this needless loss, Mother paid her the attention of the most solicitous midwife. Until the piglets were tough enough to fend for themselves she'd keep dashing out from her work in the dairy to rescue those which seemed most in danger. As litter succeeded litter, she devised scheme after scheme for the piglets' protection. One of her most successful was to strew large rocks on the floor of the farrowing pen so that if Victoria lay over them, there would be room underneath for a piglet to survive.

But, despite all this care, Victoria often disappointed her. I remember her exhausted anguish when one of her rescue attempts had failed. Hearing stifled squeals as a piglet was being suffocated beneath Victoria's warm mass, she had managed to arrive in time. She seldom swore. But I can still hear her indignant cry of 'Get up, you great bitch' as she heaved at the back legs of the piglet and kicked angrily at Victoria's vast rump.

Shocked by the unaccustomed fury, Bill had run across from the cowshed. I watched as he gently examined the just breathing piglet in my mother's arms. He'd had enough experience as a stock man to know that the frail ribs had been broken and probably the tiny lungs damaged as well. He understood, too, the significance of and disappointment in the loss of any animal on a farm. So it was with a shy and quiet embarrassment that he delivered his verdict, 'I think you better let me finish him off'.

As I began to cry my mother drew the piglet away. By then, I'd realised that the week old victim was an outstanding little piglet with a dark blue mark on its ear which we had christened Patchy. He was still alive and Mother decided to try to save him. She told me with haggard eyes the next day that he had lived in a box of straw beside the kitchen stove until four in the morning before finally dying.

Although she'd carried him to the far side of the midden and tried to bury him by lamp light to avoid distressing us further, Gladys and I saw the last of him while helping each other to stagger across the heap with a barrow of muck that evening.

When we noticed his frail pink corpse, we both stopped talking and couldn't look at each other or Patchy as we gently hid him beneath the contents of the barrow.

Thinking about the incident now makes me realise how early rural children are obliged to face loss due to death and also, in a sense, how apt it was that Patchy, a living entity which had been created on the land and had already acquired a personality, should have been returned to enrich the same soil. For by the time the midden was mature and ready to disperse on the arable fields before they were ploughed in the following autumn, millions of bacteria, micro-organisms and tiny animals would have completed their life cycles in reducing Patchy to an amorphous, life giving mass. I also realise now that the fact that Gladys and I had struggled across the midden with the muck barrow marked a significant change in my father's situation.

CHAPTER FIVE

Hard Times

Apart from being the victim of his own gregarious temperament, my father was the victim of a lot of frustration at the time. Some of his problems began two hundred million years ago. Then, most of the land we farmed was the shore of a great hot inland sea; the scene, no doubt, of epic battles between gigantic triassic reptiles. As the climate cooled and became moister, a thin carpet of vegetation developed. But the ancient sand was never far below the surface.

While it had the advantage of draining quickly, the sandy soil was easily stripped of its fertility by rain. Too frequent ploughing hastened the natural breakdown of the vital organic matter which held the sandy mineral particles together and acted as a reservoir for water and plant food. Even when dung from the cows and pigs was spread on soil in this state, the nutrients it provided were quickly liberated and washed away. To feed the large crops of potatoes which had swelled his bank account during and just after the war, our dung heap was inadequate. So my father resorted to artificial fertilisers as a supplement. Their ingredients dissolved rapidly and, with little humus to retain them, they too drained away quickly to fatten the ever lush but useless reeds on the swampy land in the valley. While it is easy to understand now what was happening then, I can't blame my father for being unaware of it. True to his creed as a progressive, he was merely adopting the most advanced techniques of his time. Both his farming brothers were employing artificial fertilisers successfully. In those days, the highly concentrated nitrogenous fertilisers produced synthetically from the nitrogen in the air by chemical wizardry were still a new miracle. Inevitably, they were used to bludgeon the land into higher productivity. On our land they became a weapon of abuse. But on the much heavier land farmed by Uncle Tom and Uncle John they increased crops without the same disastrous effect upon soil structure.

The result at Fordhall was only an accelerating decline in fertility and increased friction between my father and Jack everytime the fertiliser lorry drove into our yard. Packaging technology was not very good in those days and off-loading the heavy bags and carrying them into a dry store was unpleasant work. Apart from my father, Fred the waggoner, Bill the cowman, Jack and even a gangling fifteen year old called Tom were recruited to satisfy the impatient lorry driver's desire to return to his depot for another load. As each hundred-weight brown paper sack plumped down on to a carrier's shoulder a plume of fine irritating dust belched from its leaky seams. The adults simply grunted as they took the weight and seemed to ignore the acrid smell or the bright layer of powder which soon covered their shoulders and heads and gave them the allure of African tribesmen decorated for a ritual dance. But Tom was more distressed. The powder hurt his eyes. Rubbing them simply increased the irritation until the layer on his cheeks was furrowed with tears. Neither Jack, who considered the 'bag muck' an abuse to the land and remained mutely indignant, nor my father suggested that he should go and wash the powder away.

I suppose that Father didn't want to acknowledge to Jack his error in employing Tom. Jack had been against the appointment. Lowering yields from the land meant that the boy was superfluous and Jack knew that even Tom's meagre apprentice's pay put everyone else's wages in greater jeopardy.

But 'men on the place' provided almost as much prestige as acres farmed. And, unwilling to reveal the extent of his financial problems at the golf club or to neighbours, my father had readily taken Tom on when a Cheshire farmer asked him to train his second son.

My mother shared Jack's views about the foolishness of taking on another hand. I remember one bitter argument between my parents about a week before Tom's arrival. Wakened by the turbulence of their discussion, I had lit my candle and was passing their door on the way to the bathroom for a drink.

'But we simply can't afford him!' my mother cried with unusual anger. 'To hear you talk, you'd think we were bankrupt,' my father shouted back.

'We can't be far off', my mother commented with anguish.

Her cry made me forget my thirst and I ran back to my bedroom sobbing.

Also roused by the voices, Gladys came to comfort and
cuddle me. When finally my crying ceased, as she offered to
share her last remaining inches of liquorice boot strap, I asked
her what Bankrupt meant.

'It's a way of saving money,' she replied with schoolma'amly
authority. That puzzled me. 'Well, why does it make Mother
angry?' I found her 'Be quiet and settle down and go to sleep'
very unsatisfactory.

However, to both of us, Tom's arrival meant joy.

He was young enough to be one of our camp and a valuable
ally against the adults in the house and yard. And he, too,
being rather shy, clearly felt more comfortable when alone
with us than when Aunt Edith or my parents were present or
when he was being chaffed by Fred and Bill or frowned at by
Jack on the farm.

Gladys was nearly eleven when Tom arrived and it was clear
that his lanky figure and gaunt but friendly face appealed to
her greatly. For a while she followed him everywhere and
always seemed annoyed when Margaret and I appeared to break
up their earnest discussions.

Both Gladys and I were grateful for Tom's period at Fordhall. Being the junior, he was given some of the work on the
farm which was devolving more and more on us. For work at
that time seemed to accumulate like the logs cut by the Sor-
cerer's Apprentice. Gladys and I were growing stronger and
more able to accept our share of the chores. Nevertheless, I
shall never forget the weary back or stretched tendons caused
by massive forkfuls of moist dung or the struggle with the
forbidding and self-willed brute of a barrow as we wheeled it
across the top of the midden.

Like most farmer fathers, ours had begun by introducing us
to farm work gently. From time to time, when rushed, he'd
ask us to help him with the pigs. Fetching the fork, filling
buckets or helping to mix their meal with whey from the dairy
became our tasks. But he did all the really hard work.

However, by the time Tom came to stay, Father's appear-
ances round the pigsties were becoming rarer and rarer. In the
mornings Mother, too preoccupied with the tight disciplines
of cheese-making to appreciate what was involved, would mutter, 'Your father doesn't feel too well and says "Can you do the
pigs?" '. The more frequent evening variation was, 'He says he
won't be back in time and "Can you do the pigs?" '.

To Gladys and me both requests had initially been accepted as an exciting challenge. But as a sporadic event became a routine happening and my father's absence was never explained, we began to dread the words. For us they meant the end of childhood. And it was a state we sacrificed with reluctance. Because, otherwise, life had become exciting. I was ill less often and less shy at school. Frank Smith from a nearby farm and Jack's son, Harry, had become staunch companions in spare time and on our long walk through the lanes to school.

Being an older girl, Gladys was already too sensible and grand for us. When we reached the school yard, she'd deliver delicate Margaret to a corner among her class-mates and then join the big girls to skip and gossip while we boys plunged into violent football. But if, as often happened because I was so slight, I was hurled to the ground in the fracas round the ball as steel-tipped boots struck sparks from the hard tarmac surface, she would be first there to pick me up, dust me down or bind a bleeding knee.

However, I liked her best at home or en route for school. Then she seemed less snooty and joined our games. And even tough Frank admired her talents on a five-barred gate. Almost effortlessly, it seemed, she could run straight at it and in a single smooth movement with just a second's glimpse of pink thigh and elastic bottomed knicker she'd be over. It was an acrobatic feat, always witnessed with a shriek of delight from the normally serious Margaret and grunts of appreciation from Frank and Harry.

However, once Father began to shirk his responsibility for the pigs, Gladys' performances became rare. There simply wasn't time. Going to school after a leisurely breakfast had previously taken nearly an hour and coming home, if the weather was fine or the blackberries ripe, even longer. But now the pace of life quickened. There was hardly time to scrape the pungent pig muck from our feet after morning feeding before having to scuttle down the lane. We used to drag Margaret, whose smaller legs were forced to work like racing pistons. Complaints to Father about black marks received because we'd arrived in the yard after the bell had stopped ringing, the roll had been called and classes had been lined up and marched into school, only provoked a bleak smile. And the smiles became less frequent and cooler as the months passed.

Trying to escape the reality of a collapsing bank account, he left the farm earlier and earlier each afternoon and drank much later into the night. And although we children weren't aware of it, that is why he was incapable of working early in the morning.

The necessity to accomplish a regular task spawns an inescapable sense of responsibility. Instead of lingering on our way home from school, Gladys and I pushed Margaret through the yard gate before the final afternoon bell had ceased ringing.

On dark winter afternoons, when so little daylight was available for mucking and swilling out the pig sty yards, spreading fresh straw bedding in the houses and preparing and distributing their evening food, our urgency was particularly compelling. Then we'd move like light infantry: ten steps running and ten steps walking. It was a technique taught us by Bill when we tried to keep up with him as he strode across the meadows to round up the cows.

The warmth and throbbing circulation which the race home generated was certainly necessary. Work accomplished at a leisurely pace on a balmy summer evening became much more forbidding in winter. Water almost frozen in the pipes when splashed in the rush seemed to scald naked skin. And the icy galvanised metal handles of buckets actually cut into the flesh of numb blue fingers. Brimful of whey and suspended from a yoke across the shoulders, they provided an almost intolerable burden during the trudge across the muddy winter yard. I developed an odd paddling gait in my efforts to cross the quagmire quickly and discharge the hundred pound load. It used to amuse Bill who would shout, 'There goes the scared duck'.

When finally Gladys and I reached the kitchen fireside, we'd be glowing inside from the effort and almost frozen round the edges. The temptation to bake ourselves was irresistible and lead to monumental chillblains and screams of pain as the blood once more began to surge through our hands.

In retrospect, the contrast between that short-lived anguish and our joy when Aunt Edith bustled us to the table is most marked. She seemed to time the cracking of eggs into a charred black frying pan on the range to perfection. And their lively gasp as they struck the hot fat seemed always to occur as we raced across the kitchen to the fire. It was Aunt Edith at her bustling best. Like a great conductor, she could control a different operation with each hand. While the left broke the eggs and disposed of the shell in a smooth arc-like movement from the heaped brown bowl on the shelf past the pan to a garbage bucket at her feet, the right delicately nudged sausages, black pudding, rashers of bacon and wedges of fried bread with a spatula to prevent them sticking in another pan. Meanwhile, she'd be deep in conversation, almost shouting to make herself heard over the sizzling of the fat. Her habit of emphasizing a point by gesticulating with the spatula always irritated my mother. Because, when most vehement, it sent a spray of hot fat across the kitchen floor. But, if this was pointed out, Aunt Edith only laughed. She couldn't understand why people became so upset since the congealed droplets were yet another justification for almost incessant cleaning which was her habitual activity when neither washing, sewing nor cooking.

For Gladys and me, High Tea was the vindication of our efforts in the yard. Apart from the bread and pastry, nearly everything we ate was a product of the farm.

We were always involved in the chaos when a butcher from Drayton came out to help us kill and dress the pig we kept for the Fordhall larder. Protected by Mother from the anguish of watching the squealing act of slaughter, we were soon used to ferrying the frothy buckets of viscous, still warm blood to the kitchen where Aunt Edith used it to concoct her memorable black pudding. And in the days that followed, we'd have aching arms from trundling round the handle of a cast iron mincer or mixing the mounds of mince with herbs, dried bread and middlings to make sausage meat in giant enamel bowls.

It always surprised me to discover that the pig, which appeared such a smooth and compact animal in the court of its sty, should contain so many parts. Even an animal which had progressed so disappointingly while alive seemed capable of totally filling the kitchen and larder when dismembered. Only the strong arms and domestic competence of Aunt Edith could have marshalled the array of bones, flesh and offal into any semblance of order. And to do it, she adopted a demeanour which became quite imperious.

However, her attitude didn't scare away particular friends who quickly learnt of our pig killing over the borders of the county and conveniently timed their arrival to coincide with High Tea in the days following the event. For that was the time when the parts of the pig which we didn't preserve as bacon or ham were greedily demolished. Then, the air in the kitchen became blue with the frying of chitterlings, liver, kidney, sausages and puddings. It was a sight and sound irresistible to Urban Major. A friend of my father, his visits were always welcomed by us children. Unlike Father's late night revellers, he was a frequent day time visitor because that gave him the best opportunity of a few minutes alone in which to tease Aunt Edith. At least, when we children were about, their dialogue seemed to consist of 'Tell me, Edith, who makes your shoes? That new man in Shrewsbury?' Urban would ask, staring pointedly at her tatty slippers before turning his always amused eyes in our direction.

Edith never replied directly. Instead, crossing to the table to clear plates, she would gently massage his bald head with the tips of her fingers and mutter, 'He's done a beautiful job, that barber of yours'.

Then we'd all laugh. Urban's round face flushing crimson with pleasure as he savoured the joke of which we never wearied. My father had started it when we were tiny and it was becoming clear that Urban's frequent visits, on the pretext that he just dropped in on his way back from the barber in Drayton, were developing into a knockabout courtship of Edith.

'I must say, I've never known a man with so many acres of bare skull spend so much time in the barber's stool!' my father had exclaimed. And it had stuck.

Of course, Urban and Edith may have had their serious moments before marriage, but we were never aware of them. Laughter seemed to permeate the whole ethos of their relationship. In fact, to Urban, everything was funny. It would be difficult to determine whether his general demeanour actually imbued incidents with their comic aspect or whether chance merely conspired that he should be present when humourous things happened.

He was certainly present on one dull, freezing, February pig-killing evening, when I was obliged to leave the warmth of the kitchen to shift some hay from the barn and throw it over a field gate at the end of the yard. It was an annual chore when the grazing was scant and the pregnant ewes needed additional food to build up their supplies of milk before lambing. I was reluctant to move until Urban kindly offered to help.

Normally, it was a blind offering. Sufficient light from an

oil lamp hanging in the barn diffused across the yard to permit
the loaded forks of hay to be carried to the gate. But while the
gate was just visible, the sheep beyond could be detected only
by slight changes in the intensity of the darkness, the occasional glow of an eye or the delicate vacuumatic drawing sound
as their hooves were lifted from wet land. Occasionally,
attracted by the noise of the barn door hinges, a ewe would
approach the gate expectantly and be waiting with its patrician
nose stuck through the bars. On the night that Urban helped,
we were astonished by noses of quite a different tilt. Sharper
and backed by eyes which smouldered with greater intensity,
their nostrils were twitching to sample the air like radar
antennae. We realised on approaching the gate that they
belonged to a pair of foxes.

'Bugger me, they were so mesmerised by the fug of Edith's
frying as it wafted across the yard that they hardly noticed
Arthur and I carrying the hay,' Urban explained when we
reached the kitchen excited and laughing. My mother had
come in from the dairy to warm her hands and drink some tea.
'They looked hungrier than the crowd that Alf brings back
from the golf club. And just about as honest.'

I suppose that in me the fox incident provoked more curiosity and excitement than laughter. It stimulated an interest in
wild life which has never waned and made me aware that
Fordhall was far more than just a farm. The woodland, hedge
banks, pond, river, high pasture and low damp meadows
seethed then, as they do now, with untended life; the subject
of study which has brought me compensation for many disappointments.

As they became fully conscious of our approach and fled
from the pool of light, I felt that I recognised the vixen by her
strange gait. She seemed to have a stiff left foreleg due,
perhaps, to some injury which had healed badly.

She was undoubtedly a fox I'd seen several times in daylight
standing rigid downwind from the orchard, watching our hens
with compelled interest. Her moonlight escapades were probably responsible for the frenzied clucking which had woken me
and left our former cock as just a trail of bloody feathers and
entrails across the field.

But the dog fox, with his proud brush and younger allure,
was a stranger. Lured probably, Urban speculated, to come
courting from many miles and then distracted temporarily

from his amorous intentions by the wonderful scents of the pig killing and Aunt Edith's fine cooking.

'Do you blame him?' Urban said with a satisfied smile.

In fact, I realised later, blame would never be imputed for actions, no matter how violent, to animals unconsciously obeying patterns of behaviour dictated by aeons of evolution.

CHAPTER SIX

A Cruel Experiment

Blame was something I was unwillingly forced to accept for a consciously conducted and cruel experiment of which I have never been proud. It resulted, I like to believe, from excess pressure on one too young. And happily, it was Urban who helped me to support the shame and salvage from it some crumbs of wisdom.

Eight months after we saw the foxes, life became much harsher. Somehow, Frank Smith and I had satisfied the Grammar school that the reading, writing, arithmetic and general knowledge which we had acquired at Morton Saye warranted the encouragement of a secondary education.

I had felt a natural but unexpected elation some weeks after being taken (scrubbed and in Sunday clothes) to the school one Saturday morning, to discover that I had passed the entrance exam.

The whole atmosphere surrounding the school was more majestic than that of the homely building at Morton. I was so overawed by the solemnity of the hall that writing anything seemed difficult. In such surroundings, my natural shyness was paralysing and the brief interview with the headmaster seemed interminable. But pressure for places was less intense in those days and they found one for me.

It was becoming fashionable for the sons of small farmers as well as those of bank officials, merchants and the more prosperous tradesmen to acquire the veneer of a secondary education and my father was delighted by my success. He gave me half a crown and an air pistol and smiled frequently for several days. And since smiles had become much rarer as his misfortunes grew, I temporarily forgave him his general grumpiness which had begun to dominate our days. However, the smiles which sat so naturally on his face soon vanished again as economic ills increased. Even by the time I had started the Grammar School in September, he was beginning to complain of frequent and inexplicable headaches. Their occurrence seemed unrelated to his other excesses. And, as they grew in intensity, his enthusiasm for late nights at the golf club and even for the game itself began to diminish. At the same time, his capacity for work dwindled and more and more of the load fell on Gladys and me. So that my change of school, rather than being a release into a new land with limiteless academic horizons, became an almost intolerable burden.

One of the principal handicaps was the distance to school. As it was almost four miles away, in an epoch when bus services were infrequent, the choice was either to walk or cycle. My mother, still fearful about my general health and the notion that I should bicycle along roads carrying cars which were travelling faster and faster, refused the second alternative. So each day before and after school no matter what the weather, I had to face a walk of more than an hour. While developing lungs and muscles dwarfed by early illness, the daily trudge robbed me of time needed for tasks about the farm. By the time they had been completed, after a hastily gobbled high tea, I was ready to collapse into bed. But my new found scholarly status forbad that.

While, at twelve, I found it hard to relate Caesar's conquest of Gaul or a study of the characteristics of the Halogen gases to the demands of greedy porkers for more swill, to my masters both the Grammar School education and the homework were a privilege.

They made it clear to me that they couldn't understand why someone who always arrived smelling of the farmyard and found it difficult to stay awake or satisfy their demands for progress in learning, should ever have been accepted. Too blinkered and intolerant to try to discover and make allowance for the reasons for my growing distress, most of them simply treated my efforts to please them with contempt. And, in days when corporal punishment was considered a healthy compo-nent of a young gentleman's education, I often left school with my hands red and burning where they had been beaten with a strap.

Happily, ours was a progressive school where the cane on the backside was reserved as a punishment for only the grossest insubordination.

I must have been an irresistible target for the bullies on the staff. After the exciting newness of the first few weeks at the

Grammar School, I soon began to envy the comparative calm of Harry's life. He had stayed at Morton Saye and hadn't even attempted the entrance exam. As the son of our foreman, he had merely to breakfast before school and could play on his return. But apart from helping Gladys to look after the pigs, I was now expected to help Bill with milking the cows before leaving home.

At weekends I often assisted with the afternoon milking as well. When, after the spring calving, the cows were flushed with milk and it took a long time to empty their bags, even Jack used to milk. As each of us in turn filled our milking pail we'd tip it into the two five-gallon buckets which swung from a yoke carried on the shoulders. When the second of these buckets was brim full, whoever filled it would stagger with the yoke across to the dairy and return with them empty. That was often my lot and I must have been at it six months before I suddenly realised why I always noticed Jack and Bill exchanging conspiratorial looks on my return.

With the slow guile which only countrymen can deploy, they always timed their visits to the buckets to ensure that I would be the last to fill them and have to carry away the full load! When I discovered their treachery and ran to tell my father, I think I heard him laugh really heartily for the last time.

Bursting into the kitchen, I found him stretched out in a chair with his eyes closed. After helping to chain up the cows in the shippen, he had complained about his headache and disappeared into the house to take aspirin and try to sleep. On first opening his eyes he seemed annoyed. All the skin on his face was drawn and taut. But as he listened to my stumbling description of the cowshed perfidy he relaxed and began to chuckle. Then, with much brighter eyes, he laughed out loud.

His reaction made me even more annoyed until he explained that I'd suffered the penalty of being a boss's son and described how he'd been similarly duped when young.

However, even though I subsequently avoided an unfair share of the work, I found the milking on top of looking after the pigs very irksome. Apart from the physical fatigue, it carved the heart right out of the golden afternoons in summer.

Because, although harder, life was broadening. When I could escape from farm work or homework it had begun to acquire real zest. Less rigid timetables and greater freedom of action meant that Harry, Frank and I could range further in the pursuit of schoolboy enthusiasms. Collecting train numbers involved hours of sitting with our feet dangling over the railway bridge on the Longford road waiting for steam engines to roar beneath us, hauling coaches and trucks to places like Nantwich or Crewe in the north, Wellington and Shrewsbury to the South.

Their land-trembling passage filled the air with steam and smoke which momentarily warmed our legs and covered our skin and clothes with damp soot. It was as exciting as an electric storm. And when their din had died away and the plume from their smoke stack had dissolved in the warm air, I always felt a strange sense of anti-climax. Perhaps, without formulating the idea, I sensed that the passengers whose blurred faces I'd seen rushing by were destined for adventures in a world beyond us and from which I was excluded.

However, this wistfulness was soon dissipated in the race across country to plunge naked into the deeper, cool, brown pools of the Tern. Or, sometimes, it was banished by Gladys' generosity. She'd let us gallop her pony bareback about the high pastures.

In a life associated with livestock, I can remember hosts of cantankerous wall eyed carthorses, peevish cows which seemed to sense inattention and snatch the perfect fraction of a second to raise a hoof and topple a full bucket of milk, or truly treacherous rams, but I can never remember an animal as long suffering as that pony. It's docility was as astonishing as its looks were bizarre. Although never asked to charge at a windmill, a true Shropshire Rosonante, it would put up with almost anything. A birthday present to Gladys, the official duty of this sway-backed bay gelding Welsh cob was to pull our pony cart. However, once my father bought his car, its main function was to amuse us children. And he seemed willing to pay for his early retirement in boundless good nature.

He would stand patiently alongside a gate while the now robust Gladys straddled him just behind the shoulders clinging on to the still slight Margaret who actually sat on the base of his neck. Either Harry or Frank with their longer legs, would sit in the saddle position proper and provide stability for the other while I perched precariously on the rump. Even with this almost insufferable burden the pony would respond to Gladys' commands. He'd even try to trot — an action which culminated in at least three of us left in a heap on the ground.

The descent was always softer and sweeter if the field had been cut for hay. And once we were ruffled by the fall, the piled haycocks became bastions to defend in tumultous wrestling marathons. While Margaret was too delicate to participate, Gladys was as tough as any of us and, if helped by her chum, Doris Jones, she became a formidable adversary.

When the girls were involved in the chases and wrestling, or even looking grotesque while playing rounders with their skirts tucked into their knickers, the atmosphere was always more hysterical and exciting. Slightly older than the boys, their difference in sex was becoming more obvious. Their filling blouses made us confusingly embarrassed or desperately curious in turn. And a melee in the hay permitted at least some of that curiosity to be satisfied.

At the time, my attention and mute devotion was directed towards another school friend of Gladys, called Joyce. She was much taller than I, and her long straight chestnut hair was always plaited in a mane which often in play swung round her neck to land its bow of ribbon like a butterfly on her heaving chest. I'd watch it almost mesmerised. And, frequently, I'd think about it with my eyes closed as I leaned my forehead into the flank of one of the cows which Bill or Jack had dragged me reluctantly back to milk.

If, later, Gladys and Joyce came into the shippen I became so shy that the only way I could communicate my admiration for Joyce was to subtly change the direction of a cow's teat and spray them both with a pencil thin jet of warm aromatic milk.

I suppose that my interest in Joyce must have become more intense following an incident which made me aware that there were more possible relationships between men and women than just rows across the kitchen table.

Since I'd been walking to school in Drayton, I had become more conscious of personalities and activities in the district. And two characters in particular obtruded. One became known later as 'The Mayfair Boy' and the other was Megs Edwards. Megs seems now like the stock barmaid character of the twenties and thirties. The daughter of a farm worker, she lived somewhere South West of us beyond Ternhill and worked in a pub on our side of Drayton.

Life had clearly been too quiet for her in the village where few people can have appreciated her peroxided, bobbed hair or

the livid carmine of her finger nails. As she strained to cycle up
the incline past the end of our track, with her lips set tightly
closed to make a vivid scar in the pancake of her floury white
make-up, she was quite a forbidding sight. So frightening to
me that I almost passed by without speaking when one day I
saw her standing enraged looking down at the chain which had
slipped off and become entangled with the pedals of her bike.
When she looked towards me, I could see that the blobs of
mascara on the ends of her eyelashes were beginning to coalesce
in rising tears.

Offering to help, I was rewarded by an angelic smile which
suddenly made her look pretty and very vulnerable. In the
strongest of Welsh accents, she explained, 'Bloody thing
always does it when I'm in my best and late for work. But, I
can see I've fallen on a proper brick.'

From that moment on, my fear was dispelled. Recognising
my talents as an engineer, she was clearly a woman of the
greatest discrimination and there was something daring about
the way she swore with such conviction and confidence. Our
girls at the farm swore too when anything went wrong in the
kitchen but both my mother and Aunt Edith disapproved, so
their wrath was always choked back and weakened.

I'd often meet Megs going in to Drayton to work as I was
returning from school. She'd always make some mischievous or
cheery remark before leaving with a resigned, 'No peace for the
wicked, bach – it's all work.' And I'd watch as, standing on
the pedals in the most inappropriate garb for cycling, her pert
satin clad bottom swayed from side to side as she pushed on up
the hill.

I was clearly not alone in admiring those taut muscles. One
day I was just about to continue my plod home when I was
surprised by a plummy voice charged with enthusiasm.

'Like a pasha's dream, aren't they. Those glorious buttocks,
my boy.'

Startled, I turned to see a bronzed giant. Although I was
small, he must have been at least six feet two. And I remember
him as extraordinarily handsome. By his muddy boots and
leather knee guards, I knew that he must have been one of a
gang of labourers who were digging a ditch across a nearby
field. To provide work for the unemployed, some of the local
farmers had offered small pay and food to gangs willing to

provide trenches to carry water lines to cattle troughs in outlying fields.

On most of the men, who seemed scrawny and ill fed, their
digging gear was somehow demeaning. But, the 'Mayfair Boy'
wore the knee guards like the cuirasses of a roman gladiator.
From the waist upwards, his fine torso was naked and his skin
was burnt a deep reddish bronze — a dark ground for the
yellowish streaks from the wet clay he'd been digging.

As he watched Megs cycle away, he stared after her with
eyes of such an intensely lambent blue they could have been
enamel. An almost female shock of straw coloured hair kept
blowing across his eyes and he flicked it impatiently away from
a radiant face in which the main feature was a rather haughty
nose above two rows of fine white teeth. When Megs had
disappeared, he turned back to me holding his hands towards
the sky.

'What a vision of ecstasy, my boy. What pure and absolute
bliss.'

With that, he vaulted the gate and set off to his companions
in the trench shouting loudly about his intentions towards
Megs, while they jeered in reply.

I was too surprised to pay attention to the repartee. Because,
as the blond giant walked away, I realised that his back was
crazed with a pattern of livid looking scars.

Someone told me later that they were the indelible relics of a
beating with a cat-o'nine-tails, administered as a punishment
for a crime committed when he was a member of a London
gang. It was rumoured that he'd been an Oxford undergradu-
ate who couldn't adjust when his father was made bankrupt,
and had turned to crime.

After the incident with Megs, apart from winking at me
conspiratorially, whenever I saw him, I don't think that he
spoke to me again during the few days he remained in the
district. But, in his coercive Mayfair tones, he must have had
lots to say to Megs. Sufficient at least to persuade her to allow
him to walk her into Castlehill woods one fine Sunday evening.

I had finished milking and after slowly walking the cows
through the field gates to the bottom meadows, where they
were to graze through the night, I decided to walk on towards
the mound.

On a bluff above the river on one margin of our land, iron age men had created an impressive earthwork. It is easy to understand why the Cornoviae tribe which peopled our district chose the site. It was perfect for fortification. With steep slopes down to the river it only required minimal digging to make it impregnable.

By the 5th century A.D. the Romans had long been occupying their fifth largest British town at Wroxeter nearby and, judging by the amount of stone still on the site, they too realised its defensive value, as must the Saxons who followed them. The mound's capabilities as a fortress had by the 16th century given our farm the name 'Le Fort'. Which corrupted later became Fordhall.

But I was less fascinated then than I am now by the historical associations of the land I tread daily.

On that Sunday evening I was trying to catch a glimpse of some furry warriors whose family still possess the crest of the mound. For when the defences decayed, giant sycamores and ash rose to take their place, and it became a wonderful bosky haven for badgers. They clearly enjoy the free draining sandstone soil in which it is so easy to burrow and make cosy sets. I always tried, sometimes successfully, to catch sight of them as they emerged in the evening and were still too sleepy to be vigilant and too dazzled by even the fading light to be aware of my presence down wind. I suppose that it was my necessary stealth that evening which allowed the 'Mayfair Boy' to imagine that he could attempt to seduce Megs unmolested.

I don't know how long they had been in the wood before I crept silently into the shelter of a large hawthorn and sat down to peer across a small glade which contained two badger sets. And I shall never know how provocative Megs had been. But they were certainly silent for at least ten minutes while I waited for the badgers, lulled by the dappled light filtering through the branches and strong smell of leaf mould.

When suddenly, I heard the words 'Come on, damn you,' ring out across the glade in an angry Mayfair accent followed by Megs' anguished scream of 'Let me be you big sod'. I'd hardly stepped out of my cache and was still wondering what to do when I heard the report of Megs' hand landing on the Mayfair Boy's face and she had broken through the undergrowth into the glade.

Seeing me, she stopped abruptly. Underneath her smudged

make-up, her usually pasty skin had flushed scarlet and she was trembling with rage. The front of her blouse hung loose and she clutched the jacket of her suit in one hand. She must have been aware of the question in my astonished gaze. And, almost as a challenge, she hurled the jacket to the ground shouting, 'He's a bloody swine that man'. And then slowly and deliberately she hitched up her skirt and pointed to a vivid scratch which scarred the soft flesh at the top of her thigh.

'Look at that. I'll kick the bugger to death if I ever see him again. Just because I was sorry for the way he'd been treated, he took me for a bloody whore. But, I'm going to tell the police and he won't come molesting people hereabouts any more.'

Clearly realising that I was still a child and regretting having met me at all, she then grabbed her jacket and ran off down the hill muttering about being late for opening time.

I was too confused to follow and wandered slowly across the glade. I could see where, in lying, they had crushed the pale green, slightly furry grass which grew beneath the trees. But there was no sign of the 'Mayfair Boy' and I never saw him again.

The incident drove all thought of badgers from my mind and kept me awake and puzzled long into the night.

It seemed certain that the blond giant had attempted something forbidden and unspeakable with Megs which, I reflected, might have occurred between Joyce and myself. For weeks the idea was strangely provocative. And in the period which followed, while I was still greatly inhibited, the fascination of the incident seemed to compel me to try to spend more and more time with Gladys' friends, and Joyce in particular. While participating in all the activities as boisterously as anyone else, she retained a tantalising remoteness which I found challenging.

Perhaps that's why, at a time when with gathering confidence I seemed to be more at ease in her company, I was furious when deprived by work of time with her. And, I'd like to believe that it was this frustration which led to the first step in my worst crime.

As potatoes grow, it's the farmer's practice to keep ridging the soil up towards their stems. This provides a deep bed of nice loose soil in which the tubers can develop and it protects them from being greened by the light on the surface. It's a job accomplished by passing between the rows with a ridging plough which, like the prow of a ship, cuts deep into the soil at the bottom of the furrow and then throws it out on either side.

Jack had been grumbling to my father that the soil in Cottage Field which we were using for potatoes that year was in such poor heart that ridging up mightn't even be necessary. But a good shower and some warm weather had made them a bit less pathetic and in the hope that ridging might improve them, my father decided that they must be ridged.

He made the decision on a Saturday morning when Jack was busy in Villa field singling turnips with a hoe. Bill was helping the vet to deliver a badly presented calf by pulling on a rope that had been fixed to the two feet which had so far emerged. I was helping him to heave. Fred had cut himself badly on some rusty iron and had gone off to Drayton to see the Doctor 'for stitches'. And my father, who as well as his headaches, had begun to suffer crippling back pain, felt that he couldn't handle the plough and horse. But, in view of our sagging fortunes, he seemed to feel that any action which might improve our potato crop prospects was vital.

By the time he had laboriously harnessed the horse and spent some time bending, hammering and swearing in an effort to let down the plough wheel to travelling level, he was clearly in great pain. He let out an anguished cry which we heard in the shippen. Running the rope round a pulley on the wall and leaving me to tug at its end, Bill ran to help my father to the house.

When he returned, anxious to get back to helping with the calving of his cow, he told me that he'd attached the horse to the plough and since no one else was about to help, I'd better go and do the ridging.

'And mind you pay attention. We don't want all those spuds dragged clear of the ground', he warned as, protesting, I went away.

Like all farm boys who want to feel manly and that nothing is beyond them, in the past I had often asked Fred or Jack to 'let me have a go' when I'd been watching them ridging potatoes. And, while they let me plough a furrow or two, they always walked alongside and helped me with the heavy job of heaving the plough round when we reached the headland. So,

I'd always boasted to my mother and sisters that ridging was easy.

When I was alone on that Saturday, the task seemed much more forbidding. The horse seemed bigger and more immovable than I remembered and trying to keep the plough sole from dragging on the ground as I took it to the field, while clinging on to the rope reins put frightening stress on my short arms. However, I began to feel less distressed and rather proud when, after tremendous efforts, I'd turned the plough three times on the headland and paused to look at the darker brown, weed-free earth banked up to the potatoes in the rows I'd ridged.

Remembering that day, I have always since been aware of how quickly situations and moods can change. Because only minutes later my elation at having overcome what had seemed insurmountable difficulties was literally crushed under the hoof of the horse.

At the end of the next furrow, I allowed the horse to draw the plough too far towards the hedge before attempting to turn it. Cramped for space, I had to try to lift it bodily and it fell over taking me with it. In the confusion as I was struggling to right it, the horse moved and placed its iron shoe heavily on my foot.

If I'd been wearing my usual strong boots with steel reinforced caps, I should probably have come to little harm, but for some inexplicable reason, I was wearing a pair of old brown sand shoes which Gladys had discarded. Considering the weight of the horse, the initial pain might have been worse. But I suppose that my foot was momentarily numbed. Punching the horse's flank, I got him to move and sat back on the ground looking at the black rubber cap of the shoe which seemed to have been almost completely flattened. And then, frightened and crying, I limped my way back to the house.

My mother used her tough long dress-maker's scissors to cut the shoe away and reveal a pulpy mass of blood and sock. Before the feeling fully returned, she had bathed and bound my battered toes. And muttering about the stupidity of horses Aunt Edith had fed me soothing broth as I lay propped up on a sofa.

When, later in the afternoon, my whole foot began to throb, the pain was exaggerated by the knowledge that Joyce

was coming and she had promised to let me take her to see the
badger sets in Castlehill wood. And such is the heartlessness of
women that when she did arrive, she didn't look very sympathetic while Gladys was explaining my plight. And, I suppose that being too inexperienced to know quite how to react
in the presence of an invalid, she was just embarrassed and
seemed relieved when Gladys suggested that they go out to
collect wild flowers.

A few days later, as soon as I could limp about, I was back at
school and my injury was forgotten in the general concern of
Aunt Edith and my mother about my father's health.

They took it in turns to prepare hot compresses to try to ease
his lumbago or to moisten flannels with cold water for him to
hold to his aching head. And I was expected to resume my
farm work because the rest of the staff were busy with making
hay.

Sitting down to milk cows wasn't bad, but lugging food
about for the pigs was slowed up by my limp. By the time I
reached that stage in my evening chores, I was in a fairly
exhausted and grumpy state, infuriated by the fact that my
duties were depriving me of the chance of freedom with Harry
and Frank or the girls. That's when I began to deprive Victoria
out of spite.

It wasn't long after the injury when the old sow, in her
impatience to get at the bucket, rushed me as I entered her sty.
In the bustle she trod on my bad foot and almost knocked the
bucket out of my hand. Angry, I took the stick which I'd used
to mix the meal and bashed her savagely across the snout. And,
in a rage, I rushed out of the sty taking her bucket of food with
me. I resolved that in future I'd teach her a lesson and refuse to
pander to her greed.

Since she was feeding a litter of piglets at the time, she
always seemed to be doubly hungry.

For three days, I didn't feed her at all, but I couldn't resist
peeping furtively into her sty to see how she was reacting.
What seemed to me to be the mean look in her eye when she
saw me, only hardened my resolve to be tough with her. But, I
knew that what I was doing was wrong and, scared unless
Gladys or anyone else noticed that her trough was always
empty, I decided to just provide her with infuriatingly little
meal each day.

On the fourth day when I entered the sty with quarter

rations, her normal greed seemed to have turned more vicious and I hit her across the snout again to prevent her from knocking me over as I poured the food into the trough. Undeterred, she buried her head into the gruel of meal and whey before I'd finished pouring it. Looking round before leaving, I noticed that there seemed to be fewer piglets because they too, since it was approaching their weaning time, were also taking some of their food from the trough. And they seemed much hungrier than usual. For a second, I had a twinge of conscience when I realised that my starving their mother was depriving them of milk because she was receiving insufficient food to make enough for them.

However, that emotion was banished by the shock of seeing a piglet's carcase at the back of the sty. When I picked it up, I was horrified to discover that great lumps of its flesh and entrails had been gnawed away. I then realised that its discovery would reflect badly on me and I ran with the gory remains and hid them in the midden before returning to vent my wrath on Victoria for her horrific cannibal behaviour by kicking her hard several times in the rump.

She was so absorbed in mopping up the food I'd given her that she barely reacted.

Her cold-blooded ability to slaughter one of her own young goaded me into depriving her further. And for several days after, I only fed her enough to make her trough look normal after the food had been consumed.

Of course, I was too young and stupid to realise that this action would lead to the death of three other piglets, or that I couldn't teach a sow which was reacting instinctively to cease killing her young in order to prevent herself from starving.

It was only later when Gladys, Bill, Fred and Jack had all noticed the disappearance of the piglets that, questioned by my father, I'd admitted starving Victoria and I learned a great lesson in biology. Suffering badly from his headache and back, my father couldn't rise from his chair or I believe that I should have received a thrashing to remember to this day. His fury seemed boundless and he bellowed at me so frighteningly that before he'd half done, my distressed sobs were almost louder than his shouting. At one moment, my wailing angered him so much that he tried to rise from his chair and I began to bolt for the door and ran straight into the arms of Urban Major.

Unable to regain his composure, he shouted at Urban, 'Get

him out of here before I tear him apart!' Even Urban seemed frightened by the threat in my father's voice and hastily turning about, he dragged me out into the fields to hear the whole tale through choking sobs.

For once he lost his habitual smile and, becoming grave, made it clear how wicked I'd been. But he had a genius for teaching and never lost a chance to take lessons out of life. When I'd calmed down and we were sitting on a fallen tree in Mill Meadow, far from the house, he told me that as Victoria had starved, the piglets would have infuriated her by biting at the nipples which couldn't supply the milk their fast growth demanded. 'With those sharp little teeth, it would be like someone constantly sticking needles into the end of your cock, my lad, and how would you like that, eh?' After giving me a moment or two to contemplate that excruciation, he explained that, aggravated by the biting and starving herself, she killed the piglets in a dumb urge for survival.

'Because that's something we don't share with the rest of the animals, my boy. In desperation, a human parent would starve first to see the children fed, but that is hardly ever the case with animals. In nature, the mother always tries to ensure her survival. If you take an egg from a nest, the hen will never return. She will abandon the nest and build and lay again elsewhere. Presumably, her instinct tells her that if an egg has gone, a predator must be about and might return. The same sort of instinct must suggest to a sow that if she survives, there is always a chance that she will have another litter, whereas, if she dies, the piglets would all die because they wouldn't receive her milk.'

CHAPTER SEVEN

The Year of the Rabbit

I don't know what the Chinese called it, but 1927 for us was the year of the rabbit. For that seemed to be about our best crop. I suppose we should have been grateful for them, for, as our financial situation deteriorated and my mother found it harder and harder to feed us properly, we ate far more bunny than beef.

But, for the first time in my memory, my father didn't participate in the annual rabbit slaughter when the corn was cut. In previous years, sunburned and happy, he had always been there shouting instructions to Bill and Fred or chastising her terrier. All three of them, armed with shotguns, would surround the dwindling island of uncut corn in the centre of the field as Jack reduced it swathe by swathe with the chattering Binder.

Rabbits trapped in the field when cutting began were driven by the noise further and further into the crop, seeking cover. As the machine approached and the distance across the open cut stubble increased, they would begin to bolt for the safety of the hedge. And then, headed off by the terrier and confused and terrified by the cries of the men, they would zig-zag frantically among the sheaves of corn which the Binder had jettisoned on the ground. It was the best chance in the year of reducing the rabbit population on the farm and was taken in a violent, barking fussilade. Shot after shot was fired as, in the end, rabbits began to flee everywhere. A few escaped. But most of them were simply transformed in mid flight from lissom leaping creatures into lifeless patches of blood-flecked fur.

Despite its horrifying element, the carnage aroused in the participants all the primitive excitement of the hunt. And, although I was upset when I saw the corpses strung in pairs by their feet, hanging bleeding and fly encrusted from a stick over Bill's shoulder as he carried them back to the farm, while the

rabbits were running and the guns were firing I was as excited as anyone.

The whirring of the great wooden reel on the Binder which pushed the brittle rustling corn stalks towards the oscillating cutter bar; the occasional sparkle of sunlight on its work polished triangular knives; the noise and reciprocating cunning of the gadgetry which bound the heaped corn into sheaves with twine; the straining rump muscles and lathered sweat of the team of three horses as they sensed that their daily task was almost completed; the gesticulations, through the din, of a red-faced Jack as he tried to warn the marksmen that another rabbit was about to escape; the percussion of the guns and the barking of the dog were to my father the high point of his farming year. It was the sort of animation he adored.

But, in 1927, orchestrating the din would have been too painful and have made him scream. And his absence made everyone realise just how serious his illness had become.

When the dew had been burned out of the yellow corn in Drayton field on that bright September day and Jack had decided it was ready to cut, I went indoors to tell my father and ask the maids to prepare cold tea and bread and cheese for our lunch. He was slumped in his chair in the kitchen with his palms pressed to his temples as though trying to force the pain away. Hardly acknowledging my announcement, he just closed his eyes and nodded.

I soon forgot his plight in the bustle of preparations for cutting. In the absence of my father, Jack seemed to move with more urgency and be more voluble. He too enjoyed the harvest and had spent days working on the Binder knives, fidgeting with adjustments and shrouding everything which moved in so much thick yellow grease that it exuded a strong paraffinic odour when it was dragged from the cover of a shed.

I was sent to fetch the mammoth reels of scratchy sisal binder twine which were stacked on a shelf in the stable. It was twine I was normally forbidden to touch. 'I'm buggered if I'm going to run out of twine in the middle of cutting just because you need a bit of string to hold up your breeches', Jack always warned.

Passing the dairy with the reels, I peeped through the open door and noticed the regret on Gladys' face. She had left school in the July and life had become serious. She was learning to help Mother with the cheese making. Although, later in the

day with the maids and even my mother and Aunt Edith she
was recruited to stook the sheaves to help them dry, at that
moment she was confined to the habitually wet, rather dark
and cool dairy, while I was going to work in the sunny field.
She was clearly jealous.

Raising her eyebrows, she grunted, 'It's all right for some',
and then returned to measuring out the correct amount of
rennet to coagulate that morning's milk.

I often wonder whether she, like Bill and I, realised that
there seemed to be less and less milk to make the cheese and
butter as the weeks went by. Since I was regularly involved in
the milking I had noticed that cows which had previously
filled my buckets rapidly had become stingier in their supply.

Normally at that time of year, milk production peaked as
the cows enjoyed the September flush of grass. Bill was
puzzled too. 'I can only think that the old buggers ain't getting enough out of the grass to do us well', he speculated. His
habitually cheery face looked troubled. 'Your Dad will be mad
when he learns just how much expensive cake I've had to use to
keep up production. But, it seems as though the land's flogged
out and won't carry wholesome grass any more.'

For a man whose knowledge of the science of animal nutri-
tion was confined to knowing roughly how many scoops of
dairy cake or crushed barley were needed to keep a cow content in winter, his diagnosis then proved to be very accurate
later.

When my mother and I had mentioned the drop in milk
supply to my father, he seemed as disinterested as he did that
morning when I told him that we were off to cut the corn.
Perhaps, it's as well that he was able to be resigned to the
farm's collapsing fertility. For if he'd come to the wheat field
that day, his anguish could only have been increased.

After he'd been cutting for a couple of hours, Jack paused to
eat some bread and cheese. As he collected it from Betty, he
looked thoughtful and instead of joining the rest of us strewn
out in the shade along the hedge bank, he wandered off among
the sheaves alone. Holding his bread and cheese between the
fingers of one hand, he gnawed at it absentmindedly while
stooping to pick up sheaves with the other. I watched him
intrigued as, still chewing vigorously, he cast them aside and
then used his forefinger to count the sheaves and paced out the
distances between them. After a period of what was obviously

hard mental arithmetic, he started to shake his head and began counting again. He hardly seemed to notice the deference when Joan carried him out an enamel mug of cold tea. The rest of us got our tea by up-ending old brown beer bottles, but Jack was given the respect due to both a foreman and a farmer. She had to follow him round for some minutes to get him to accept the mug.

Drinking the tea thoughtfully, he continued to gaze about in disbelief and then, walking back, he flung the tea-leaves out of the mug, handed it to Joan with a curt nod and said to Fred who had been watching the performance.

'It's at least a third down. I've never seen anything lighter.'

With an annoyed shrug, he went back to the Binder and began cutting again. Fred slowly stood up and looked at me. 'Come on, young 'un, we'd best get on stooking.' But I was reluctant to move until I'd understood fully.

Fred seemed embarrassed by the question and then muttered, 'Jack thinks your pa has poisoned the land with too much chemical muck'.

Fred's short explanation worried me. Without being quite sure of the implication for the future, it had a sinister ring. It could have accounted, I supposed, for the extra dust. Harvesting was always a dusty, gritty affair. But that year there seemed to be more dust than usual.

Once the dew had been cooked out of the soil surface, it seemed to break up like face powder and the horses' hooves made it rise in thin clouds. In the afternoon, it was even stirred up by our lighter tread. It seemed to have no goodness and substance left to hold it to the earth. I remembered how, after it had been ploughed and sown in the previous autumn, a great wind had eroded its surface, tearing out the wheat seedlings and carrying dense clouds of our soil across the hedge into the neighbours' fields.

At the time, I'd heard Jack say to Fred, 'If he isn't careful, he'll have nowt but a dust bowl.'

But, at the time, I hadn't understood what he really meant.

Jack frowned his way through the hot afternoon as he bounced on the sprung Binder seat. None of the rest of us said much as our forearms became chaffed and reddened by the action of collecting stooks in each arm and then standing them with the bases apart and their heads together in groups of eight. It was only when Bill appeared, accompanied by my father's terrier, with guns for Fred and himself, and the rabbits started running, that anything like the normal harvest atmosphere was restored. There were so many rabbits that year that as he urged the horses towards the last swathes, even Jack's eyes began to twinkle.

After the dreary repetitive and back-breaking task of stooking, I was delighted to have a chance to run about picking up the rabbits and take them out to Joan and Betty who were busily arranging them in pairs on the headland. It was an operation I preferred not to watch. Using sharp pointed knives, they deftly pierced the skin of the back legs and made a passage between the bones through which they forced a paw from the other rabbit. When coupled, they were hung over a stick.

The noise of the knife scraping the bone made me shiver. So when I'd collected a pair, I'd run into the area where the girls were working and simply drop them and dash away. Since the girls seemed to work faster than I could run, I was becoming exhausted when Harry and Frank turned up, attracted by the shooting.

The three of us began to collect rabbits quicker than they were being shot. So we started to compete by rushing in as soon as the guns were fired. Realising how dangerous the game had become, Jack stopped the Binder and shouted to Bill, 'Send my Harry home', and then turning to me, he said, 'Young Arthur, help Bill by going down to round up those cows for him'. And then, nodding towards Frank, he commanded, 'You will be enough to pick up the rest, but for God's sake, stay clear of them guns'.

With that, he got the Binder under way again and I realised reluctantly that I had better obey him. I'd seen him annoyed and wasn't brave enough to risk his wrath. Nevertheless, I was peeved by the way in which Jack had spoilt our game and loitered on my way to fetch the cows.

Instead of cutting through the woods down to Mill Meadow where the cows were grazing, I decided to go via the house where the water from the well was always so deliciously cool. And to get there I skirted the top of Cottage Field which contained the potatoes whose ridging had earned me the bad foot.

By this time, even on our depleted land, the haulm had closed over the top of the furrows to form a straggly mattress of solid green. I was sweeping it with my gaze, fascinated by the way in which the heat made the air shimmer when I realised that towards the middle of the field the colour of the foliage abruptly changed.

Forcing my way through the web of stems, I finally reached what looked like a pool of desolation. In a radius of about fifteen feet, a whole patch of the crop was rotting. So many of the leaves had become blistered and distorted that the soil could easily be seen. And already many of the stems were going dark brown. Leaning over to peer more closely, I could see fungus sprouting from them everywhere. I was still bending when I became conscious of the stench and nearly vomitted. Moving back to the headland, I scanned the crop again and realised that many small rotting patches were developing all over the field. Aware by now of just how destructive the blight could be, I raced to the house to tell my father.

He wasn't in the kitchen and when I shouted for him there was no reply. Waiting for a moment, I shivered. It was much cooler in the shade of the kitchen than it had been in the fields and the running had made me sweat. All I could hear was the heavy tick of the clock from the hall and the buzz of a bluebottle which was trying to fly through a bead-fringed net which covered a pitcher of milk on the side-board. Its drone made me even more impatient to tell my father the dreadful news. 'Pa', I called again more loudly. And when there was no response, I ran upstairs to his bedroom. But the bed was made and he wasn't there.

I was looking out of his window to see if he was in the yard when I heard his pathetic cry of, 'Arthur'. Running downstairs again, I found the kitchen empty. And then I realised that the cellar door was open and the cry came again.

I was about to plunge down into the cellar when I saw his beseeching pain-racked eyes in the dim light. He was trying to crawl up the cellar steps on his hands and knees.

When I reached him, he seemed relieved and, holding my arm tightly he closed his eyes for a moment and then muttered, 'Find your mother and help her to get me to bed and then run to fetch the Doctor'.

Mother told me later that he'd been in so much pain with his back and head that he had gone to the cellar where he kept his fine blended whisky in the hope that a drink would help. But, before he reached the shelf he had fainted and on regaining consciousness had tried to get back to the kitchen.

From that day onwards, he was really a permanent invalid and played no further active role on the farm.

CHAPTER EIGHT

Nine Months

It takes nine months to make a baby. And it took only nine months from that harvest to transform me from a timid schoolboy into a scared man.

Because from the day my father collapsed in the cellar, he took no direct part in running the farm. He spent much of his time in bed and we children rarely saw him. My mother spent all the hours she could spare from the dairy trying to comfort him, But the best she could do was to administer the painkillers which the doctor left, to try to suppress the terrible anguish caused, it was thought then, by persistent migraine.

His back too, perhaps worsened by lying in bed, needed attention. To ease the pain Mother prepared great poultices of a hot and sticky clay. While the tin was being heated in a pan of water on the stove, the whole house was permeated by its strong mentholated smell. Even today when I sense menthol, I am immediately reminded of those grim months.

To be effective, the poultice had to be very hot when initially applied. Trying not to burn herself, Mother would rush from the kitchen with the steaming rectangle of lint held gingerly between her thumbs and forefingers. Seconds later we would hear Father shriek as he felt the heat on the bed-sensitised skin of his lower back. The intial shock was soon followed by a loud sigh of relief as the heat and menthol anaesthetised his aching muscles.

Often, for up to a week at a time, those frequently repeated sounds of shock and pleasure were the only intimation we children had that he was still alive.

Occasionally, when reprieved from the worst of his agony for a few minutes, he'd ask Mother to bring me to his bedside. Then, refusing to acknowledge that he was incapable of running the farm, he'd give me the orders he wished to pass on to Jack.

I dreaded those interviews with a man whose sinister

demeanour and increasingly cadaverous appearance seemed
totally unrelated to the essentially carefree characteristics of the
father I had known throughout childhood. Usually, before
he'd finished telling me what he wanted the men to do, his
pains returned and the frustration of being unable to escape
them soured his temper. As the weeks passed I was more
frequently subjected to his outbursts of bitter irritability.

As his suffering increased, my misery grew. Because I
seemed unable to report any event on the farm which pleased
him. The situation I faced in the farmyard was far from comforting. Jack obviously missed the decisiveness of my father
even though he disagreed with most of his policies. Father's
decisions on the work schedule bore little relation to the status
quo. But in ignoring them, Jack wasn't happy in choosing
between the alternatives. Later, I realised that he was a marvellous lieutenant, but a poor general; a sound and valuable
critic rather than a creator of policy. So that without my father
to argue against he felt confused and lost.

Conscious that at times his indecision prompted barely concealed sceptical looks between Fred and Bill, he became very
cantankerous with me. More aware than anyone of the depressed state of our land, his fears for the future must have been
the most haunting. I suppose that's why his normally phleg-
matic approach to problems sometimes deteriorated into a
panicky confusion and in the worst moments to a senseless
brutality.

By the time that year's stooks were dry and ready for stacking, Jack already had ample grounds for despair. He always
master-minded and carried out the construction of the giant
stacks of corn in which the stooks were packed so tightly that
the autumn rain could never penetrate to spoil the grain. He
was justifiably proud of his skill as a stacker. In previous better
seasons his great straw bastions temporarily transformed the
horizon along the Drayton road. In 1927 so few stooks were
collected that he realised they would make a negligible impact
on the landscape. He was, therefore, moody and short-
tempered before the work began.

Working on the stack with Bill as his aid, he shuffled his
portly body across its awkward surface quickly and with surprising ease. He concentrated on the vital construction of the
corners, leaving Bill to lay the stooks between. And, just as
when wielding a billhook or sickle, he handled his two

pronged fork with wonderful dexterity. With disarming casualness, he would lean out to pick a stook held aloft on a fork by Fred or me from the waggon below and, in a simple deft movement, place it exactly where it was required.

However, it was essential that the stook was presented to him in just the right place and with the ears of corn pointing towards him. Otherwise, his rythm was destroyed. Similarly, his assistant on the stack had to move quickly to keep pace with him. On that disappointing and heavy autumn day, Jack had several times shouted over his shoulder to Bill to stand clear and stop getting in his way. His irritation spread a gloom over the operations which several inane comments from Fred to Bill did nothing to dispel. In fact, they prickled Jack further and ultimately, I became the butt of his ill humour.

Fred and I worked at opposite ends of the waggon which was parked alongside the growing stack. As our load diminished, the stretch to heave the stooks to its top became longer and longer. When it was my turn to feed Jack, I was too anxious not to keep him waiting and I always became flustered. As a result, on numerous occasions, I presented the stook the wrong way round. Since the strain on my short arms was so great and the stooks shed tiny cutting particles of dust, I often closed my eyes when making my final skyward thrust. Then, I'd wait with nagging pains in my calves and forearms until I felt the load removed and I could turn to spike another stook. Each time that happened, I longed for Jack to make an error or become dissatisfied with his work and pause to correct it, so that I might have a moment of relief. But, that didn't happen often and when my stook went up ears outward, Jack deliberately waited to make me hold it a moment longer. As I opened my eyes, I'd face his fierce scowl as he bellowed down, 'Other end'.

He seemed to enjoy my plight. I'd reached a state of almost whimpering exhaustion when a row flared between us which could have destroyed our relationship for ever.

Quite rightly, my father and mother had always insisted that I treat Jack with great respect and obey him at all times when I was working and they were absent. But, co-opted into doing more and more farm work, as the boss's son I had begun to resent his authority. In fairness to Jack, it was power he rarely abused. His superior craftsmanship imposed a willingness to adopt his methods on Bill and Fred as well as on me.

There wasn't much need for him to command. Off duty, he was so uncommunicative and I was so shy that we seldom had real contact.

But the whole atmosphere that day seemed to vibrate with conflict. He had shouted at me on several occasions, each time louder. Then I made the unforgivable error of passing up two wrongly presented stooks in succession. As the second arrived, I felt a numbing pain shoot down my arm as the fork and stook was knocked flying from my grasp. In his flaring anger, he had spun right round and used the shaft of his fork like a cricketer hooking a four. To infuriate him further, his fork had snapped off just below the shank when he made the stroke.

When the report of the clashing shafts died away, he said nothing for a moment and then, hurling his broken shaft far into the field, he pointed down at me with a threatening expression and said, 'Don't you ever get me angry again'.

The meanness of his look and the slight note of hysteria in his voice finally broke my spirit and I began to cry.

'And don't start to blub either', he admonished. Summing up what little courage I had left, I hurled back, 'I'm fed up with being bullied'. Then, throwing my whole fork after his broken shaft, I jumped down from the waggon and fled.

I was going to race to the house and plead for justice from my father but as my anger faded I realised that in his depressed state he would probably take Jack's side. Leaving my job at such an important time was, I knew, unforgivable. But I was determined not to return.

Instead, I plunged off down through the long covert and hid among the grasses on the edge of our landlord's lake below the Hall.

I was very depressed and lay for a long time looking at the heavy sky and wondering why my parents tolerated such an ogre. But, slowly, I was distracted from my resentment by the activity on and around the lake. In the still air diaphanous mosquitoes seemed almost static as they hovered just above its surface, provoking a fat trout to jump. The splash and slap as it landed back on the water made them rise a foot or two in unison before dropping to their former position.

From time to time their patterned aerobatics were disturbed by the skidding arrival or gaggling jumpy take-off of a flight of Mallard duck. Meanwhile, overhead, a flock of white fantail doves from the cote at the Hall performed a whirling serial ballet against the backdrop of smokey grey clouds. They were so beautiful that I resolved to buy a pair which Fred had said he could get me cheap from a friend. As they spiralled, banked and soared and tumbled, I became entranced by the notion of a flock of my own. Taking a last sighting on the position of the trout which I planned to try to catch after dark, I set off for home. Fred, I estimated, would have returned because when I had deserted the team, there hadn't been too many stooks still to stack.

As I approached the house the gravity of my behaviour began to worry me again. Uncertain whether the moment was propitious for a return, I hid behind the wall which separated the yard from the meadows. I was still wondering how to explain my absence from the corn field and looking away from the yard when I was surprised by the click as Fred flung open the gate to release the horses which, watered and fed, were being turned out for the night.

To avoid looking at him, I followed their liberated antics as, freed from the harness and the load of the waggons they frisked and whinnied joyfully and then galloped off down towards the river, leaving a cloud of dust in their wake.

'How's the deserter then?'

He gripped a short stemmed clay pipe firmly between teeth stained brown by strong tea and nicotine. They were very strong he once assured me when using their serrated edges to wear through some sisal twine, 'Because I always clean 'em with a chewed willow wand.' Now they were exposed because he had drawn back his lips to produce what he called his comic smile.

I chose to ignore his question and said rather diffidently, 'Fred, those fantails?'.

'Want 'em do you?' I nodded. 'Righty ho then. See about it tonight.'

With that, he winked decisively and stalked back through the gate leaving it to judder closed behind him. Reassured by the mildness of his rebuke, I stood thinking about the house.

Sadly, I needn't have worried. When I reached the kitchen, Gladys was sitting at the table with her chin cupped in her hands, weeping. 'He'll be all right, you'll see. It's the best thing, the doctor said', Aunt Edith was saying reassuringly.

But Gladys remained unconvinced and sobbed more loudly. Through her tears, she wailed out to me, 'They've taken Father to Hospital, in Newcastle'.

Tom, who was driving by then and had become increasingly interested in the car, had taken my father to the hospital and my mother had gone with them.

It was after dark when they returned. Tom went straight off to do the rounds of the stock and look at a cow that had been unwell. Mother came into the kitchen looking very subdued and tired. As she remained standing and distracted, sipping the tea which Aunt Edith handed her, she said quietly, 'They think it's an abcess on the brain and they will probably operate tomorrow'.

The significance of Fred's conspiratorial grin as he led a pair of horses to the large trough in the yard the next morning escaped me. His large brown eyes seemed to sparkle every time our looks met.

Tired by the late night discussion of my father's plight and numbed by the notion that he might die, I felt his barely suppressed mirth inappropriate. So, as our paths crossed when I was preparing food for the pigs, I tried to ignore him. But, whenever I went about the yard and buildings, Fred seemed to have a reason for being there before me. When I reached for the scoop to measure out the barley meal, I'd be obliged to nod my thanks and notice the amused look on his boney face as he handed it to me. It wasn't until just before he had finished shackling the horses to a plough and was about to move off to the field which I'd deserted on the previous day that the reason for his odd behaviour became obvious.

'Be a pal,' he shouted. 'I've forgotten me pipe. It's on top of the grain bin.'

I was annoyed but, glancing across the yard, I could see that he already had the reins in his hand. Posing a brimming bucket of whey, I ran into the store room which opened off one end of the stable and was Fred's personal domain. Although it was a bright morning, so little light penetrated the dust and cobwebs which clad its small window that it took my eyes several seconds to adjust to the gloom. I had just found the pipe and was about to run out again when the soft cooing of a dove made me jump.

At first, I couldn't find them, but when finally I saw the

pair of fantails, my delight was boundless. Grabbing the rough wood and wire netting box, I stared at them with joy.

I was still trembling with proud excitement when I reached the dairy and showed them to my mother. Despite her depression, she smiled kindly and agreed that they were lovely. Gladys, who was turning cheeses in the maturing room, was equally enthusiastic. Even the maids and Aunt Edith, who were at the height of their morning household bustle, gasped indulgently in turn at the sleek whiteness of the doves.

Each time I bolted across the yard from door to door clutching the cage, Fred, who was still waiting for his pipe, bared his brown teeth, and looking like a goat, bayed with laughter. My obvious happiness was his reward for so much careful plotting. But I didn't learn about his most cunning plot until my mother told me about it much later.

When I finally reached him with the pipe I was also carrying thirty pennies. They were from the personal hoard which was kept in a Gold Flake Tobacco tin on my dressing table and grew slowly every time I sold chestnut conkers at school or received small tips from kind people like Urban Major. And thirty pence was the price which Fred's friend had been asking for the doves.

He took the pipe but ignored the money. 'Here's the money', I said as he stuck the pipe in his mouth and picked up the handles of the plough. Fussing with the the grease-smooth, worn rope reins, he looked away and muttered. 'We've had a bit of luck. He says we can have 'em free because he's got too many for his cote.'

He didn't give me time to react. Making the ropes ripple over the horses' rumps, he urged them forward. The jingling of the chains and wheeze of the plough wheel as it began to move across the cobbles sounded like sniggering laughter and drowned my grateful 'Thank him for me.' But Fred owed the fantail breeder no thanks. Because he had paid for the birds out of his own scant wages.

His charitable gesture turned out to be a wonderfully appreciated act of kindness. Watching the doves provided the calmest and happiest moments during the last few months of my father's life. Before he returned from hospital, I had confined them to a pigeon's loft above the stable for a few days' familiarisation and then, gradually increasing their freedom, had settled them as part of the Fordhall scene. I believe now that their grace and beauty helped to lighten everyone's spirit during those dark days at the end of 1927 and during the first months of 1928.

Although he was confined to bed, when the ambulance delivered my father back from the Hospital in Newcastle, we all shared his belief that he would soon recover completely.

He was obviously still very weak, but Aunt Edith's confidence that 'a few weeks of our good food and we'll soon have him on his feet' seemed justified by his own lighter spirit.

Even as he was being carried into the house, he raised himself on his elbows on the stretcher and turning to Jack said, 'I've been thinking it over and decided that we ought to try sugar beet instead of potatoes in Banky Field next year'.

Jack didn't reply but, as in the old days, shook his head slowly as though seriously considering the idea. He was clearly shocked by my father's wraith-like appearance. But his eyes, which had seemed dull and unresponsive over the past months, twinkled with pleasure because his boss was regaining his former enthusiasm for life.

Sadly our optimism soon dwindled. Mother had only pretended to share it because the Doctor had told her that the surgeons weren't sure that he wouldn't be permanently damaged by the operation or even that it would be a lasting success. And it is obvious now that the mere fact of being home again had boosted his own euphoria for a few days.

Instead of gathering vitality, he became increasingly listless. By Christmas, his melancholia had begun to return and his back was troubling him again. I think I was probably the first person to realise that what we all dreaded most was beginning to happen. When I entered his room with some snowdrops I'd gathered in Castlehill Wood, I thought he was alseep. But, I realised that he was merely pressing his eyes closed to avoid the sunlight aggravating the pains in his head. He admitted to my mother that since early January, they had become worse daily. By the time we'd finished lambing, in mid-March, he was so badly afflicted that once more Mother was obliged to dose him with painkillers and to prevent anyone else visiting his room to avoid his being disturbed. I was grateful when I thought that at least I shouldn't have to convey the dreadful news about the lambing.

Our pastures had become so impoverished that the ewes had been in a very low state at the vital moment in their pregnancy when the unborn lambs were developing fastest. Many of them were born dead. Or, if they survived, their mothers didn't have sufficient milk to feed them and despite our best efforts to wean them onto cows milk in a bucket, many of them just faded away in the first few days.

Although some of the ewes died as a result of their debilitating experience in that harsh winter weather, they survived better than the lambs; demonstrating again the rule that in nature the survival of the breeding adult seems to take priority over the fate of the offspring.

As a lowland flock, we should normally have expected that since some ewes would give birth to twins, or even occasionally triplets, the zero return from barren ewes or occasionally stillbirths would have been well compensated for and our breeding mothers would have returned an average of one and a quarter lambs each. But, owing to their inadequate diet in 1928, the average dropped to less than one.

The weight or volume of crops harvested and the number of offspring born to a flock of sheep, or a herd of cows or pigs has always been the most obvious way in which farmers measure and boast about their successes. Thankfully, Father didn't have to admit to his friends at Drayton Market how poorly we fared during the 1927-28 year. Mother was happy that, at least, his illness helped him to avoid that humiliation. Even his brother Tom, who was always at his most infuriatingly superior when comparing farm outputs, was sensitive enough to discuss other things on his rare and inevitably short visits to the bedside.

However, I couldn't escape facing the brunt of his disappointment. Since his return from hospital, we had kept up the facade that he was still in charge of farm affairs. So that whenever his head pained him least, he'd send for me to issue orders. A month before lambing, worried about the poor state of the grass elsewhere, Jack had decided to move the ewes into Mill Meadow. On the flanks of Long Covert, although less of a swamp than our other riverside meadows, it still tended to be damp. But Jack thought it worth risking the foot troubles and debilitating humidity because the supply of grass seemed better.

When I told Father, he was furious. Lambing had always

taken place at Fordhall on the high well-drained fields he explained. 'They are colder but healthier. How many times have I told you that sheep don't like it damp under the hoof when they are lambing,' he shouted. 'Tell Jack to move them back immediately'. Alarmed by his raised voice, Mother arrived and sent me away before I agreed to obey.

Since his headaches became very bad in March, I hardly ever saw him and believed that he would never ask about the lamb crop. But he did. And I was forced to admit its failure. When he learned that the flock was still in Mill Meadow his bellowed 'Young Fool' could be heard all through the house and terrified me. But the shrieked admonition, 'You'd better bloody well learn to obey me if you want to stay on this farm', was almost inaudible against the pounding feet of Aunt Edith and Mother as they rushed up the stairs. Bursting into the room and realising my distress, Mother momentarily forgot his illness and began to shout back. 'Alfred, for God's sake, stop.' She had hardly finished the sentence before he started writhing round the bed while clutching his head. When she reached his side and threw her arms round his shoulders, he gasped and shuddered in a mighty effort to escape the pain and then implored her to fetch his tablets.

That was the last time that he ever shouted in anger. Tragically, in the weeks which followed, despite heavy sedation, his suffering frequently became so intolerable his anguished cries could even be heard in the yard. Feeling impotent because we couldn't help, the rest of us tried desperately to ignore his calvary. Gladys, Aunt Edith and the maids spent most of their time behind closed dairy doors trying hard to compensate for Mother's absence, while she hugged and comforted him and shared his ordeal.

To escape, I spent most of my free time in the pigeon loft tending the doves. Mother told me later that she was sure that their swirling gyrations beyond his window or their coy flirtations on the stable roof which he could watch from his bed were the only activities which would momentarily distract my father from his suffering. And even though the massive doses of morphine pain killer which the doctor had begun to prescribe left him barely conscious, Mother always swore that when he first saw their grown family of three flutter down beside them on the roof his eyes lit for a second with joy.

It is comforting to think now that this was one of his last

true moments of awareness before he lapsed into the coma in which they took him away to the hospital, where he died in the May. I'm sure that Fred too, if he were alive now, would share that sentiment.

CHAPTER NINE

Uncle Tom

'Idle boy'.

I only heard the last syllable the first time the science master said it, And, suspended as I was by the lobe of an ear firmly pinched between his thumb and forefinger, I was obliged to turn away from him to lessen the pain. 'Idle boy', he shouted again as he disdainfully released me and I became fully conscious.

The warm, late June afternoon, my general exhaustion and the gentle purr and fume of the bunsen burners had made me feel sleepy within ten minutes of entering the chemistry laboratory. Twice I'd found myself dozing and tried to fight off the sleep by shuffling on the high lab stool. But, in the end, drugged by the monotonous drone of his flat industrial midlands voice, I leaned my head down on an unopened book and collapsed into a welcoming oblivion.

My nervous astonishment on awakening must have fostered his talent for bullying. The class, which had begun to giggle at my discomfort, relapsed into a terrified silence as he grabbed my jacket collar and pulled me to my feet. 'I'm sick and tired of you Hollins,' he shrieked. 'This is a laboratory not a dormitory. But week after week you are dull and inattentive.' I found it hard to face him. Even when calm, he was an unattractive man. But, in anger, the veins seemed to glow beneath a scaling, plaster white skin which in places appeared to have been blotched brown by years of exposure to the vapours from his acid bottles. Apart from a nose long and thin as a shark's fin, designed, it appeared, for sneering down, his most outstanding feature was an unruly mop of hair that was more carrot coloured than auburn. His worst and most intimidating features were, however, frosty blue eyes which bored out from narrow slits and a tiny mouth which seemed barely large enough to take the stem of his off duty pipe. But, small though it was, he used it like a master to jet abuse in my direction. As he saw the tears beginning to rise in my eyes, his attack became more vitriolic.

'It's perhaps a blessing your father is dead. At least he won't have the shame of witnessing your dismal performance.' Pricked, perhaps, by my distress, he drowned his guilt in a torrent of further abuse and then roughly pushing me towards the door: 'Get out. Get out and leave the place free for people who are intelligent enough to learn.'

His unsympathetic blindness prevented him realising that what I most desperately wished to learn was how to manage a farm. The products of distilling coal were of far less importance than the chemistry of feeding plants, ways of making the soil yield crops or the understanding of the acquisition of authority over men, subjects about which, despite her talents in the dairy and her sympathy for my snivelling plight after I'd trudged unhappily home, my mother could teach me little.

If prolonged misery induces a necessary catharsis after death, the weeks following the loss of my father must have served me well. It began immediately we reached home after trailing glumly back from his funeral; Mother and I riding in Uncle Tom's car. Between brisk sips of funeral breakfast sherry, punctuated by authoritative and self important undulations of the tongue as he savoured it against his palate, he coldly reviewed our situation.

'As I continually warned Alfred, things are not good at all. Having been through the books, I can't see how the enterprise can survive. While sympathetic, the bank manager says without a guarantee from me, he is not anxious to allow you to carry on.'

As I watched him from a chair in a corner, the side of his well fed face towards the window was lit by the bright May sunlight. It seemed to reflect a pompous satisfaction at our plight.

'We'll have to see what can be done. My bailiff will keep an eye on things once a week. I'll send him over on Mondays. If anything special needs looking at, I'll come over myself. You and I will meet at Drayton Market so that I can sign all the cheques and give you the money to pay the men. But, I'd better warn you now, there will have to be changes.'

There was a nasty menace in his voice and we all waited apprehensively as he paused to establish his authority. Gladys drew her breath as he pointed towards our student who was standing with the tray of drinks near the scullery door. 'Tom there will have to go back to his father. Because you can't afford to keep him. And I don't know how long you can go on feeding those two strapping lasses Edith has about the kitchen. Meanwhile, young Arthur will have to face the inevitable. And he and Gladys will have to do a great deal more about the place to see if you can't do without Bill or Fred because nothing eats up profits like men's wages.'

He had put down his glass decisively on the table and was beginning to draw on his driving gloves with slow exaggerated precision as he issued his last ominous threat. 'I want to make myself perfectly clear. I can only go on trying to help as long as my orders are obeyed. It will take a great deal of thought and effort to make this place pay and there won't be room for two masters on the ship.'

'We'll do our best, Tom', my mother quietly but firmly replied as she walked him to the door.

But, as the weeks passed, it was clear that no matter how hard we tried, he'd never be satisfied. The extra efforts made to please him involved my rising at 5.30 and working until 8.30 or 9 in the evening when I returned from school to try to compensate for the loss of our student, Tom. It created conflict with most of my masters, who made no attempt to discover why I was habitually exhausted and found it difficult to stay awake in class. Ultimately, six weeks after my father's death, it led to the stinging humiliation of my expulsion from the chemistry laboratory.

I hadn't been home long and was carrying the first yoke of milk over to the dairy when Steve Fuller entered the yard. Although the original stone cobbles were mostly covered in a sun-baked carpet of mud and manure, he dragged his iron shod boots so quickly and harshly over the ground that he made more noise and raised more dust than the horses.

It was a walk which betrayed his gross insensitivity. Matching his coarse face and brutish manners, it no doubt served Uncle Tom's interests well. In an age of high unemployment, when workers were afraid to argue, Fuller must have been a perfect bailiff, shouting and bullying his way about my Uncle's farm, dragging his boots quickly from one field to another. That afternoon he was clearly in a black mood. He had been rowing with Jack in the potato field. Blinded by his wrath, he nearly ran into me and upset my pails of milk.

'Where's your mother?', he shouted angrily. I was as afraid of him as his own men and simply nodded towards the dairy.

When I reached the door, he was already haranguing my mother. 'It's no damn good, missus. Mr. Hollins won't like it at all. I told them to wait until we'd had a shower — upsetting the soil about them tatties now'll only make it dry out. But he's nowt but sheer pig headed that man of yours.'

After several weeks of bullying from Steve Fuller and trying to appease him to obtain good reports to' Uncle Tom, my mother had begun to fight back. I saw her hand tighten its grasp on the wooden paddle she'd been using to stir the rennet into the milk in the coagulation tank as she eyed Fuller coldly and replied with equal force. 'Jack has been looking after potatoes here for a long time now, Mr. Fuller. And, if he thinks they need ridging to tear up and dry out the weeds, I dare say he's right.'

Unused to being contradicted, Fuller simply glared at my mother in silence. But, as he turned to leave, he grunted, 'We'll see what Mr. Hollins has to say'.

'Doubtless we will, Mr. Fuller, doubtless we will,' my mother said quietly as he stalked through the door.

It was as he was leaving that I realised how overcast it had become. On my way home from school I'd noticed clouds building to the West and heard the rumble of distant thunder. By the time Fuller arrived, the sky was almost as dark as his frown. And, when he left the dairy, the first heavy spots of rain had begun to fall. Before he reached his car, the down pipes were spilling out torrents of water from the roofs and the whole landscape was hidden behind a dense grey-white curtain of hissing rain.

As we peered out from the dairy door, my mother squeezed the back of my neck tenderly. And looking around, I was astonished by the brightness of her eyes and the radiance of her smile. Without saying anything, we both began to laugh.

Sadly, our victory in the skirmish with Steve Fuller only gained us temporary respite from my Uncle's interference. But I suppose that it was useful in stiffening our resolution to be more independent. At least once a week, everyone groaned when Uncle Tom's immaculate car was seen turning into the gate at the end of our track. It always heralded an hour of carping criticism, even when the situation seemed temporarily to have improved.

If the potatoes looked better, the corn was rather thin. The smooth roundness of well-fed thriving pigs never compensated for unthrifty looking cattle or sheep. He didn't believe in encouragement. I suppose that in some way he must have felt it would undermine his authority. Perhaps it was his restless dissatisfaction and desire for perfection which made him into such a good farmer on his own land. But that was land much richer and in better heart than ours. The methods he applied so successfully over in Cheshire achieved little improvement at Fordhall.

It seems clear that when undertaking to guarantee our over-draft, he had little intention of helping us for long. If the instant application of what he believed to be sounder methods could extract heavier crops from our worn out fields, and there seemed some chance of his getting his money back, he prob-ably intended to continue his aid. But, by mid July, this obviously wasn't going to happen. The early corn was as thin as in the previous distressing year. The potatoes which while relying upon their own store of foodstuffs had come through the ground well, were becoming very straggly and unpromis-ing. The heavy thunder storm which had drenched Steve Fuller, while temporarily greening up the summer pastures, had come too late to affect the light hay crop which was already in the smaller-than-usual stack. That made us fear for supplies of livestock feed in the coming winter. Only the pigs, fed as usual on a mixture of corn, offal and nutritious whey from the dairy, looked well. But, as the great industrial depression was beginning to strangle the economy, the price obtained for fat porkers at the market was very low.

These were the facts, which, my mother told me, Uncle Tom put before her when they met at the Drayton market on that fateful day. Their discussion began in the cafe they always used for a light snack at lunch time — a time when she was most tired. Not only was the early period of the market most active, but she had been up since just after dawn in the dairy, separating cream from milk and packing it in wax cartons, weighing up and wrapping the pound circular discs of the butter which she had previously churned, or selecting the cheeses which were ready for sale.

It is hardly surprising that she wept when Uncle Tom made his blunt announcement. 'So I've put two weeks wages in each of these packets and that's the best I can do,' he said as he handed her the money. Mother was too tired and gaining too much relief from her cup of tea to react immediately. He continued just as she realised what he meant.

'It's no good,' he said. 'That farm will never support you all. So you will have to give the men a week's notice. You can fetch most of the livestock over to me and John will have to use your equipment to harvest the crops before the sale.'

John Hollins was my father's older brother. A much more compassionate man than Uncle Tom and less forceful than either he or my father. He was nominally also helping to carry our burden. Since Father's death, he had agreed with the suggestions which Tom had made for running Fordhall. They were similar to the methods he also used successfully on his own farm near Nantwich. If he hadn't turned up at the cafe, at Uncle Tom's request, to discuss the details of our giving up Fordhall, it is doubtful whether I should have been farming the land today. After she had recovered from her initial shock, my mother would probably have accepted its full implications.

'The family will have to be split', Tom said brutally. 'You and Gladys can come and live with us − my two in the dairy will soon be too old to work and you two can take their place to earn your keep and feel independent − because I know that's what you'd want.'

'But, what will happen to Arthur and Margaret?', my mother asked through rising tears. 'Well now, Eva and I have given that a lot of thought', Tom explained. Mother said he seemed less embarrassed and could ignore her crying when asked to apply his thrusting decisiveness to practical questions.

Although she had visited us at Fordhall at times of large family gatherings like Christmas, his wife, Eva, had always been a rather shadowy and remote figure to us children. Reserved and somewhat demure, she didn't participate much in discussions and never attempted to contradict Uncle Tom. My other aunts seemed jealous because, while obviously running Tom's household impeccably, she had never worked in the dairy. Some mysterious illness in her youth, which we children were discouraged from discussing, had left her unsuited to hard physical work. And, although she seemed fit enough to us, she gave the impression that her past complaint made her merit special consideration. When she was absent, the other Hollins women obviously resented her privileged situation and didn't hesitate to remark that, despite the gentility of her table manners, she ate more than most of them. It was clear that whatever Uncle Tom felt, Aunt Eva wasn't prepared to lodge all our family.

'There simply isn't room, you see. So we thought that Arthur and Margaret had better go to John and Stella.'

Even then, Mother was astonished that Tom could have contemplated parting her from her youngest children. It was only later that she realised he was less interested in humanity than in obtaining cheap and useful help about his farm. Margaret was still a shy child who needed supporting and he didn't need my help with the cows or in the fields. Mother's wonderful skills in the dairy which he had always openly admired, supported by Gladys, who was becoming a fine assistant, could, however, have been profitably exploited.

Believing that my mother's hostile silence was provoked by the notion of working for him, Tom hastened to reassure her. 'You'd be your own boss in the dairy, my dear. No one would interfere.'

She was further upset by the way he began to smile at the prospect of the added prosperity her talents could bring. It made him become quite animated. 'We are not bad milk producers, you know, Lillian, and it's quality stuff with plenty of good cream. You could spend a bit of money on modernising – get some of that newer equipment you've been telling me about.'

He became short tempered when she obviously wasn't enthusiastic, and sighing, said flatly, 'What's to become of Edith?'. 'Well, we don't need a cook, but she's good at it and she will just have to find a place.'

The notion that any of our family, which had been independent yeomen farmers as far back as we could discover, should have to enter domestic service, was intolerable to my mother. Her distress began to embarrass Tom greatly. As he glanced round, it was obvious that other people in the cafe were beginning to stare at him belligerently. He was relieved when John arrived. Seeing my mother sobbing loudly, he said firmly but quietly, 'This is no place to discuss family matters, Tom. We'd better get her back to Fordhall'.

I was upstairs changing into my working clothes when they arrived. But all the doors were open and I was conscious of the commotion as they entered the kitchen. Uncle John was supporting my mother and when she looked up from the stove, Aunt Edith was shocked by her condition.

'God love us, what's happened?', I heard her cry. I was running down the stairs buttoning my shirt when my mother wailed in reply, 'Tom wants us to give up Fordhall'.

Drawn by the noise, Gladys rushed across the yard from the dairy. And Margaret, who had been watching her work, followed in her wake. Confronted by us all, Mother, who had had only to face our plight in abstract in the cafe, realised fully what Tom's proposals meant. She broke down completely and began to cry hysterically.

As Uncle John helped her into a chair and stooped to hug and comfort her, we all stared reproachfully at Tom. 'God, it's hopeless,' he shouted, pricked by our anger. 'She can't see reason. Doesn't she realise when she's well off?'

He was still ranting as he turned to my mother, 'You'd think the end of the world had come. You are not doing a bit of good to yourself or anyone else going on like this. You've got to face the facts, woman.'

My mother's rending scream in reply of, 'The facts, the facts', provoked unusual courage in me. 'Leave her alone,' I shouted as I rushed forward and tried to drag him away. But I was still slight. Shrugging me off, he continued to bellow at my mother, leaning forward to emphasise his point.

'Yes, woman, the facts. You are bankrupt and I'm offering you your best chance of survival. You must face reality. Without the help of John and me, you'd have been out of here long since. You have simply got to . . .'

I wouldn't let him finish. I, too was now crying, more in frustration than despair, as I tried to pull him away from her again. I shouted, 'Don't listen, don't listen, don't listen. We'll run the place ourselves'.

It was a notion, almost a fantasy, which had been slowly germinating in my mind for weeks. Life had become intolerable at school. And, on my returning home, the frequent presence of the sinister Steve Fuller or my pompous uncle had simply added to the misery. I was as much a butt for their bullying ill-humour as my mother. I knew that I was old enough to leave school and I resented the freedom which Harry, who was a month or two older, had already obtained.

As, daily, I had suffered the increasingly scathing remarks

from masters about my inattention and bad work, I had compensated by withdrawing into the dream of leaving and becoming a fully fledged farmer. But when my fourteenth birthday arrived and I made the suggestion to my mother, she had dismissed it. Proud that I was at the Grammar School and anxious that I should complete my education, she insisted that I carry on to obtain the prized School Certificate. Her courage in the circumstances was remarkable. Uncle Tom allowed her only the minimum cash necessary to meet the farm bills from week to week. Margaret, the cleverest of all of us, was now also at a fee-paying girls' school. To pay the bills for the autumn term, Mother knew that she'd have to face great hardship. Tom had made it clear that he thought I should leave school as soon as possible and that Margaret should transfer to a free school the week after Father had died. But Mother had refused to listen.

However, despite her previous resolution, she listened then as I urged her to throw off the yoke imposed by Uncle Tom. 'Tell him, Ma, tell him; I'll leave school and we'll get by on our own.'

Surprised by my unexpected outburst, Uncle Tom fell silent. Straightening up, he eyed me sceptically. 'So you're going to run it, are you? Leaving school's one thing, but what are you going to do for brass to pay the wages?'

That was a problem I'd skirted round when enjoying my dream of liberation.

'Don't you worry. We'll find a way', I stammered out, sounding, I believe, more confident than I felt.

Uncle Tom looked at Uncle John and sighed heavily. 'Tell him, John. It's bloody ridiculous – the bank would close them by the end of the week.'

He was furious when instead of agreeing immediately, John paused for a second and then said quietly: 'Listen, Tom. I think everyone's too upset to start making decisions now. Let's give it a week or two and see what can be arranged.'

Uncle Tom wasn't used to opposition. He tried to suppress his anger and appealed to Uncle John. 'There's nothing better to be arranged, you know that. And there's no point in dragging the business out. Let's stop wasting time and money and settle the matter now.'

Before John could say anything, my mother interrupted. 'That's right, let's settle it now. We'll do it Arthur's way, we'll run it ourselves.' As she spoke, the notion of dispensing with the humiliating need to have to account for everything to Uncle Tom clearly began to lift her spirits.

'What are you going to run it on?' he asked contemptuously.

'I've no idea,' she replied with a weak smile, 'I've no idea, but we will find a way.'

The strength of her last words made him realise that to argue would be pointless. Nodding his head in disbelief, he began to move towards the door.

'I don't know. You can't help some people – but I'll have to make it clear that if that's the road you choose, you will have to tread it on your own.'

CHAPTER TEN

The Master of Fordhall

Betty's gesture seemed as courageous as Captain Oates' decision to sacrifice himself for the sake of the group by crawling off into the Antarctic twilight.

She'd been lurking behind the scullery door with Joan while the row with Uncle Tom raged. Some strong rural intuition must have made her realise that we could only survive with fewer mouths to feed.

Before Tom had driven away, she was confronting Mother with her second shock of the day. 'They've been at me to go and help over at the Manor. They need more hands now that there are children. So, if you've no objection, I'll go.'

Her announcement stunned us more than Uncle Tom's departure. She was an intimate part of Fordhall life, as much a member of the family as anyone else. Although her leaving would reduce our food and wages bill at a time when only paring back our cash requirements to the absolute minimum could help us to survive, more than anything it made us conscious of our precarious situation.

It was a situation which became even more obvious to me when Mother unlocked my father's roll-top desk that night. We were alone, talking quietly when everyone else had gone to bed. The act of turning the key in the lock seemed to strengthen her resolution. The last of the summer evening light cast a soft pink glaze over features that had become drawn and hardened during her recent ordeal. She seemed to be smiling confidently as very slowly and deliberately, she handed me the key. We both knew that it was an important moment. She was making me the master of Fordhall.

Although she'd allowed Uncle Tom access to my father's papers after his death, she'd never been able to face them herself. Despite his irrational behaviour and the trauma of his last years, she was missing him greatly. Outwardly she was being brave. But loyally attributing his faults to the developing illness, she fretted for him when alone. Continuing to use their bedroom, she cried herself to sleep each night. However, her decision that we should continue to farm and that I should be responsible for everything outside the dairy marked the end of her worst suffering.

Although Uncle Tom was right and we should have called the creditors meeting which would have been a short prelude to our liquidation, her faith that we could survive provided me with the strength I needed. But I can't pretend my confidence didn't fluctuate violently during those early days. While he was still fit, I was too young for my father to make me aware of his financial problems. And he was too impatient and too seldom at home to teach me much about practical farming. As his illness developed, although I was older and a more willing and appropriate pupil, he had been too cantankerous and defensive to answer even simple questions. Although I only half understood them, the vital papers in his desk told me why.

When I had isolated the bank statements, bills and rent book from the golf club fixture lists, sheafs of notes about the port, madeira and malt whisky he'd laid down in the cellar (and a mound of invitations to smart social functions he'd attended in the past) the true grounds for Tom Hollins pessimism stuck out from the plain of our euphoria like a forbidding crag.

Even in an epoch when a bank overdraft was considered by puritanical countrymen as a sin, Father's ability to talk with conviction and authority had enabled him to build up what seemed to us like a formidable £500 debt. In those days, that was more than the annual salary of the manager who approved the loans against insubstantially based promises that repayment would be certain and prompt. Unpaid bills to Clive Thompson, the corn merchant, for the additional food we needed for our animals almost doubled the debt. Faced with another difficult winter, when we'd certainly need more grain and concentrated feed than usual, that liability seemed all the more daunting because Clive Thompson was also our landlord and the books showed that we owed him three quarters of a year's rent — a further £270.

It was well into the night before I realised that my career as a farmer was to begin under the burden of more than £1,000 of debts. The initial excitement I'd felt when first allowed to touch what had formerly been sacred and confidential business documents had evaporated. I needed more reassurance from Mother who had left me to calculate alone. But when I gently opened her bedroom door, I realised that she had quickly fallen into a deep restorative sleep for the first time in weeks. So my glum conclusions had to wait until the morning.

When I came back into the house from milking, there was little time for discussion or decision making. There were still five days of the school term left and, despite my protests, Mother insisted that I complete the year. She wanted me to arrive at school early to deliver the note which she had written to the Headmaster explaining our predicament and her decision to take me away. Handing the letter to his secretary gave me more satisfaction than anything since I had naively welcomed the news that I had passed the entrance exam. Temporarily banishing my fears about our future, it strengthened my spirit during the encounter with the chemistry master.

Since it was our last lesson of the term with him, he had abandoned studies and set us the traditional recreational task of composing a chemical crossword. But, ungenerous to the last, he spoilt our pleasure by using the time to hand back our corrected exam papers.

1 Across — The best of what we breathe   OXYGEN
1 Down — Seaside Tonic   OZONE
6 Down Most of the rest of what we breathe   NITROGEN

I was quite proud of those but already becoming frustrated by words beginning with X or Y and was blacking in the squares below them to have a chance to start again when he threw my papers onto the desk.

'Another disaster, Hollins, another disaster ' Without looking up at him, I could tell from his voice that he was already sneering. 'You will have to do a lot better than that next term.'

He was indulging his favourite affectation with his empty pipe, moving it in and out with his lips like a moth flexing its proboscis when, staring at him hard I replied. 'I won't be here next term, sir.'

Although clearly astonished, he tried to appear disinterested as he spoke languidly. 'Where, I wonder, will you be?'

'Helping my mother to run the farm, sir.'

A master of sarcasm, his sneer began to return as he nodded

and turned towards the rest of the class. 'Perhaps it's as well, Hollins, perhaps it's as well.'

Although he didn't quite smile, he raised an eyebrow in acknowledgement of the laugh his remark provoked. There were few opportunities for levity during his classes so they couldn't be blamed for sharing his scorn. But I tingled with resentment during the seemingly interminable ten minutes which remained of the period.

My pride was still sadly deflated as I slowly gathered together my papers and pushed them into my satchel. All the class had left the laboratory when a sympathetic mate looked back into the room and, ignoring the master, shouted, 'Come on, farmer — you'll be late for the match'.

I'd forgotten that we'd been allowed to miss lessons for the rest of the morning to begin the interform cricket matches. Cheered by that thought, I began to move quickly to the door when he called me back. 'Hollins, er . . . Hollins.' Expecting further abuse, I was surprised by his obvious embarrassment. 'Hollins, I just er. . . .' Holding his pipe by its bowl, he gesticulated with its wet gnawed stem as though he was trying to prick the right words out of the air. But, abandoning the attempt, he turned away and looked down into his open desk where he must have the found the courage to urge out a quiet, 'Luck, Hollins, good luck', before nodding decisively to indicate that the interview was over.

I was too astonished to do more than mutter my thanks as I ran off to the cricket. However, the abrupt change in attitude of the man I'd feared most during my three years at the school added greatly to my enjoyment of the game. I ran harder and hurled the ball with more vigour than ever before. It even added spring to my steps as I half ran, half walked home.

Urban Major was in the kitchen when I gabbled out the news to my mother and Uncle John. He shrugged his shoulders and laughed. 'They are all the bloody same. Terrorise you for years and then try to apologise when you are growing up so that you won't hold it against them.'

Although when crossing the river below Castlehill, skirting the lake and clambering among the trees on the opposite slope I'd seen sections of the Hall from a distance, I was overawed by its complete facade.

As we swept round the gravel turning point at the end of the drive, Mother warned me firmly not to interrupt the coming discussion. She was obviously very nervous but divined that my presence at the interview with our landlord might induce extra sympathy. Uncle John, too, was quieter than usual and seemed very grave in his dark blue 'going to town' suit. In my Sunday grey flannel, which I was starting to outgrow, I felt foolish and dreadfully constricted. But we must have looked serious and respectable enough to be shown straight into the morning room by the maid who had answered the bell.

While we waited, the silence was only broken by the roosting argument of some rooks in a nearby group of elms and the distant chink of cutlery on plates as the Thompson family finished its supper. Mother sat in obvious discomfort on the edge of her chair, clenching and unclenching her fists. Inwardly rehearsing the way in which he would present our case, Uncle John was peering distractedly out of the window. I stared at them both in turn and, obtaining no recognition, settled to absorbing the details of the impressive mahogany furniture in the lofty room. Compared with the simple domesticity at home, it hinted at a way of life and a grandeur which I could barely comprehend. It obviously added to my mother's unease. She must have felt that our problems would seem quite inconsequential to a man used to such august surroundings.

Although we were present by appointment and he responded quickly to the announcement that we had arrived, the few minutes before Clive Thompson entered the room seemed interminable. To me they recalled similar anxious times spent waiting to enter the dentist's chair, because we had just as many gruesome thoughts to occupy us.

Before leaving home, we had all been speculating upon Thompson's willingness to refuse what sounded like an unrepeatable offer. In that era of agricultural depression, people weren't fighting to become farmers. But the landlord had told Uncle Tom that if we wanted to give up he'd had an unexpected offer of a higher rent from a potteries business man who wanted a house in the country so that his wife could keep horses. Now that we were so much in his debt we could hardly have avoided eviction if he wanted to foreclose.

Earlier that day, Mother and Uncle John had visited the bank to arrange an increased overdraft supported by a long term guarantee from Uncle John. That would enable us to pay some bills and provide money for day to day expenses until we had harvested some of our crops. It wouldn't however, be any help if we had no land to farm. Only Clive Thompson could decide our fate. So, in our minds, he became a terrifying figure.

He must have detected something of our anxiety when he entered the room. Switching on the light, he quickly dispelled the evening gloom, and with the most convincing bonhomie, made a great effort to make us feel welcome. When we refused coffee, he insisted that we all join him in a glass of port. He swept aside my mother's reluctance to allow me to drink it with a laughing, 'Nonsense, my dear. He's the master of the house now and, like his father before him, he must learn to enjoy his glass of port'. Previously, I had only seen him on a few occasions, when he'd called to see Father. Too preoccupied by their business, he had done little more than nod briefly in my direction. His recognition of my new role, then, gained him my respect for ever.

There is no doubt that my gratitude wasn't misplaced because without his immediate and long term help, our bid to survive as farmers would have failed. He had clearly liked my father and had been saddened by his business misfortunes and long illness. The reputation of Uncle John, as a sound farmer and man of impeccable integrity, must also have helped to attract Thompson's sympathy.

He didn't take long to reassure us. 'It would be better,' he said, 'to draw a line below the present account and start again. You can consider the debts to date as a long term liability to be paid off as and when you can. I'd be obliged, however, if in the future you could let me have the rent at the beginning of each quarter and if you would pay your feed bills at the end of each month. And, if you can't settle, don't let it mount up. Come and see me immediately so that I can see what we can do.'

When the period is considered, this warm and paternal approach was really quite remarkable. Although he too had benefitted greatly from the agricultural prosperity of the war years, his income was obviously being restricted by the depression. To even the blindest optimist, our chances of ever repaying my father's debts must have seemed very remote. Clive Thompson was not only allowing us to try to survive, but virtually making us a present of a large sum of money which he must have known he might need if the financial depression deepened. It was a spontaneously generous gesture which I shall never forget.

At the time, my mother was so affected that she could barely prevent herself from crying. Her confusion and relief was so great that I am not sure whether she even remembered to thank him formally. But, I am sure that her delighted expression was sufficient recognition for Clive Thompson.

Urban Major was so pleased by the news when we returned to Fordhall that he rushed out to his car and returned with a bottle of port he'd bought to take home. 'This calls for a little celebration,' he shouted while rummaging in the drawer for a corkscrew.

He rapidly overcame Mother's abstemious resistance to the idea of having a second drink within the hour, a lapse which quickly reddened her cheeks and prompted her to giggle continuously. If I hadn't already begun to feel light headed myself, I believe that I'd have noticed her becoming drunk for the only time in her life.

There was undoubtedly a lot to celebrate. Only one important problem remained. How to feed the animals during the coming winter? To give us a chance of obtaining a good second crop of hay in September, Urban suggested that he and John should each provide summer grazing for some of the beef cattle and sheep on their farms. This would enable us to close off a portion of the meadows to allow the grass to grow undisturbed.

Urban felt that this decision warranted yet another drink. He filled the glasses again and even Aunt Edith, stimulated by the cheering news and growing animation, stopped bustling about the sink, accepted a glass and laughing hysterically, allowed herself to be dragged onto Urban's knee to drink it. After a few sips, I began to feel very heavy and a little sick. Realising that no one would notice, I slipped out into the gathering dusk. Taking my rod from the porch I walked slowly down to the river. It was almost dark when I arrived.

When fetching the cows up for milking that morning, I'd seen a sizeable fish rising just under the the bank of Broad Meadow where the current was swiftest. Reaching the place, I stood quietly waiting. The air was very calm and still quite warm. I could hear a steer occasionally coughing as it grazed among the tall reeds in the low meadows half a mile away.

From somewhere towards the Hall a barn owl hooted her proc-lamation that the time of the night creatures had arrived.

As I breathed deeply, trying to gasp the alcohol away, I caught the heavy scent of a fox which must have crept behind me; but peering into the light haze which was collecting over the grass I saw nothing.

While still staring away, I heard the first plop as the trout rose to take a late fly. I turned back to the water, annoyed that I'd missed it. Concentrating hard, I waited for it to happen again. It clearly wasn't hungry; satiated, I supposed, with the midges which had been annoying the cattle all day. I could feel my feet getting cold as the dew from the grass soaked into my socks in the five minutes which had passed before the fish rose again. Then I shook with excitement, realising why I'd missed it before. It was almost below my feet, barely three yards away.

I had just pulled out a short length of line and flicked it a few feet upstream beyond the rise when I was startled by a high pitched squeal from over the water. It was one of those persis-tent nerve-shredding sounds which can make the rural night terrifying to the uninitiated. Undoubtedly a stoat had caught a rabbit – a creature normally so silent which can shatter the calm of the night with its wailing distress.

While I was distracted by the last whimpering chords of the rabbit's death, the fish struck. It was as though it had been tempted to snatch at the Black Gnat I offered under the camouflage of sound. And it only took a second before it expressed tempestuous anger at its mistake. Plunging for the gravel of the bottom, it made the tip of my rod bow violently. Only the elasticity of the finely seasoned, close grained greenheart which had belonged to my grandfather could have withstood the strain as I fought to raise the fish. At first I thought it must have been one of the monster pike which Fred had spotted maurauding our stretch of the river.

Soon the erratic cunning of its gyrations betrayed that it was indeed the trout. Twice I thought I'd been able to shorten the line sufficiently to draw it unsuspecting onto a gently sloping bank of pebbles. But sensing shallower water it thrashed away and I was obliged to play out more line. It took nearly ten minutes to land the fish. While I was groping about for a stick to stun it, it writhed and leapt about over the wet grass and I had to fling the rod aside and grab it or it would have reached the water again. Once it was quiet, I tried to remove the hook but it was too far into the back of its mouth to reach easily. So, leaving the line attached, I carried the fish by its tail in one hand with the rod in the other as I walked as quickly as possible back to the house.

Sadly, no one was downstairs to greet my triumph. Urban and Uncle John had left. The rest of the famliy had gone to bed. The glasses were stacked in the sink and the empty port bottle stood, a momento of their guilt, on the window sill behind. Deflated by their absence, I realised that I was very tired after such an eventful day. Not bothering to extract the hook, I cut the gut cast and used the free end to hang the trout from a hook in the window lintel. The best fish I ever caught, it must have weighed almost fourteen ounces. Slowly turning on the end of the line, it made a pretty mobile, showing its freckled brown back and silvery white underside alternately.

When I turned down and snuffed the lamp, I was surprised to find it still illuminated by beams from the rising moon which had just reached the window. In that light, the silver glittered even more brightly. It's an image I retain vividly. At the time, it seemed to reflect the promise of a day in which our major immediate problems had been solved. But later, when I began to grapple with our land more seriously, it became the symbol of an ambition. For then, I wished to convert the stagnant water which made our low meadows an acid swamp into an active stream which would support such beautiful fish.

Sheep are fitful grazers. Stupid and incomprehensible to us humans, they must have a wisdom of their own or they wouldn't be able to survive under such widely varying and frequently testing conditions. I still wonder what makes them such uneven performers. Withstanding the burning heat of Europe's Southern plains in summer or the sub zero temperatures of alpine regions in winter, they can still die of pneumonia in hours if, when brought into a building during a difficult lambing, they are let out again on only a mildly chilly day. 'Farming's perpetual pensioners', as the old hands say. 'They are all bad chests and feet.' For while some of the best graze our marshlands, if they are confined for a month on pastures which are too damp, half their hooves will have turned into a putrid rotting mass.

Watching them on that sublime summer morning, I was puzzled. Their progression as they brushed dark streaks across the glinting dew was like a strange and halting pavanne: a dance to unheard rhythms. Alone, or dispersed in groups of twos or threes, they paused — straggling along a rough line. Then, after a few minutes of quiet nibbling, the line would move on, passing tussocks of grass looking equally succulent to those which they had previously grazed. Somehow, when they halted again, the groups had changed. An imperceptible variation in step allowed stragglers to catch up and enlarge groups ahead or the more preoccupied to drop behind. They were antics which made my task difficult and left me feeling rather foolish.

It was my first day as a farmer. Like all good husbandmen, I felt it my first duty to count the outlying stock. My mother and Gladys were responsible for the welfare of the chickens and hens. I was daily in contact with the pigs and calves when feeding them. Having just milked the cows, I knew they were all present. Ten minutes search among the high reeds of the low meadow had located the last of the beef cattle. Only the sheep remained to be counted.

My inability to control the dog with any skill didn't help. It was something I regretted not having learnt from my father. Responding to a minimum of effort, gesture, whistle or occasional word, the dog had worked like another, much swifter and perfectly comprehending man. My father's economy of communication had been as fascinating to watch as the simplicity of a golf swing which allowed him to propel a ball a hundred and fifty yards into a feckless wind and land it a few feet from the hole on a hidden green.

Trying to count a new group of sheep individually, I'd get half way along their line and then they'd move. It was becoming frustrating. By the time they had settled again and lowered their patrician noses to the ground, I couldn't decide where to continue and had to start again. I began to despair. Fred's joking repetition, a few weeks earlier of the old adage that you should count the legs and divide by four didn't seem to be very helpful. It would be absurd and foolish, I knew, not to be able to volunteer a number when later Jack asked if everything was all right with the sheep. Despite his doubtful look, I had remained self assured when earlier I asked him to get on with lifting some early potatoes and leave the stock count to me.

I had made many false starts and concentrated so hard for so long upon the line of sheep that I suddenly began to under-

stand how experienced flock masters counted. With their trained eyes, they glanced at a group and, without thinking, realised exactly how many animals it contained. Never attempting to count singly, they swept their gaze along the line registering inwardly three, five, eight, ten, thirteen, fifteen, etc. I tried it that morning and convinced myself that the total was twenty eight.

Jack received the news very sourly. He was kneeling to examine the sample of potatoes and I adopted what I hoped was an attitude of authority. Both my thumbs were firmly behind my braces just below my shoulders and resting confidently on a chest I had deliberately expanded. Although Jack was only a short man, it wasn't often that I could hover over him.

I saw him glance first at my boots. One of them had a hole in the toe from which I realised a demeaning scrap of turnip leaf protruded like a scornful tongue. He made no attempt to joke as he looked directly up into my face.

'Twenty eight you say.'

I nodded nonchalantly. He grunted. 'Funny that — your Uncle Tom told me he only bought twenty seven.'

He grudgingly admitted that my stammered explanation that perhaps one had joined our flock from outside was possible. But it was obvious that he didn't believe it. Fred didn't try to hide his amused grin.

Trying to re-establish my position as master while they continued to throw the newly dug potatoes onto a riddle which allowed the smallest rejects to pass, I examined the marketable crop which they had already put into bags on a cart. Although most of them were clear skinned and pearly fleshed I found a worrying number with hard scaly surfaces which had obviously been attacked by a disease known as scab. Others had a tell-tale black hole on the surface which, when broken open, revealed that they had become a cosy home for plump and wriggling wire worms.

I knew that scabby wormy potatoes should have been discarded, otherwise a merchant finding them in a sample would drastically reduce the price he offered. But I didn't know how to say it to Jack.

Jumping down from the cart, I carried several attacked potatoes with me and showed them to him. Afraid to look at him directly, I mumbled, 'they shouldn't be in the bags'.

Clearly resenting the criticism, he stared at them and said antagonistically, 'They were good enough for your Dad, my lad'.

Since it had always been 'Sir' to my father or uncles, his 'my lad' stung.

'Well, that's as maybe. But you better take them out otherwise they won't be fit for sale.'

I noticed that Fred seemed surprised by this show of authority. Jack was more upset by the strength of my reply and, saying nothing, turned away and threw a forkful of potatoes he'd been holding at the riddle with a violence which betrayed his feelings.

Not knowing how to continue and hoping that he'd obey, I left them and returned to the pasture to single out a sheep which needed a hoof paring and dressing. I'd noticed it limping during the count. When I'd driven it to the yard and cut away the infected horn with my father's knife, I struggled to apply the curative sticky stockholm tar without dribbling it all over the fleece or onto my clothes. As I fought to calm the ewe and remembered the recent encounter with Jack, I realised that I faced more problems than merely farming the land.

Just about everything changed in the first five years I was in charge of Fordhall except the niggardliness of the land and my relationship with Jack. The crops sown before my father died were as ungenerous as Uncle Tom had predicted. Arguing from successful practice elsewhere, no matter whom I turned to for advice, they always recommended the same thing: more artificial fertiliser and a continued rotation of the same crops on the higher land. Sadly it always seemed to provide similarly disappointing results.

As one bad crop succeeded another, Jack became increasingly morose. Although he grudgingly accepted me as the master, he continued to call me 'lad'. He knew I was bound to ask his advice frequently and that I nearly always took it. So that in some way he felt personally responsible for our poor yields. They puzzled him as much as any of us.

He was at his most melancholy for months after the great experiment had failed. That was in the year after father had died and we were all unloading fertiliser prior to planting potatoes. I was upset because, in pausing to wipe the sweat from his brow, he had uncharacteristically set one of the paper bags down in a puddle in the yard. Normally, though trying to sound firm, I always spoke to him with the respect which I felt was appropriate because he was so much older. But in my irritation, I must have shouted more rudely.

'Watch that wet now, we can't afford to waste it like that.'

Clearly annoyed by his own carelessness, he shouted back defiantly. 'I don't know why you buy the bloody stuff at all. It's doing as much good there as it is in the field.'

The other men were obviously intrigued by our battle of wills so, to avoid further argument, I stalked away, leaving them to finish unloading. I had realised that though he spoke rarely, he could argue convincingly and that if he seemed to win, it did my authority no good. Even before my father died, Jack only became really loquacious when condemning bagged fertiliser. I was tired of his eternal complaints about its use.

That night I plunged once more into the books and papers which I had read and re-read on the advice of Urban Major and Uncle John throughout the winter.

'All the experience from experiments at Rothamstead and elsewhere suggests that provided the other ingredients are balanced, for every extra unit of nitrogen you apply, you will obtain extra yield', I told him with confidence the next day.

He must have been as sick of the word Rothamstead as I was of his complaints. 'Aye, well, what works down there won't work up here,' he replied dogmatically. And then, nodding towards the proposed potato field, he added with conviction, 'You'd be better off applying none of it up there'.

Exasperated by what I considered his pig-headedness, I flung back without thinking, 'All right — we'll try a patch your way to see'.

Too late I realised that Fred and Bill were both present to witness what must have sounded like an intriguing challenge. The eager way in which they were nodding approval of the idea betrayed their delight. It meant that for both Jack and me a lot of prestige was at stake.

Trying to be extra scientific, I insisted that we wait for a flat, calm morning before we broadcast the fertiliser on the field. I jokingly explained that I didn't want any of my bag muck to float onto Jack's plot as we had begun to call the ten yard strip of land across the field which was to remain unfertilised. My issuing the challenge must have strengthened Jack's opinions. Sure that the outcome of the trial would be in his favour, he was becoming quite animated and good humoured.

'That's right, we don't want my tatties contaminated with that stuff,' he agreed laughing.

They were main crop potatoes. Hardly any disease infected foliage in our area that summer. The autumn weather remained fine and, since the plants continued to grow, we left them in the ground to make more weight until mid-November. Unfortunately, it became clear when we harvested the field that even the good growing conditions hadn't done much to improve yields. The crop from the fertilised area was well below the average for our district; but the crop from Jack's plot was much lower.

He was so anxious to discover the results that he drove the digger plough himself. As it split the ridges of soil and threw aside the tubers he could begin to estimate the crop. Wanting to be scrupulously fair, he had insisted on working the fertilised area first. As the ordinariness of the yield became apparent, he became more and more eager to lift his own plot. When his defeat was so obvious, he became very crestfallen. Although delighted about my success, I was sorry that it was so evident and that he should feel so beaten.

When I tried to soften his disappointment by saying that his plot had always done a bit less well than the rest of the field, he found it no consolation. He saw Fred wink broadly at Bill and that didn't help. Quietly saying that he'd take the plough and horse back to the steading, he didn't return to help with beginning to gather the crop although there was nearly an hour to go before we normally stopped work. He was obviously too depressed to face us. Standing up to stretch and relieve the ache after half an hour of continuous bending I saw him leaving the buildings to trudge off home. His shoulders seemed unusually drooped and he looked terribly forlorn.

I realise now that his step would have been far jauntier if we had understood then what we know today – that while wrong in some particulars, his general opposition to the use of synthetic fertilisers on our land at that time was substantially justified. But it took more than a decade to make that discovery.

Even from the perspective of only a few weeks, my victory seemed very hollow. Receipts from the poor potato crop had made little impact on our annual bills. And, it was only my mother's stringent management, coupled with increased output from her growing flock of chickens and hens which made it possible to face them at all.

Later, we always jokingly said that we only survived the 1930 winter because Urban Major's bid finally succeeded. Since we had been alone, he no longer needed excuses to drop in to court Edith. He was aware that advice based on his farming experience at Chipnal was always welcome.

His big square Austin often sagged on its rear springs and resembled a speed boat as he drove up our track. The bags of poultry feed which weighted it down were sold to my mother at half their value. He claimed to have found a cut price merchant in Shrewsbury. But since he was evasive about the address when questioned, I'm convinced that he was merely being kind.

He would brush aside my mother's effusive thanks with an embarrassed laugh saying, 'It's only chicken feed, Lillian, only chicken feed'.

He sometimes claimed that the difference in price barely compensated for the amount of Edith's cakes or tarts he had eaten. She told me later that he had proposed to her soon after my father fell ill. However, she had asked him to wait because she felt that my mother needed her support at home. When he died and Betty left, she'd been torn by indecision. Mother's work in the dairy and with the growing flock of poultry had increased. Meanwhile we had lost some of the help she needed in the house. And that at a time when all the family were growing and we still had Fred living in. But, she was aware as anyone of the constant pressures on our scant income, so when Urban proposed again, she accepted, feeling, she said, that her most useful contribution at that stage was to go away. Because, it would mean that we had one less person to care for and one less mouth to feed.

CHAPTER ELEVEN

A Fordhall Winter

'We'll have to eat cold at lunch times because I really won't have time to spoil you like Edith', my mother announced after Urban had driven his bride away. We were all slowly stacking plates and trying to tidy the house after the wedding. The return to domestic chores had reminded her that we had lost the help of the person who had most made her hours in the dairy and poultry houses possible. They were activities upon which we increasingly depended and she was obviously worried about the extra time she would have to spend in the kitchen.

She was delighted that her sister should have married a man she liked and admired but clearly unsure what her departure would mean to our lives. Since they had lived together from childhood and always loved and respected each other, my mother knew that, apart from her practical help, she would greatly miss Aunt Edith's moral support. The prospect upset her and worrying about it made her head ache. Usually reluctant to succumb to minor ailments, that evening she took little persuading when we urged her to take a cup of tea up to her bed.

She was more amazed and pleased than anyone when she came into the house at lunchtime next day. Requesting that Joan should fit in an extra wash that morning to cope with linen dirtied at the wedding, she thought that after her work in the dairy she would have to start searching in the pantry for something to feed us. The table, however, was beautifully laid. Two large serving dishes were heaped with boned and tastefully arranged morsels of the chickens left over from the wedding. A big bowl of freshly made mayonnaise stood beside them. A pan of vegetable soup filled the room with the savoury aroma of chicken stock as it gently simmered on top of the kitchen range.

Pleased to witness her happy astonishment, Joan dramatically swept open the oven door, 'There's an apple pie nearly done in there for pudding', she announced with pride.

When we had all experienced the shock in turn and eaten the meal, it was clear that Fordhall had found another in its sequence of remarkable women. Edith had always complained that although Joan was cheerful, infinitely willing, stronger than an ox and domestically talented, she lacked initiative and always had to be told what to do. This time, it seemed that circumstances had done the prompting and for many years we were sincerely grateful.

By that time too, Gladys, who was nearly seventeen, was beginning to play a fully adult role. Apart from helping Mother in the dairy and with the poultry she did her share of feeding the young stock. While this left her little time for housework, she had absorbed some of Aunt Edith's abilities as a cakemaker and pastry cook. So that at least twice a week our tea times were gladdened by cream-filled sponge cakes whose texture was like whipped gossamer. We weren't the only people to discover these talents. Just seeing the quality of our produce, when Mother and Gladys took it to Drayton Market, must have made Tom Williamson first suspect them.

In those days the weekly mart had, for country people, some of the characteristics of the Southern European Sunday promenade. Apart from playing a vital role in the sale and exchange of stock produce, it was a foyer of intrigue and a chance to see and be seen. The only day time opportunity most farm folk had to escape from their land to meet other people, it was also an informal marriage bureau.

Like many other youths, each week when Tom Williamson had completed his family's business — selling surplus stock, negotiating with corn and produce merchants, buying feeding stuffs, machinery or cattle to fatten, he would wander round the market gathering information or listening to salesmen extol the virtues of the novelties they were offering. A bright, dusty, noisy animated place, it provided an exciting contrast to the calm of the fields. Real ale which clung to the side of the glass like a web, or for the more affluent, on cooler days, Scottish spirits, made good-humoured eyes sparkle. It also fuelled the violent rows which frequently added zest to the occasion.

Even in that otherwise depressing epoch it was an optimistic atmosphere. Prices were dreadfully low. But since nearly everyone was sharing a similar fate which they believed could only improve, there developed a community of hardship. Without expressing it, all knew that they were more fortunate than the poor of the industrial towns. People with skill and access to land always believe that they can survive.

Too young to be oppressed by economics, Tom Williamson was inflated with the satisfaction that his growing skills provided. The second son of one of the district's best and more properous women farmers, at eighteen he was rapidly gathering responsibilities as his competence grew. A wiry, keen-featured boy, he had surprising strength which was combined with great sensitivity: qualities which enabled him to cope with a team of heavy horses or heave about awkward implements as easily as a mature worker; yet his touch was so delicate that he could plough as straight and even a furrow as any man in the country or pick out an ailing animal in a group from such slight clues as the inclination of its head or the unusual droop of its haunches.

Although thoughtful and retiring, he was evidently something of a skilled fancier of women too. Gladys had hoped he'd pay her more attention from the first day she'd noticed him talking seriously to Mother. Disappointed by the cattle offered for sale, he was trying to buy five steers privately. 'We have an extra flush of grass and desperate for something to eat it. But we are looking for real doers not the rubbish here today', he explained.

Glancing at him from the other end of the stall where she had been cutting cheese, Gladys was surprised by the eagerness of his eyes and the quiet authority which his voice conveyed. Mother, too, was impressed by such certainty in someone obviously so young. Uncle John was at the market and she suggested that Tom should speak to him. Luckily for Gladys, John had just what Tom wanted and they struck a deal. Before he went home, he called back at the stand to thank Mother for the introduction. From then on he often stopped to tell them about the progress of the steers.

His calls became a habit and went on long after the animals had been fattened and sent to the butcher. As he overcame his shyness, he gradually spent more and more of the time talking to Gladys. She was greatly encouraged and began to feel that the extra care and attention she gave to preparing herself for the weekly visits to town, which we at home all noticed and joked about, were having the desired effect. For such a strong, bustling and forthright girl, she displayed great patience and discretion. When either Bill, Fred or I saw her with unusually well set hair and discreetly made up eyes and lips, helping Mother to load the trap before leaving for the market, and teased her about her mystery boyfriend, she became embarrassingly demure and didn't shout back at us as she would formerly have done. So the slow progress of the courtship began to exasperate the rest of us. Mother often chastised us when we referred to Tom as 'Mr. Slowcoach' who was 'certainly taking his time'. However when even Margaret, who had reached the romantic early teens, was beginning to despair that Tom would ever appear at home, Gladys knew exactly what she wanted, refused to discuss him with us and simply waited.

Although Mother obviously knew about the arrangement, she didn't tell us until the evening she returned from market without Gladys. We were all very astonished when we realised that the longed-for day had arrived. She announced quite casually while pouring the tea, 'Gladys won't be home until later. She and young Tom Williamson from Peplow are having tea in town and then going to the Young Farmers dance.'

Her delight was quietly evident. While Margaret and I speculated about the intentions of the man we had never met, Mother sat silent, smiling. To Joan who was cooking at the stove, Gladys' date was an event of tremendous romantic moment — the sort of adventure she absorbed avidly from the flour-streaked, fat-blotched women's magazines which she pretended to read for the cooking recipes.

Fred, who was still living with us and shared many of our meals, made his pleasure obvious in an extra spectacular show of his pipe worn teeth. Normally, he discreetly ignored family matters. But, before going back to the yard he, too, risked a comment. 'I hope Ma'am, that this fellah is good enough for your Glad.'

Embarrassed by his lack of restraint, he escaped before she could reply, muttering, 'I didn't like the look of the sky so I think I'll stuff some sacking in the stable windows'.

Roused by his concern, after lighting my lamp, I followed him into the yard. It was late February and had been very cold for days. People said that there had been heavy snow in Wales but so far we had escaped. However since noon the sky had become increasingly heavy. Just before dark it had had a threatening liverish yellow look. I was surprised by the unusual warmth of the air as I crossed to the shippen. It was the cloying warmth which in summer can mean thunder but in winter often heralds snow; the sort of sign which farmers respond to instantly but townfolk frequently ignore.

I hurried to join Bill whose activities were creating what used to be husbandry's most lovely sound. Moving quickly from stall to stall, he was hurling mounds of fresh straw on top of the cows' bedding, so that they would have extra insulation to sink into if they became really cold. Curious to discover what he was doing, they craned their heads round, moving the chains which strung round their necks, kept their muzzles near the manger. Tumbling or being quickly drawn through their iron retaining rings, the chains jingled tunefully. If a cow, too confused or incomprehending, refused to move quickly enough to allow Bill to throw straw onto an area of bed which needed it, his moaned, 'Move over, you great bitch' as he nudged her by leaning his shoulder heavily into her rump, added a familiar lyric.

They were all sounds which for me since infancy had provided reassurance and made the shippen such a special place. Its appeal must, I suppose, have depended on the harmony created out of so many sharp contrasts. Fresh cold air by the walls and doors hemmed in a blanket of musky warmth surrounding the animals. Their plume of condensing breath, which made the cobwebby windows trickle, hovered as a thin mist above the summer dried straw which crackled beneath their hooves. The glistening brown-green wetness of the concrete dung channel behind their tails balanced the softness of their doleful eyes in the manger. Lamplight, yellow as Jersey cream, made the iron of buckets, barriers, chains and shovels gleam out against the dull whiteness of chalk-washed plaster walls.

Even in the nostrils the shippen's smells conflicted. The sweetness of fresh dung was always pricked by acrid carbolic disinfectant. Beneath these obvious odours, the faint oily fragrance of cow cake always lurked. A byproduct from the extraction of oil from cotton seed, coconut flesh or a variety of nuts in the great Merseyside Mills, it never completely lost a hint of its exotic tropical origin.

While Bill was laying the straw, spreading it out with the prongs and then patting it into place with the back of his fork, the thick dust he raised made our skins itch and for some minutes its slightly musty aroma became dominant. Aware that I was watching him, he nodded towards the windows. Our years of working together had generated a splendid empathy. Quite frequently, I knew what he meant without his speaking.

'I think you are right. It feels colder already.'

As I crossed the yard to find the sacks to seal the windows, it began to snow. Large, very dry flakes disappeared with a crackle as they hit the hot glass of my lamp.

Inside the stable Fred, having settled his horses, was fastening on his winter ploughing gear. Seeing him in it one morning, the postman said it resembled more a yacht's rigging than outdoor wear.

Everything was held in place with binder twine. The strips of sack he bound round his ankles as puttees, the army greatcoat which he had worn almost tissue thin, but insisted on calling his 'British Warm', his outer mantle — a shining olive green, rubberised waterproof from which the belt and buttons had long disappeared, the 'Flying Corps' pilot's helmet with a torn chin strap — all were fastened on to him with an intricate series of bows. When he was fully cocooned with a long khaki scarf spiralling round his mouth and nose and his hands hidden inside his 'Tank Commander's' leather mittens, the only thing I could see of him in the lamplight were a pair of bright eyes.

Giving the bows on his waterproof a final tug, he nodded to confirm his satisfaction and made a final adjustment to the water supply of the acetylene drip lamp which hissed on the bracket of his ex-dispatch rider's bicycle. Mumbling through the wool of his scarf that he didn't expect to be late, he pushed it through the stable door. As he rode away, I could see in the beam of his lamp that the snow was becoming very heavy. Fred's nightly excursions with their mystery destination had become the cause of constant speculation at Fordhall since Betty had gone away.

'Like a randy old Tom Cat, he is', Bill observed with a grin when he joined me in the stable.

Our boots made quite deep prints in the lying snow as we went back to the shippen with the sacks. Crossing the yard had only taken a moment but we'd been whitened in transit.

'My God, rather him than me!' Bill exclaimed, banging his cap against the wall and pulling it back on his head. 'I hope it's worth it because he could get lost forever on a night like this.'

Mother's worry about allowing Tom Williamson to take Gladys dancing didn't turn out to be justified. It was about half past seven when I returned to read and cook myself by the fire in the kitchen. The snow had become much heavier and a rising wind was making it drift. For the next two and a half hours Margaret, who was writing an essay at the table, kept looking at me and raising her eyebrows at twenty minute intervals as Mother let the cold in by opening the scullery door and peering out at the weather. So we were all pleased when they arrived home early.

While Mother declared that he shouldn't have done it and was worried about the state of his suit, Margaret was impressed by Tom's evident gallantry. Looking rather regal in a sprinkling of snow, Gladys was wearing his smart tweed coat, draped over her own top coat like a cloak. If he hadn't had to struggle through the deep snow on the track while carrying her from the car which they had been forced to abandon near the gate, he would undoubtedly have been very cold. As it was, the effort and the warm air in the kitchen made his cheeks glow.

While he drank the hot cocoa which Mother insisted he have before we went out to dig out his car, I noticed a characteristic which remains to this day. Instead of slumping back in the armchair, he leaned forward, holding his arms out in front of him. I realised that it was the attitude always adopted by a man guiding a plough.

It meant that he had to turn his head upwards to explain to my mother that since most of the dancers were farm folk who daren't risk being caught away from home because stock needed attention the next morning, the dance had finished early.

However it had clearly continued long enough to convince Gladys that her patience had been justified. Putting on her Wellingtons, she insisted on coming back to help get Tom's car moving. After a lot of digging, wheel spinning, shoving and heaving, we managed to get him back onto the track he had lost in the blizzard, turn him round and head him for home.

As he switched up his headlights and was hooting us farewell, they revealed the comic figure of Fred. Only his waterproof was free from a thick crusting of snow. With his arm through the main frame he was carrying his bicycle on one shoulder. He used his other outstretched arm to try to maintain his balance as he staggered towards us. We realised that he was smiling broadly and singing barely coherently as he approached.

'To plough and sow
Reap and mow
To be a farmer's boy, oi oi oi oi
To be a farmer' boy.'

He seemed momentarily puzzled by our presence on the track but didn't reply when I proclaimed, 'Hell of a night for cycling, Fred'. Sawing again into the chorus, he just nodded and lurched past us towards the house.

When I looked at Gladys she laughed knowingly.

'He obviously thought it was worth it.'

It snowed heavily again before morning. I can't remember many worse storms. The wind had swung to the north east, congealing the previous night's fluffy drifts into steely waves of ice. Some, making barriers across doors, had to be broken down before we could begin the normal day.

Fred, Bill and Jack were all working in pools of lamplight with crowbars, picks and shovels before I reached the yard. Tracks had to be hewn to connect the food stores, pigsties, stable, shippen, midden and dairy. In the darkness their job was made hazardous by unnoticed chips of ice which, once dislodged, rapidly froze onto the area previously cleared. Two nasty falls did more to shake Fred out of his alcoholic coma than air which was so dry and cold that it seemed to burn the membranes of the nostrils and the throat.

Jack had been the first in the yard and climbing about everywhere had assessed the priorities. He was aware of the dangerous paradox that housed livestock are most at risk of suffering from thirst when their buildings are blanketed in water that is frozen. He knew that I had never been in charge after a blizzard so his voice was quite imperative when he glanced up and saw me trying to understand the situation.

'All the cisterns are solid, so you better get that standpipe thawed.'

Nodding my agreement, I instantly remembered the excitement which that operation had generated when I had watched my father make the fire as a child. By clinging to projections from the walls, I managed to skid and clamber over the frozen drifts and fetch straw from the barn.

Lit after being heaped about the iron pipe and soaked in paraffin, it flared furiously, filling the still dark sky with sparks. Until the paraffin had gone, flames reflecting from the frozen snow and icicles which clad or hung from everything provided illumination of arc-light intensity. Initially it was too bright for Fred's drink sensitised eyes and he was forced to stand with them half closed. Watching him, we all laughed.

We laughed again when, as the flames subsided, he patted the top of the pipe and brass tap with his mittened hand and then turned it on. At first nothing happened and he was leaning towards it when, with an angry snort, like a steam engine beginning to turn, it ejected a few gobbets of water and then a chilling stream. For an instant, he was lost in a halo of violently splashed droplets before he leapt clear, cursing.

Our laughter however was short lived. Apart from mixing wet concrete with a shovel, there are few more laborious jobs than carrying water in buckets. By the time daylight arrived, we all had aching arms and backs. That was before we began to face the normally heavy tasks of the day under appalling conditions.

Even in the shippen, cluttered with extra buckets of water because the supply to the automatic drinking troughs was frozen, the cows were more restless and cantankerous than usual. We were late for the milking and their over full udders were becoming burdensome and painful. Also, it seemed in resentment, they spoiled their reputation for patient docility by constantly shuffling and attempting to push Bill and me away with their back feet, sometimes upsetting milk into the straw in the process. In consequence, milking lasted longer than usual and I was exasperated and famished by the time I reached the kitchen for a late breakfast.

Gladys was furious because she had fallen badly when trying to get more hay to the calves. Apart from the bruises, she had been covered with muck and had to bath and change her clothes. Mother was worried about the prospect of having to get food and water out to the poultry houses. Only Margaret seemed pleased by the blizzard. There seemed little chance of her being able to reach school. That gave her an extra day to finish her French homework. While we glumly chewed our toast, she sat with her earphones on listening to the crystal radio set Urban Major had given her for Christmas. While still a novelty which was distracting her from her work in the evenings, it gave her a new status in the household. She was always first with the news. That morning she seemed delighted when announcing that unless something drastic happened to a depression which was moving down from Iceland there was worse weather to come.

This forbidding forecast added greater urgency to our morning's activities. Muffled like Esquimaux and carrying blow lamps and hammers, Jack and Fred set about thawing pipes which, when the water was flowing, they lagged with newspaper held in place by strips of sacking.

It is easy now to reflect upon the improvidence of farmers in those days. Of course the pipes and cisterns ought to have been protected in the autumn against likely freeze-ups in the winter. But, inevitably, in the rush of activity in fine weather they were forgotten.

Most of the more arduous work on the land had to be done by hand. There were seldom surplus hands available for anything else. Certainly there was too little capital to build the vermin-proof, insulated cow palaces which many farmers use today. So that even if the pipes were crudely lagged during one autumn, by the following winter much of the primitive lagging would have been nibbled from the pipes by rats and mice for use as bedding in their winter nests.

When he had fed the cows, Bill volunteered to help Mother with the poultry while Gladys and I set off to see what had happened to the sheep. As usual, when bad weather threatened, we had moved the sheep into the end of Villa Field nearest the yard. That, we knew, would make it easier for us if we had to carry food.

The pregnant ewes had followed a sheep's instinct to spend the night at the top of the hill where in harsh weather the temperature is always a degree or two higher. Since this was near our buildings, they had gained shelter by huddling on the lee side.

Most of the flock could be seen through the yard gate. They had given up trying to break through the hard snow to the remnants of the winter grass and were simply waiting for something to happen. Since reaching and using a cart was impossible, they had to wait for over an hour before Gladys and I could carry sufficient fork loads of hay to satisfy their appetite.

The effort had made us very hot, but we cooled quickly as

we watched their determined chewing when we paused to rest. Although the sun was now nearly at its highest and the sky was cloudless, it was clearly not strong enough to banish the pre-dawn cold. The surface of the snow on some of the south facing roofs had begun to melt a little and there were drips running down to increase the length of the icicles which hung from the gutters. It offered scant encouragement. Elsewhere it was obvious that winter had us firmly in its grip.

While beginning to shiver, I counted the flock and realised that there were three ewes missing.

When Tom Williamson was leaving, I had noticed some sheep in his headlights near the end of the track where for a time the eddying wind had swept odd patches of grass fairly free from snow. Dragging on one of Father's top coats, Gladys came with me to try to find them. As she walked ahead, trying to maintain her balance on the undulating ice, I wondered what he would have thought of the state of the garment of which he had been so proud. A three-quarter length, simply cut, officer's type, buff coat with a half belt and plaited leather buttons, it had been superbly made by a tailor in Chester to whom he'd been introduced by an affluent member of his golf club. When he wore it with a shallow black bowler hat, it made him indistinguishable from a group of men he clearly admired — the stewards he saw in the paddocks at the local hunt race meetings.

He had worn it so proudly on the day when he returned from Chester. I remembered him replying to my mother's question about its cost with an offhand and slightly annoyed, 'Much cheaper than I thought'. It was an answer which didn't satisfy her. Because earlier, in error, she had opened a large, unpaid bill from Clive Thompson.

For two years after his death, the coat had hung like a sacred relic in Mother's wardrobe. Until, one cold morning, when Gladys' own old top coat wore too thin, she was allowed to use it. Although the distinction it retained gave her a certain style as we slowly made our way towards the road, the crusted areas where, morning after morning, it had been splashed with whey or calf feed banished the allure of gentility it once provided for a vain man.

As we approached the hedge along the Drayton Road side of the field, I began to worry. There was still no sign of the ewes. On one place, the top of the hedge was obliterated by drifts which, beginning in a neighbour's field beyond the road, had tumbled right across it like a giant breaker.

Climbing to its ridge, I felt all the strangeness of a suddenly distorted perspective. The familiar landscape acquired quite a new character. Distant house roofs and church towers which normally remained unsuspected came into view. The air was so dry and clear that vision seemed limitless. As we stood panting, it seemed as though the only thing we couldn't see was the group of sheep we sought. I had a shovel and my grandfather's old hazel crook with me and we started probing every probable mound of snow along the hedge.

Because of the thick frozen crust on which we could easily stand, it was very tough work. We took it in turns to hack away at the surface with the sharp corner of the shovel until we broke through into the softer snow below. Then, using the crook, we probed for signs of life.

After two hours, we were exhausted and hungry. Neither of us dared suggest that we give up the search because we both knew what a financial disaster the loss of three ewes and the lambs they carried would mean to our pitiful turnover. The dog which had initially considered our activities a game had long vanished. The arrival of Jack, Fred and Bill to help gave us more courage but for nearly another hour provided no result.

Although I was in charge of the sheep, Jack, who never hesitated to advise me about how they should be treated, was clearly beginning to take the loss of any of the flock as a personal affront. The crowbar he wielded allowed him to work quicker than the rest of us. As his frustration grew he moved quickly away from along the hedge. But even his enormous reserve of stamina gradually began to wane. He'd stopped and was leaning on the bar breathing heavily when he saw the tell tale sign and shouted. Rushing to join him, we watched the tiny wisp of vapour escaping from a half-crown sized hole just below the crest of a low mound.

Gently breaking away the smooth ice around the mouth of the hole with the point of his bar, Jack revealed the startled ewe. She was crouching in an ice cave which she had managed to keep open by slowly rocking on her feet as the snow had built up round her. Ultimately only the warmth she generated and her efforts to keep her nose in the air had kept the breathing hole open and prevented the cave from becoming her tomb.

Gladys shrieked with delight when Jack pulled the ewe clear and then, plunging his arms into the cave again, withdrew a clearly astonished five-week premature lamb.

It was while still enthusing over the discovery that Bill cried, 'Well, bugger me – look at that'. Only a few yards further along the hedge, almost hidden behind the curling lip of a wavelike drift, the other two ewes were standing silent and motionless, peering out at us. When we went to drive them back to the yard they seemed to resent our discovery of their wonderfully cosy shelter and find the indignity of their heavy bellied, slithering return before such laughing and satisfied spectators highly distasteful.

When Gladys and I had finished throwing the now complete flock of expectant mothers sufficient hay to last the night, the sun was beginning to drop behind the Welsh mountains. We stood quietly watching it disappear as it threw the finger of the obelisk into a silhouetted relief. When it had disappeared completely, a thread of green light seemed to cling to the horizon while everything above it became the colour of pink junket.

'My, that's pretty', Gladys said breaking the silence. 'But it looks as if its going to become very cold. Unless we are very lucky this lot will be with us until Saturday.'

She could see that I noticed the heavy regret in her voice and, looking away, explained.

'Well, Tom Williamson asked me to go to a twenty-first birthday dance in Peplow.'

Since the prospects of his even being able to reach Fordhall to pick her up by the Saturday seemed remote, I understood her disappointment.

'Bad luck that.'

'Aye, it is.'

I could see that she was nearly crying as she turned to walk back to the dairy to prepare the calves' evening meal. Her step seemed to perk up a bit as I shouted after her from the shippen door, 'Nice fellow, that Tom'.

Tom Williamson turned out to be even kinder than Gladys thought. Few snow ploughs operated in those days, but teams of men with shovels had managed to clear the roads to Tern Hill, the village just South West of us. Leaving his car there, Tom tramped the remaining mile and a quarter to our door.

It was quite dark when he arrived and Gladys had become

very glum again because Margaret's recital of the evening weather forecast promised enduring cold with no immediate sign of a thaw.

The note he carried to my mother happily made the forebodings of the man at the meteorological office irrelevant. It requested permission for Gladys to stay with the Williamsons after the dance on the Saturday night because a return to Fordhall might be too difficult.

Although rather diffident when handing the letter to Mother, Tom became quite animated after she agreed. He must have become infected by our excitement. For to us it was a great event. None of us had ever stayed away with strangers overnight.

Worried about the roads, Tom didn't stay long. Perhaps it was as well because within minutes of his departure Gladys and Margaret had rushed upstairs, dragged one of Father's pigskin cases from under a wardrobe and begun to pack it for her stay away.

Mother and I sat listening to them running from room to room, opening and slamming drawers, gabbling excitedly and then breaking down into gales of laughter. After one particular shriek, they both burst back into the kitchen. Gladys stood posing like the Mikado in a very tattered Chinese style dressing gown which had been the favourite early morning garb of Aunt Edith.

'Will it do for her ladyship?', Margaret asked in mock seriousness before they both began to laugh again and disappeared upstairs.

Mother, who had been reading a newspaper which Tom had thoughtfully brought for her, didn't say anything but raised her eyes towards heaven and adopted a slightly martyred expression. When I laughed, she simply said, 'Ah well' and turned back to her paper.

She seemed to be smiling whenever I glanced across at her during the rest of the evening and I could tell that she was well satisfied. Certainly, from then on, she made it obvious that Tom was a welcome guest at our table.

In many respects, he adopted the role in our household formerly occupied by Urban Major. While Urban and Edith were frequent visitors, they were building a new life together and Urban came less to Fordhall than in the past. So I began to discuss our farming problems regularly with Tom. Lured by an opportunity to see Gladys and sample her wonderful cakes, he paid for them with sound advice.

Uncle John, too, since he had become our guarantor and mentor was a frequent visitor until he died in that summer of 1932.

They both tried hard to think of ways of wrestling better crops from our land. Their sound views confirmed all the ideas I was developing as the result of wide reading about modern practice. But none of us really understood the fundamental problem.

Looking back at the figures I am still amazed that we survived. In total, our sales of cheese, chickens, eggs, fat pigs and potatoes yielded just under £1,400 per year. When we had paid the wages and rent, less than £700 was left to cover all the other farm expenses and feed and clothe a family of four.

When prices were so poor neither the Williamsons at Peplow, where Tom and two brothers helped their mother to farm, nor John and Stella Hollins near Nantwich were very prosperous. But at least their well-farmed land provided bigger yields and the margins they produced made them seem incredibly rich to us.

Compared to the industrial poor, we were, of course, well off. Thanks to the domestic skills and ingenuity of Gladys and Mother, while we still had access to the land, we knew we wouldn't starve. Practically everything we ate came from the farm or garden. Our diet had a seasonal excitement which has become obliterated by the deep freezer. Spring meant crisp, irony lettuce or green cabbage, raddishes munched with salt and butter or rare delicacies like rich beesting custard sneaked from the first flow of extra nutritious milk a cow had created for her newly born calf. Summer brought gooseberry pie, strawberries, raspberries, tomatoes, new potatoes and bowls full of eggs. Autumn yielded apples for memorable tarts and dumplings, pears, plums, damsons and crunchy carrots. In winter we shared the turnips and swedes with the cows. They provided the cheese whose toasted aroma often filled the kitchen before we gobbled nuts from the woods or watercress from the brooks and ditches. The men furnished us with at least a rabbit a week. A sympathetic gamekeeper provided the occasional treat of a pheasant or wild duck.

By waving her wand over such a cornucopia, which also included fowl and a host of products from a pig, Mother made

rustic poverty into an enviable situation. We lived a sophisticated, stone age existence. Although our clothes became
ragged and we hardly entered a shop, our bellies remained
gratifyingly full. But behind this repletion, there always
lurked the ogre of eviction.

It terrified me as I lay in bed at night trying desperately to
think of other ways of increasing our income. No matter how
hard we tried, our debt to our landlord continued to grow. If
he lost his patience and threw us out, I knew that we would
have absolutely nowhere to go. I was fit for nothing except
farm work and few farmers wanted to increase their wage bill
at that time. Pride would have prevented us from appealing to
Uncle Tom for help.

So long as we could stay at Fordhall, I knew that we were all
right. The question was, how were we going to cling on to the
land? Since I'd become quite adept at growing vegetables, in
what I thought of as our survival garden, I began seriously to
wonder whether I could grow them as cash crops. If I had
something to offer besides potatoes, I thought I might be able
to sell vegetables in the local markets and earn the full retail
price.

Both Uncle John and Tom Williamson agreed that it might
be worth trying. They supported my argument that land
which was seemingly too light and drained too freely to support field crops might prove more satisfactory for vegetables.

Even Jack agreed, but he raised the best founded objection.
'It's easy enough growing a patch. But a patch won't get you
much further ahead. And as soon as you want to plant a field
you will need more hands than you have got.' His own large
vegetable garden easily supported the three of his family who
remained at home. However he pointed out that working it
occupied nearly every moment of his spare time and even its
abundance wouldn't provide much income if sold at the market.

More impetuous and desperate then than I am now, despite
Jack's objections I decided to try.

CHAPTER TWELVE

The Thirties

The row of perfectly formed beans nestling tightly into the woolly white fibre in their pod meant as much to me as rare gems in an expensive jeweller's box. Laid across a palm browned and calloused by hours of hoeing, raking and singling in the five-acre vegetable area I had created, the first well filled pod which I split open seemed to justify my optimism. I wished that John Hollins had been there. He knew that I intended to plant the vegetable crops and I should have liked him to see how well they were growing.

Since the soil hadn't carried anything similar for generations, all the crops were remarkably free from disease. Though a lot of them were still immature, it was time to start picking the broad beans. Their bright green lower pods already stood out well against the freshly hoed soil, trembling gently as they were rocked by a light June breeze. Higher up the sturdy stems, a fine show of flowers had become a stageing post for the hundreds of bees, attracted by their heavy scent. It smelt like sweet success to me. Crouching to inhale it deeply, I didn't notice Jack come over the brow of the field.

I was startled and a bit resentful when I realised that he was kneeling among the fine feathery heads of the carrots. Although he had provided valuable advice, I had done most of the work. I felt that the success was my own, something which I wanted to savour alone. I had chosen the vegetable area in the previous autumn. When he had ploughed it well while working on the rest of the field, he had insisted that I should apply the fifteen tons an acre of dung that he claimed the vegetables needed. Day after day, before and after my normal work, I had filled and lead the creaking cartloads out to the field, spreading it carefully along the furrows with a hand fork. I deliberately refused help from anyone else because I was determined that other farm work shouldn't suffer and we couldn't afford to pay overtime. Now that back breaking toil seemed to be rewarded. Perhaps it would help to restore our fortunes. Uncle John would, I felt, have approved the effort and thought that his wonderful confidence in us was justified. Unhappily he was never to share my joy. He died suddenly before even the rows of autumn sown beans were in the ground.

Glancing round at them, I became momentarily very sad when I realised that I should never again witness the approval for my suggestions in his warmly encouraging eyes. Jack's rather grudging, 'They ain't too bad', as he approached dangling a bunch of carrots from their leaves like a rabbit by its ears, seemed therefore niggardly.

For a second I had to look away to conceal the annoyance his superior attitude generated. As our farm crops had dwindled his tenativeness had grown. But now that I was growing vegetables and had entered a domain in which he was the district's acknowledged master, he felt qualified to comment freely.

I realised that even if I had possessed his skill the scale on which I was growing made it impossible for me to provide the attention to individual plants which ensured his success. However, as well as his habitual, rather harshly expressed criticism, I should have been more encouraged if occasionally he had found something to praise. I was still only eighteen and while others of my age were gaining prestige at sport or in the admiration of women, since I worked so hard my only rewards came from success at Fordhall. Little notable had been achieved since my mother and I had taken over, so I was understandably proud of the hard won vegetables.

Unaware of my feelings, he was slicing across the carrots with the scimitar sharp blade of his cherished hart's horn handled knife. 'Mm, not bad at all' he said, after inspecting them carefully. 'Hardly any core at all — they'll cook well enough.'

When it came, I was astonished to realise that I found such guarded approval embarrassing. Since at that age he still sought respect not gratitude, I just nodded as though the good quality of the carrots was what I had expected.

Any slight softening of my attitude following the compliment was quickly banished as he hastened to establish his authority. 'Of course they are not all ready — you better leave them for a day or two yet.'

I wish I hadn't taken his advice. A careful selection of those early carrots might have made a bit of money and been as profitable as the first picking of beans. When I finally took them to market, I realised that I was competing with good carrots which were wholesaling at thirty new pence for a hundred weight sack. If anyone else had received wages for the work, it would have paid simply to let them rot in the ground. I hadn't been attending the vegetable market for many weeks before I learned the horticulturalist's hardest lesson: when it's a very good year, nobody does very well.

In an excellent growing season with just the right amount of bright sun, warm nights and gentle rain when it was required, vegetables throughout the North West grew splendidly that year. Bolstered up by the dung, even our thin land provided reasonably heavy crops because the weather was so much in their favour. But, under such circumstances, every pound of extra yield and every fraction of a penny gained by being a day or two earlier in the market is vital if vegetable growing is to pay.

My yields were heavy enough to make me nearly scream with pain as the result of bending to collect them until the last glimmer of daylight had gone. However, they were no heavier or earlier than those obtained by more experienced men on better land. By July the work trap into which I had fallen became pitifully obvious. Large, tight-headed, flawless white cauliflowers were selling for less than half a new penny each. Lush green, crumbly edged savoys which occupied a whole square yard of ground, pretty as a cabbage rose, did no better a month later.

Fine sprouts in November, or broccoli in the following March, sold equally poorly and did nothing to compensate for the ludicrous twelve new pence per hundred-weight sack which was the best we could obtain for our usual low crop of potatoes.

Tom Williamson could only commiserate when we realised that my plan had failed. I mustn't be too discouraged, he insisted, pointing out that even at those prices, the land had made a better contribution to our income than it might have done in other crops. I knew that what he said was true. The country was still in the depths of the depression. Eggs had tumbled from seven and half to four pence a dozen. Cheese was down to a derisory three and a half new pence a pound and all other farm prices reflected the same situation.

I was so depressed that it was perhaps only Tom's own courageous example which helped me to face another even more disastrous farming year. He and Gladys were deeply in love. There was little he needed to learn about crop and stock production. He didn't want to increase his own family's burden by taking a bride home. Since he was a second son who, despite his strong attachment to the family had a very independent spirit, he was anxious to begin farming on his own. Within hours of learning that with his mother's help he had managed to gain the tenancy of a farm near Audlem, he had proposed marriage and been accepted by Gladys.

We all admired him greatly. The farm at Audlem was, he said, 'Weed infested and badly run down', but that was obviously a challenge he relished. However, despite his skills and confidence, we all recognized and appreciated that it was symptomatic of the strength of his love for Gladys that he should have willingly unhitched himself from the security of his family when still so young and in such a deplorable farming epoch. It turned out to be a period of both mature and youthful initiatives.

While we admired Tom's positive move, it came as no surprise. However, when Fred shyly announced that while he hoped to continue working at Fordhall, 'Me and Betty have decided to take the plunge and I'll be moving to a cottage we've found over Ternhill way', we could hardly believe it. His nightly excursions confirmed our belief that his fourteen year joking relationship with Betty had continued. But we all thought that it had settled into a comfortable companionship upon which they both depended without wishing to take the relationship any further. Whenever Bill challenged Fred by asking him when he intended 'to make an honest woman of Betty' he always provided the same answer. 'Who would want Jack for a father-in-law?'

However, Jack repaid the compliment with a rare flash of malicious humour. When congratulated on his daughter's imminent wedding, he spat loudly, nodded incredulously and said, 'Can't understand why she's done it. Must be marrying him for his money'.

If anything, Margaret's show of resolution was more astonishing than Fred's decision to marry. It certainly justified my mother's determination that, as academically the brightest of us, she should receive the longest education. Always treated as the baby, while quietly seeming to enjoy being protected, she had matured without our realising it. Specialising in commercial subjects in her last year of school, she acquired sufficient competence as a shorthand typist and bookkeeper to become a useful secretary although she was still very young. These were talents quickly appreciated by the hard-headed businessman in Wolverhampton where she had attended an interview without our knowing. She maintained her habitual calm and reserve while twice carefully reading the letter offering her a job.

Mother's initial reaction must have been very disappointing. Everything seemed to be developing too swiftly for her. In six years, Father and Uncle John had died, our relations with Tom Hollins had been ruptured, Edith and Gladys in turn had left the house. Recently, Fred had gone too and now her youngest, Margaret, wanted to go as well. The whole world that she had known seemed to have lost its permanence and to be crumbling. Meanwhile, everything she had left was in obvious jeopardy. Her instinct to fight for its preservation made her reluctant to let Margaret go.

In the end, it took the combined efforts of all three of us to persuade her that for Margaret, at a time when employment of all types was so scarce, the post she had been offered was too good to reject. Leaving eventually with her blessing, Margaret never forgot the sacrifices Mother had made for her education. Until well after we were prosperous enough not to need it, she always sent home each week what money she could spare from her wages when her lodgings and other outgoings had been met. Although initially that was very little, it probably saved us from the pauperdom we would otherwise have had to face.

I watched the tops of the trees in Long Covert across Drayton Field lose their distinctness as the Western sky darkened. Although I could still feel the summer warmth radiating from the ground, the air was cooling rapidly. Pulling on my sweater, I pushed my back harder into the hedge back and waited.

From where I sat, the line of fourteen low wooden arks we had built for the pregnant gilts resembled the bivouacs of a sleeping army. Those to my right stood out in hard silhouette against the flare of light from Jack's cottage.

We were still in the honeymoon period after being connected to mains electricity. The release from the daily chore of filling oil lamps and trimming their wicks had made us all profligate with a supply of power at the rock of a switch. Jack and his wife were still not in bed and I doubted if there was a bulb in the house which wasn't lit. As I grew colder, I found the light comforting. It also made the irregular thudding from inside the arks more tolerable. Impatient with the harness and chain which was for weeks ahead to limit their movement to a radius of fifteen yards from a stake in the ground, the gilts were venting their irritation on the ark walls.

After days of coming and going as they pleased, it was the first time that we had driven them in and bolted the door for the night. Getting them through the door onto the cosy bed of straw had been easy enough. But, after five minutes of struggling to get the harness strapped on to the first cornered gilt, Jack and I wished that we had accepted Bill's offer of help. Although with a belly full of piglets they were heavier than front row forwards, they jinked, bobbed and weaved like the most mercurial rugby three quarter. Once they began to move quickly, they acquired an overwhelming momentum. Several times when they rushed straight at me, I was hurled to the ground. Frequently, when hanging over their backs trying to grab a strap under their shoulders, I was pinned to the stake. My ankle still throbbed painfully where it had received the full impact of a flying hoof.

Jack, who did what he could to still the turbulent gilts by clinging to an ear and a foreleg, was obviously not prepared to try and fix on a harness. Being essentially a plantsman, he always made his slight disdain for livestock clear.

Several weeks of prenatal grazing on some rich clovery sward had made the bowels of the expectant mothers satisfactorily loose. Sensibly reluctant to work anywhere near their back legs, Jack left me to receive the blessings they so freely bestowed in their excited, squealing agitation. When, with the job completed, we went back to his cottage to drink tea, he made no effort to disguise his disgust at my dung-soiled garb. More aware in the confines of the kitchen of the cloying smell of pig muck which was developing like an envelope around me, I hurriedly drank my tea and went to my post in the hedge to wait and see what happened.

In the air, the reek from my soiled clothes was less overwhelming. The herbs I crushed with my back provided a counter aroma. Breathing really deeply I caught the resinous perfume from the deal of the arks which had cooked all day in the sun. An overlay of pig seemed more acceptable out there as I listened to their dying protests.

Determined not to sleep myself until certain that the pigs had settled I was grateful for the occasional diversion of late revellers from the Drayton pubs passing along the road beyond the hedge. The hollow metallic knock of bent pedals colliding with bicycle frames or the jolting slip of loose chains was followed later by the chillier scrape of hobnails on the tarmac. Incoherent snatches of drink-slurred conversation penetrating the vegetation provided a kaleidoscopic impression of the major concerns in rural England at the time. 'Now it's really got going that Milk Marketing Board is helping to get us better prices.'

'Francis was saying their Harry found work again because they have taken another two hundred back at the ordnance factory in Wolverhampton.'

'She says there were terrible queues for that Snow White at the Picture House and she'd never take such a bunch of kids again.'

''E said that corn and tattie prices will be higher than they've been for years.'

'Herbert Sutcliffe says that Hutton is the best batting prospect since Bradman.'

'Never should have let the bugger march into Alsace Loraine. Our Dad says that if we aren't careful, we'll be back in the trenches.'

'Give over — I've told you before — you'll have to wait.'

While the previous messages had been anonymous, I recognised Megs Edwards' voice making the last determined statement. Plumper and more florid by that time, she had remained unmarried but was obviously still the object of ogling attraction at the Drayton pub.

In the country, we were just beginning to think about Hitler. The prices of produce obsessed us more than the activities of a small Austrian who was never mentioned in the *Farmers Weekly*. At Fordhall, we were so obsessed with survival that events beyond Market Drayton seemed to count for very little. Our hopes were firmly pinned to the success of the new pig enterprise.

In the three years that Mother and I had been alone, nothing much had changed. Joan, who had previously helped in the dairy during high summer when milk supplies were greatest, now had less to do in the house and had replaced Gladys as Mother's fulltime assistant. Our farm production remained pitifully low. Prices had begun to improve marginally as the country slowly started to drag itself out of the great depression. But at Fordhall, the difference in our income was barely significant. We continued to limp from one crisis to the next and were never sure how we would pay the rent for the coming quarter. It was the fruitfulness of Jack's garden which prompted us to try a new way with pigs.

One evening in August, 1936, I had been out to Drayton Field to look at a steer which Bill said he though was a bit lame. Jack and his wife were working on his vegetable patch and her cheery and respectable 'Evening, Master' made me pause to talk to them across the fence on the way back.

Despite Jack's superior early 'Lad' which had slowly deteriorated into an unrecognisable grunt of recognition now that I was twenty-two, his wife had called me 'Master' from the day I had succeeded Uncle Tom.

It was her warmth, kindness and shrewd understanding that made dealing with Jack possible in the early days. Then, after eight years of working together as boss and man, we were gradually learning to tolerate and respect each other.

If ever he disagreed violently with my policies, I usually found that I could obtain his fuller co-operation by talking to his wife when he was absent. She had known me since the day I was born, so we were firm friends.

He was moving slowly backwards plunging a wide fork into the ground to loosen a double row of delicious looking little yellow globe turnips. She was following him to collect the crop. I stood fascinated by their harmony as a team and by her dexterity. There was something wonderfully accomplished about her hands. They seemed to epitomise all that was laudable about a rural wife. Despite the pommelling they took as the result of endlessly washing dishes and clothes, pounding dough to make pastry or bread and the skin cracking work in the damp soil of the garden, they always looked strangely elegant and well kempt when she darned or held her cup. Her fingers were so nimble that I could barely follow their movement as she collected the leaves of two turnips in each hand, tapped them gently together to knock off the soil and then twisted off their leaves and dropped them in her basket.

As she followed Jack on her hands and knees, shifting her basket each time she moved, I noticed how far her hands penetrated the rich, almost black earth. When he plunged his

fork into the soil, it seemed almost bottomless. Years of bar-
rowing mounds of selected manure from our stables, stacking
it beneath a corrugated iron cover to allow it to rot and
mature without its goodness being washed away by rain and its
autumn incorporation into the ground had created something
very special. No longer just soil, it had become a rich, warm,
slightly spongy, always moist but never sodden growth
medium — the perfect cradle of prolific plant life. Everything
he sowed or planted seemed to burgeon. Translated into a farm
scale, his yields of potatoes would have been twice as high as
those we worked so hard to take from our fields. His runner
beans rampaged over the ten foot high hazel rod frames he'd
erected like the wildest of tropical vines.

Faced with such a riot of green abundance, I always felt
chastened.

That year everything seemed to be particularly splendid.
Pausing to wipe the sweat from his forehead with his cap, he
realised that after staring about in envy I was looking directly
at him. He answered my question before it was asked. 'It's the
muck that does it, that's all, tons and tons of muck.'

I suppose that he could see that I was only half convinced.
Every year when the ground was dry and the cows were out in
summer, we carted the contents of our winter midden and
spread it onto the land we'd chosen for the following year's
potatoes. I pointed to the heaps from the midden which stood
awaiting spreading in Cottage Field. 'Oh aye, but there's not
nearly enough.'

Having helped to shift it, I was dubious.

Pulling his cap back on his head impatiently, he became
more vehement. 'Not nearly enough.'

He was the only man alive who had worked for my
grandfather when Fordhall had been as prosperous as any farm
in the region.

'It doesn't get the half now it got in Old Clutton's day when
every field was packed with walking dung carts.'

He clearly found my continued puzzlement exasperating.

'Well, it stands to reason, doesn't it. We had more beasts
then and less land under the plough,' he expostulated almost
shouting.

I did my best to sound disdainful as I sighed heavily when
replying, 'I know, I know, but we've been through all that
before.'

He plunged his fork furiously into the ground again. 'Well, that's as maybe, but I tell you, you'll never do any good until you get more muck onto the land.'

I knew he was right but we had discussed the golden hoof theory repeatedly and even he couldn't come up with an answer to the fundamental problem. If we ploughed less land to accommodate more grazing livestock in the summer, we would still have to feed them through the winter. As it was our pastures could hardly cope with the few stock they carried. When the weather dried out, they became niggardly and burnt looking in less than a week. Even in a good grass growing season they barely provided sufficient hay to see us through the winter.

The serpent was always chasing its tail. We could improve fertility by carrying more stock if only our land was fertile enough to carry them. Richer people might have found a solution by buying in winter feed. However we could never have met the bills. The alternative possibility of buying store animals in the spring to fatten on an increased pasture area for sale in the autumn didn't seem feasible. Our land was in such bad heart that it was hard enough to get those animals we did rear into a good enough condition to send to market. The thought of trying to fatten more and increase our susceptibility to the vagaries of poor fatstock prices was too daunting.

The autumn was well advanced before I realised that we had one asset which remained unexploited. I'd been down to look at the sheep in Mill Meadow and was panting my way back up through Long Covert when I paused to rest.

Over the surge of a strong wind through the residual leaves of oaks and beeches, I heard a louder, splashing sound like someone jumping into water. I could see nothing by the river and was still staring about when it happened several times again. Looking up, I saw a red squirrel plunging from bough to bough as it made its way across the ceiling of the wood, brushing foliage as it went.

Staring up at it, I became aware of the bumper beech mast and acorn harvest which stood out against a bank of fleecy cloud.

'He won't starve this year', I said aloud.

Few people talk to themselves aloud more than farmers. It must have something to do with the lack of an audience when they are working. I am as good a self conversationalist as anyone. When young, I believed the myth that it was a sign of madness, but now I'm convinced that it ensures the expression of many good ideas which might otherwise have remained locked deeply in the mind. Nevertheless, I am still shocked when it happens. I was then. Glancing about guiltily to make sure I hadn't been overheard, I realised that the ground was covered with a layer of fallen mast, spanish chestnuts, horse chestnuts and acorns which in places was several inches thick. Their fruity mustiness was almost alcoholic. The idea it provoked certainly made me momentarily tipsy.

Jack was just settling to an enormous bowl of his favourite sheep's head broth and seemed annoyed at the interruption when, with the briefest of knocks, I stuck my head through their kitchen door.

'What about more pigs?' I cried.

'Pigs', he repeated grumpily without looking up from the task which engaged him. With a giant serving spoon he was plunging about among the bright vegetables in the steaming bowl, trying to extract a sliver of succulent dark cheek flesh he'd spotted.

'Aye, pigs', I said as, successful, he raised the spoon to his lips and blew on its contents to cool them. I felt frustrated at not being able to communicate immediately my wonderful vision. It was straight out of school history primer. 'A typical woodland scene in the Middle Ages' I remembered the caption saying. As a farmer's son, I'd been fascinated by the poor black and white reproduction of a blue and gold illuminated capital in a medieval manuscript showing a swineherd in leather jerkin and cap with boots with curly turned up toes, watching his herd of strange looking pigs graze the mast on a forest floor.

The image had returned when the squirrel had drawn my attention to the nuts.

'We've been trampling over the extra grazing for years now', I pointed out to Jack. 'That's how we'll get more muck on the land. We'll let pigs root and forage in the covert and walk back to manure the fields.'

I wanted to groan when, instead of immediately recognising the brilliance of the idea, he continued quietly chewing and savouring the sliver of meat. But after he had plunged the spoon again to find another his reaction, if less enthusiastic than I wished, was more encouraging.

'You know, it might just be worth a try.'

Tom Williamson, whom I had come to rely on more and more for advice, thought so too. So did Urban Major. However, it was the conviction of my mother's cousin, Dick Fitton, that more pigs might be profitable which was finally the most influential. The Fittons lived not far away at Ightfield and their son, John, was about my age. We'd both been rather shy when young and although I was still very nervous when with strangers, we had become firm friends in our teens. Their farm was a pleasing and satisfying bike ride away. Since I didn't drive a car, I had become a fanatical cyclist.

It was my attempt to cure a growing complaint. Just when it seemed that I was going to need my health and strength most, it seemed likely to break down again. At unexpected moments I would become quite dizzy and my eyes would lose their focus. I would sometimes have to rest for several hours before I was fit to work again. Despite my rugged outdoor life, I frequently slept badly and found it increasingly difficult to digest food. Just about every time Joan went to market with Mother, she would return and drop numerous cartons of patent tablets on the kitchen table. I'd keep them constantly in my pocket and crunched them ceaselessly as I went about my work.

Fred, who disapproved of my general abstinence from alcohol and my consumption of tablets, told me earnestly one day that he had never suffered from anything in his life and was convinced that the secret was brown ale.

'Soothes the lining and helps the fermentation of the stomach and all the rest', he confided as though admitting me to a privileged sect.

Bill could grasp a medicinal herb from a hedgerow quicker than a swallow could grab a fly from the air. Daily he'd urge me to make complicated concoctions from the peculiar posies he thrust into my hands.

'Boil it in a pint of water 'til it's nearly dry, then strain it through a silk stocking and take it hot before bed', he'd prescribe. Some of them were so vile that I determined to die rather than continue the cure.

Fortunately, my headaches were rare but just my dizziness and its association with my head made Mother terrified. She must have been reminded by my symptoms of the horror of my father's illness. I frequently caught her peering at me anxiously while I was reading. Since on those occasions I felt fine, I'd spend much of the evening trying to convince her and myself that my problem was trivial. She never seemed very reassured by my claim that if what I had was serious its presence would be constant and its gravity increasing. I remember having doubts myself. Because the dizzy bouts did seem to be becoming more frequent.

Mother obviously felt that if my condition wasn't caused by something seriously organic, then it must have been related to an inadequate diet which she had been providing. I couldn't persuade her that just because our budget wouldn't allow us such luxuries as sea fish or in fact anything very much bought in shops, my diet was in no way defective. To compensate for what she supposed to be her former neglect, she doubled her efforts in the kitchen. More of everything, she determinedly believed, was the answer. More fresh milk, more cream, more melting pastry, more eggs, more home cured ham and bacon – the product of more home killed pigs to supply more sausage, liver ('rich in iron'), Black pudding, potted meats, pork with crackling rind and flesh so white and succulent that you could cut it with the edge of a fork.

Only my generally restless disposition and the cycling which I prescribed for myself, can have saved me from being mistaken for a sack of lard.

It certainly made me spend more and more time discussing my plan for pigs with Dick Fitton and John who had been building up a very successful pig fattening business. Since they were wishing to expand, it was agreed that our interests seemed to coincide.

'If you keep some of those good home bred females which you normally fatten for the butcher, you could rapidly build a herd of breeding sows', John enthusiastically explained. 'Putting them to your boar again would probably produce a lot of fine young pigs. But you wouldn't have sufficient whey or meal to fatten them yourself. However we are looking for more young stock than we can produce ourselves and you could sell them all to us as soon as they are weaned. That way, you'd get the benefit of their mother's muck while we got the chance of upping our output.'

He became more enthusiastic than me and when he could spare the time, he drove over to us to help with the construction of the arks. These portable homes for the sows were necessary because we wanted to confine them on the field to be improved and to move them regularly to make sure that all areas got an equal supply of manure. It was a method which was becoming fashionable again.

Sows were healthier, when pregnant or nursing young, living in plenty of fresh air and grazing new ground, the pundits in the farming journals had rediscovered. They were less prone, they said, to diseases which build up if the pigs are kept habitually on the same area.

Since fashion seems to play as big a role in farming as it does in women's dress, both John and I were extremely pleased with the plan we had devised.

But the din I heard while sitting in the hedge that summer's evening raised doubts in my mind. I was still kept alert by the constant banging from the arks long after the last stragglers from town had past along the road and were in their beds. All the lights in Jack's cottage were also extinguished. I was becoming very cold and tense. Sitting in an awkward position seemed to have increased the pains from indigestion which at times felt as if I was being stabbed in the heart with a red hot spear.

Lonely and miserable, I began to wonder whether once more our efforts to survive would be thwarted. I couldn't see how Clive Thompson could be expected to go on allowing us to be late with the rent. Fortunately, he had been as enthusiastic as anyone else when I explained to him the scheme in detail that spring of 1937. Yet again, Mother and I had been forced to go and see him and beg for charity. We were nearly a full year behind with the rent again but could only pay him a quarter. However, he seemed embarrassed to accept even that. I think he was impressed by our refusal to give up and in true British spirit wanted the underdog to succeed. He knew the Cluttons and I suppose that they wouldn't have agreed to co-operate unless they thought the pig scheme was sound.

Typically, it was the feature of the scheme which most made it possible which appealed to him most. His beam was radiant when the thought occurred. 'It's splendid, splendid. I like it, I like it. All that fertility locked up under those trees after hundreds of years of growth and leaf fall and decay being cropped as nuts by foraging pigs and then walked onto their field when they want a bit of sunshine and return to graze the grass and clover. That's a fine way to use walking dung carts.'

I remembered the words vividly and hoped they were justified as I sat my vigil waiting for the pounding of the gilts to stop.

When I reached my room I was shivering violently but happy. I had to wait for that moment before dawn when air which has gradually cooled suddenly seems to precipitate all the moisture it contains to drench everything it surrounds. When I pulled off my vest, it seemed limp and damp. Even my skin clung to the sheets as I drew them round me. I realised before sleeping that the pleasing events of the last hour had, for a while, helped me to forget the cold and my bad digestion. Despite the long wait, the gilts had finally settled down. Their anguish was easy to understand. Near to giving birth for the first time and increasingly astonished by the movements in their uterus, they had been harnessed, chained and locked in their arks for the first time. So many firsts in quick succession must have been upsetting.

The sequel came abruptly next morning. I went over to them before fetching the cows. Very late to settle, they were obviously as exhausted as I. Gingerly releasing the latch on each ark door in turn, I expected a stampede. At first nothing happened. Only a gradually increasing shuffling and dragging of chains announced their growing interest in affairs outside. One by one they hesitantly nosed through the doors as though suspecting more mischief. I walked away to encourage them to adventure further.

With deeply suspicious glances in my direction, they began to advance towards one another. As their confidence grew, their speed increased until suddenly, with a disturbing jolt, their progress was halted. They had reached the end of their chains and stood almost snout to snout a few inches from each other. When, after several minutes of determined tugging accompanied by indignant squeals, they realised that there was no way of advancing and they seemed to become more resigned.

Glancing back as I left the field, most of them had quietened and began eagerly to graze the leafy clover in the grass circle between their arks and the end of the chain. It was lusher than I had seen it for years and was already benefitting from the fertility carried by the pigs from the covert during the spring. For the first time in nearly twenty years a patch of our land seemed to be really improving.

Even Jack was stimulated by the success. 'By God, there's

some stuff on there', he proclaimed as I was urging the last of the cows through the shippen door to be milked. 'They'll have a job to clear up everything in their patch if we move them every three days."

But he forgot that most of them were feeding an average of eight developing young. They managed splendidly, cropped the grass like mowers, and prospered. No piglet ever went short of nourishing milk after it was born or failed to make excellent progress. Eight weeks later, John Fitton was almost lyrical when he saw the condition of the hundred and twelve sturdy weaners he came to collect.

After a second cycle I became more ambitious and increased the breeding sows to thirty five. So many arks disposed regularly about the fields and moved frequently transformed the appearance of the farm. From a distance, they looked like a crusader encampment.

Although I tried hard to divide the sows into groups due to farrow at different times, and thus spread the work, there always seemed to be a lot to fit in between the normal work of the farm. While grazing in the woodland, the pregnant sows could look after themselves. Beneath the trees there was plentiful nutritious food, boggy areas in which they could wallow and spring at which they could drink. If they wanted more bulky food, there was an area of adjacent meadow to graze. At night, they could slump down beneath hawthorn and bramble thickets in the covert or lurch contentedly back to their unlocked arks.

Once they were tethered, my real work began. Although portable, the solid arks were heavy and cumbersome. Moving was made more difficult by the presence of testy pregnant sows. While groping up and relocating the tethering stakes, they frequently broke free and frisked away – their normal ponderous gait accelerating to the sort of surprising sprint displayed by elderly matrons when the doors open at a post Christmas sale in a large store. By the time thirty five arks had been moved and all the stakes hammered into their new places I was quite exhausted. By then the water bowls, which we had cast for them in concrete, had to be shifted and refilled. And in the later stages of pregnancy and while nursing their young, the sows had to be fed additional meal as well. It was a load of work I had ignored when merely speculating upon the benefits which breeding weaners might bestow.

Happily, by the middle of 1938, those benefits were becoming obvious everywhere that the sows had grazed. Months after they had moved on the thicker, darker green pasture indicated exactly where the arks had been stationed. The effect was particularly noticeable on a hillside which could be viewed from a distance. From there, it could be seen years later.

Looking at the regular circular patterns left by the grazing, I realised that they spelt out a simple message to me. If I wanted my grandfather's prosperity, I'd have to find a way of getting animals to spread as much of their rich organic manure about the fields as possible. My reading had taught me that simple chemical analysis showed that pound for pound, artificial fertiliers were much richer in plant food than animal manure. But it was obvious that on our thin soils the manure had something far more valuable to bestow. It was rich in organic matter which, as it was used by the small animals and micro-organisms in the soil, broke down into humus. Once formed, this almost magical brown and slightly gelatinous substance helped to bind the mineral particles in the soil together into crumbs — greatly improving its structure. While vital air and water could filter more easily through it, the crumbs provided valuable reservoirs of moisture in dry weather. More important still was the fact that the humus clung onto and released slowly as the crop required them the plant nutrients in the manure. If it rained they weren't all washed away below root level.

Apart from their startling impact upon soil fertility, the pigs ensured our survival until the outbreak of the war.

They didn't make as much money as we had hoped. Pigs multiply very rapidly. Even in those days of less improved breeds, each sow was providing twenty piglets per year. If pork and bacon prices seem attractive, farmers are naturally tempted to breed more pigs. Quite quickly, they discover that they have all bred too many, the market becomes glutted and the price collapses. This situation creates what is known as the dreaded pig cycle.

If a farmer steps onto this moving economic belt at the right time and increases his output of pigs early enough, he will probably be lucky and make good prices. Profits made then would, he'd hope, tide him over the lean period which is bound to follow. Sadly, our Fordhall pig plans were hatched too late to take the best advantage of the market. We also discovered that the extra food we had to provide for the sows was almost too costly when compared with the prices John Fitton could pay for the weaners. Nevertheless, it was income from the weaners which helped us to catch up with our rent and other bills. Even if they had yielded no profit at all, we would still have profited from the good which they did to the land.

Despite a buttress of cloud against the hills behind us, it was a brisk and invigorating day. At nearly twelve hundred feet above sea level, we felt we could see the whole sweep of Cardigan Bay. A dark smudge on the horizon across the bright water might have been Ireland. But it was probably only the shadow of a cloud; too remote to subdue spirits which were stretching our imaginations beyond the limits of vision.

Staring about, through eyes blurred by wind sprung tears, we could see other tiny patches of emerald gleaming out from the duns and olives of the mountain's skirt. They, like the field on which we stood, were scraps of improved pasture acquiring the significance of a shrine.

Patient with his disciples, the god to whom they would be dedicated was still replying thoughtfully to eager questions as he clambered over the dry stone wall.

It had been like that from the moment he had greeted us when we stumbled out of the charabanc in Aberystwyth in mid morning. In fact he was only replying to questions which had been forming in the minds of men ploughing distant fields or milking in lonely shippens for months past. They were questions rehearsed endlessly during the long haul in the wheezing bus from the Shropshire plain through the Welsh mountains and down to the coast.

'Wasn't grass, after all, just grass?'

'Stuff that cows and sheep like nibbling and relished in winter as hay?'

'How could it be changed?'

'Would it be different if you treated it like a crop of corn, ploughing the land, sowing it with seed, feeding it with fertilisers?'

'If so, what was the right way and time to do it?'

'What would the ultimate benefit be?'

His shock of grey hair tossed by the wind and vehement nodding, bluff Professor George Stapledon, his tweed suit and slightly buccolic accent deliberately tailored to appeal to men of the land, had lost no enthusiasm during the four hours he had been supplying the answers. The questions had been diffidently posed at first. But since they were well received by a man who revelled in controversy, by the time we reached the sacred hillside, he hardly had time to pause for breath after the climb up from the track.

'This', he explained triumphantly while squatting and brushing his palm over the stiff and springy pile of the turf, 'is what the whole thing is about. More cattle feed of a higher nutritional quality for much longer every year – even here up on the hill.'

Shuffling our feet deeper into the thick sward, we were momentarily silent. We all knew that we were standing on history. Because we were on the hill land where Stapledon had first ripped into the thin and rocky soil to improve drainage, neutralised the high acidity with lime, improved the fertility with fertilisers and planted the greatly improved strains of grass and clover he had bred. It was a rich bright green patch in a niggardly brown wilderness which even in 1938 had become famous. Stapledon had been publishing the results of his research for over a decade and farmers everywhere were beginning to pay serious attention to his findings.

Only a god, we farmers felt, could interfere with nature in the way in which Stapledon had done. Refusing to accept the scant productivity which the sparse and wiry mountain grass or the exquisite but tiny native clover plants provided, Stapledon, when still defiantly young, had decided to do better. Selecting the best rye grasses he could find, he painstakingly emasculated some by teasing away the male anthers when they flowered. Then, isolating them in his own version of an intensive care unit to eliminate the vagaries of nature, he fertilised their ovaries individually with pollen from other strains with compatible characteristics and similar promise.

Thousands of hours of this tedious and patient genetical juggling had led him to produce strains of grass quite unlike their parents. Breaking the winter dormancy much earlier in the year, they produced more, larger and richer leaf. Since, after flowering, grasses become less productive and more difficult for animals to digest, by his tinkering, Stapledon had bred grass which didn't flower until much later in the season.

To compete with the oustanding vigour of his grasses and to complement the animals' diet, Stapledon had bred giant new clover too. Their broad leaflets stood out boldly among the grass stems like radar scanners to trap the sun.

Could this lush mixture be the answer to raising Fordhall's productivity, I wondered while gazing at it in awe? Would ploughing our reed-infested lower land and sowing it with a Stapledon mixture provide sufficient feed for the extra stock which we obviously needed? It would, Stapledon felt, but only if the land and livestock were properly managed. Good drainage was essential if his strains of grass and clover were to establish quickly and survive. And if they did, only sufficient stock to eat the new growth they produced, as they produced it, should be allowed to graze, otherwise the new strains would be eaten out.

'Grass is the crop which grows best in Britain – but we must treat it like any other crop', he explained, insisting that ploughing and reseeding anew every three years was the best way to take advantage of the new plants he had bred.

Stimulated but exhausted, we all lapsed into a drowsy silence on the way home.

As the bus snaked its way down through the passes, I worried about how I could best profit from the lessons learned on the younger farmers' outing which I had organised. Certainly Stapledon's new Ley Farming system sounded appropriate to our well drained higher land. But it offered little hope for the wet meadows. Remembering their boggy surface for all but a few weeks in summer, I couldn't see how we'd even get the land ploughed, let alone repeat the operation every third year.

The visit had certainly stirred up a hornets' nest of observations. My father and grandfather had fed sheep on turnips followed by three years of grass. Why did these systems improve fertility? What was the 'secret behind that mysterious word, fertility?

Jim knew, but only by intuition or, as he would say, 'I just know.' Was the answer to be found in the spent mushroom manure, in the culture in my yoghurt; a link between the fungus and the microbe cultures; something about soil bacteria?

CHAPTER THIRTEEN

The Man From the War Ag

Every word he uttered seemed backed by quiet menace.

'I'm afraid you have no choice Mr. Hollins. We want every possible acre ploughed.'

After only three visits, the 'Man from the War Ag' had already established a harsh reputation at Fordhall. One of the men charged by the government with maximising farm production, he was no respecter of land and his answer was to plough everything, even soil which would have produced more food if it remained in pasture and carried livestock. But when I had tried to outline our bitter cropping experience of the previous decade and my belief that it would be better if we continued to try to improve the land by carrying more stock, he became very impatient.

'You are a lowland farmer, Mr. Hollins. It's crops we want from you — leave meat production to the men in the hills who can't do anything else. I'll be round again shortly and I'll want to see your complete cropping plan.'

That was at the end of his first visit and he left me feeling very miserable as, without any attempt at a formal goodbye, he strode briskly to his car and drove away. Anyone less equipped to obtain the collaboration of farmers by humane and gentle persuasion it would have been difficult to discover. For me, his auburn hair and mean face seemed to promise a double threat. Not only did he possess power to affect our immediate future substantially but he bore an uncanny resemblance to the ogre-like chemistry master from whom I had escaped eleven years earlier. Initially, this extraordinary likeness rendered me more timid and incoherent than usual. I was unable to imbue my arguments with any authority as he drove me to take actions I was sure were wrong.

He hadn't been with me for more than half an hour when he made it clear that bad reports from him to his Committee could lead to our being expelled from the farm.

'To feed people in wartime, we need every bag of grain and potatoes we can get and if the Committee doesn't feel you are obtaining the best from your land, it's entitled to put in someone else who can.'

Realising how poor our yields were, compared with those of others on richer soil, I knew that it wouldn't be long before his threat could become reality. I had a dreadful foreboding about the unpleasantness of future relations with the War Ag which was confirmed at the third meeting when he insisted that I plough even more of the high fields than I proposed. When I pointed out that I wouldn't even have enough grass left to make hay to see the cows through the winter, he simply said I'd have to buy in food. I was doubtful if I would be able to afford it but I was wrong.

After years of neglect, when governments had encouraged the import of cheap food from overseas to feed the industrial poor, blockaded Britain needed its farmers again. Prices for all products greatly improved and the farming slump was over. Instead of treating the farmers' plight as something to be ignored, the government offered exciting cash incentives to increase production. A grant was paid for every acre of old pasture ploughed. There were grants, too, for many other things – spreading lime, draining land and erecting new and more efficient livestock buildings among them.

Since his tenants were obviously going to become more prosperous, Clive Thompson quickly realised that it would pay him to improve his property while the government accepted much of the cost. It was early in 1940 that he decided we should have the enlarged and more up to date cowshed which for a while turned our yard into a building site. A wise investment decision from his point of view, it created circumstances which later enabled us to survive at Fordhall. So once again, we were rescued by that generous and perceptive man.

The gasping insistent thud of the motorised cement mixer which reverberated round our buildings most of the day is the sound most reminiscent of Spring 1940 to me. When our machine was silent, many others could be heard from across the valley where the R.A.F. base at Tern Hill was being urgently expanded. There it often co-mingled with the rasp of our own hard boots on concrete and tarmac.

For our local Home Guard Unit also had its base at Tern Hill. Preoccupation with our own problems had largely insulated us from the anxiety of the months which led up to the Munich Crisis. But as the Nazi threat grew, even we began to speculate upon events beyond the Channel. In a surge of defiant patriotism I, together with many other farmers and workers in the district, volunteered to defend the homeland.

I little realised when I strapped the puttees round the ankles of my ill fitting khaki 'Dad's Army' trousers that I was donning apparel which would launch me in local society! For apart from being obliged to participate in the bawdy ribaldry generated while our ageing band exercised, I began to meet and learned to cope with many new and unfamiliar types of people. Contact with them led to an ever widening circle of voluntary wartime activities.

The experience taught me how to overcome the handicap of my innate shyness. However that took time and I could have used greater confidence in my early dealings with the man from the War Ag. Farmers weren't obliged to do anything except farm. It was clear that he considered my efforts as a husbandman pitiful and obvious that he thought my 'playing at soldiers' a ludicrous distraction from my main task. As always happens in that sort of situation, I seemed to be perpetually at a disadvantage. He nearly always turned up when I'd changed into my uniform and with boots sparkling I'd be about to leave for a parade.

I believe that pure malice made him lead me to discuss matters in the muddiest sections of our bottom land on those occasions. So that, after listening to his school masterly criticism of my inadequacy, I'd arrive late on duty to the accompaniment of scathing comment from our sergeant about the impossible state of my boots.

By the summer of 1940, the War Ag man was becoming very dissatisfied indeed. Apart from those areas of the land which had benefitted from grazing the pigs, the crops on most of the ploughed land were looking very poor. 'You'll have to be doing better than this, Mr. Hollins', he said firmly, beginning to preach again the need to apply bigger doses of the mineral fertilisers which had proved so useless in the past. Glancing disparagingly at my uniform, he left with a final admonition. 'You'd do well to give more time to thinking about the impovement of your crops.'

I couldn't really see how spending even more time worrying about them would lead to any improvement. As it was, I was sleeping very badly. Violent pains about my heart frequently jolted me into consciousness after I had lapsed into sleep through sheer exhaustion. I was more comfortable sitting up in bed and would read for hours or just sit and think until my stomach settled. I had plenty of time to think but couldn't find reasons for abandoning my former conclusions.

I tried to conceal my deteriorating health from my mother but she couldn't avoid noticing my haggard appearance early in the mornings. She believed that I was overtired because I was involved in so much outside the farm. I wondered if she was right but somehow I couldn't think of stopping. Despite my complaint, I was young and active and felt that, since I wasn't in service on some war front, I'd be shirking if all I did was farm. Yet before the disaster at Dunkirk, in the period of the phoney war, when hours of drilling or simulated patrols through our coverts seemed like just a repetitive game, the War Ag man's words made me reflect hard on their usefulness.

After Dunkirk, everything seemed to acquire a greater relevance. Everyone became fired with a stronger sense of purpose. All the playing at soldiers seemed justified if the concrete pillboxes which were hurriedly erected to cover road junctions had to be defended in earnest against a determined invader who had proved his capacity as a soldier on the continent. The evacuees from towns whose alien accents so frequently betrayed their pillaging presence in our orchards or about our chicken coops lost their pestilential image and became the nation's future which we had to embrace and protect.

When, late in the summer, the Luftwaffe (cleverly igniting the dry peat of a hillside in North Wales and using the flames as a navigation beacon) began to raid Liverpool, the children seemed to be in imminent danger. Aircraft observation was added to my list of activities. Since I wasn't sleeping well, standing upright scanning the sky through night glasses provided a fine distraction from my indigestion and taught me a lot about the constellations.

It was the window rattling, slate shifting percussion of the stick of bombs ripping craters in the Ternhill airfield which finally jolted old Jack and Fred into recognising that they were living in exciting and dangerous times. Until those ear stunning explosions, they had managed to remain practically uncommitted to anything save their work on the land. To Jack, who was over sixty, the war meant the intrusion of the

War Ag man with his insistence on undoing all the good we'd accomplished in the immediate pre war period. Hitler and the War Ag were as one as far as he was concerned. Fred, taciturn as ever, seemed more concerned with the fact that he had to black out most of his cycle lamp with dark blue paper which made riding home difficult in the winter, than in the progress of the army of the Third Reich on the Western Front.

However, the morning after the bombing, they were both clearly very resentful. When I'd finished milking and was crossing to the house for breakfast, I heard an animated mumbling from the store room next to the stable. Curious to discover what they were plotting, I peeped through the door. My father's old shot gun leaned against the wall and in the poor light I thought Fred was about to assassinate Jack with another twelve bore. However, looking closer, I realised that the gun was broken at the breach and Fred was merely holding it up while Jack was dragging a knot of oily sack through the barrel with a piece of binder twine. I crept away, grinning for it was clear that they, too, were preparing for war!

If the cleaned barrels never directed shot fired in anger, they certainly helped to feed us as the war lengthened. Our stock levels were much reduced. We couldn't fatten any beef cattle and the man from the War Ag kept a very careful note of the destiny of the few pigs he allowed us to continue rearing or the poultry we raised. Hare, rabbit, pigeon and occasionally pheasant, partridge and duck shot by Jack and Fred helped keep meat in all our larders.

With a great hiss, the last of the pea grit avalanched from the tipped cart to form a conical heap on the ground. It had taken Jack several days hard shovelling and carting to fetch it from the main pile by the road at the top of Banky Field and spread it in fifty odd heaps about the meadow. Although we had hoped to move the vital gravel on which clay drains are laid before the autumns rains, wartime transport was hard to obtain and the delivery from the gravel pits was too late.

In places, the wheels had cut ruts nine inches deep into the sodden ground and Jack had often needed two horses to get the heavy cart over the worst patches. Filling instantly with water, the ruts stood out among the crushed reeds like glittering veins. They were a reminder of the difficulties of the work ahead. After only an hour or two of rain the natural drainage was so poor that the soil became saturated.

Even the man from the War Ag had reluctantly agreed that the low meadows could never grow arable crops until they had been drained. But he wasn't going to allow this to interfere with his determination that they should be ploughed. 'Then they'll have to be drained, Mr. Hollins', he'd said decisively, while scanning them from the high land near the house.

He seemed more at home out of doors. It was only with reluctance that he had accepted my invitation to drink tea in the kitchen while we discussed my 1940 harvest results. I suppose that he felt that the tea was a form of bribe and my few months acquaintance with him convinced me that he considered the exercise of pure power alone sufficient reward.

With only the curtest of nods he had accepted the cup and immediately began to scowl as he made his announcement.

'These figures are not satisfactory at all, Mr. Hollins. The yield from your hundred and eighty acres doesn't even reach half the local average.'

My pointing out that over a third of our land was sodden meadow which couldn't be ploughed did nothing to appease him. As though he needed to face the problem before devising its solution, he quickly put the half full cup down on the table, pulled his cap firmly back on his head and walked outside. He brushed aside my objection that the local drainage contractors were so short of labour that they were booked for months ahead, with an impatient 'You'll have to do the work with your own labour'. While I was still accommodating to the prospect of such a massive task, he dismissed my rising objections, 'Of course you are a lucky man – there's a big grant for drainage which will help to pay for materials and labour and our drainage officer will provide you with a plan.'

The plan which flapped gently in the light breeze as Fred and I held it spread on a rectangular block of stacked drain pipes, reflected all the drainage officer's confidence. A few days work by his assistants with a theodolite had convinced him that the job was simple. 'Water,' as he explained with a laugh, 'always flows down hill'. That knowledge, he pointed out, had got him the job. 'Secret is', he confided, 'mustn't let it flow too quickly. Otherwise, any particles it carries get left behind while the water dashes away – high and dry so to speak, builds up a blockage. So the slopes must be nice and gradual and shallow. No problem here – no problem at all.'

Gazing about the lower end of the flat meadows while he spoke, I had found it difficult to see any slopes at all. But they were all clearly marked on the plan.

'They are slight, but definite', he explained when handing me the roll of oiled silk with its intricate web of indian inked lines.

We only had to locate six inch diameter main drains along the bottom of the slopes and connect them to a big ditch which joined the river. In some places very little digging would be required because there were already open ditches at the foot of the slopes. They would simply require deepening to lay the pipes before filling with soil.

Parallel three inch diameter subsidiary drains, set shallower at fifteen yard intervals would feed into the main drains and, as the drainage officer confidently explained, 'The whole place will dry out like the Sahara in weeks'.

'That's what he said', I repeated reassuringly to Jack as he joined us and peered at the plan.

After he'd slowly raised his head to follow the conical gravel heaps and rectangular stacks of pipes which could just be seen tracing paths through the tall reeds, he looked dubious.

'Well, looking at it now, you'd never guess it.'

With great optimism, Fred, George (the new young cowman who had joined us when Bill retired) and I began deepening the first ditch.

Nodding his head sceptically, Jack led the cart and horses away.

The deep roots of the reeds permeated the earth like thickly knotted nerves. Fortunately they sliced as easily as carrots except where they were infiltrated by the tougher fibres from the alder bushes which sprouted everywhere. Between the shallower roots of marsh marigold, buttercup, soft rush or swamp grasses caused no problem.

Without the alders, it would have been very easy digging. Because the alternative patches of gravel, fine silt, or thick black decayed sedge all yielded satisfactorily to the narrow ditching spades. But, no matter what their work-burnished edges struck, as we thrust them vindictively into the belly of the land, the sound as we strained to remove them was always the same – a vacuumatic, flatulent sucking. It was almost as if each dripping bladeful was protesting at being removed from the porridgy mass.

Although the water lubricated the penetration, it made the lifting very difficult. Since each thrust of a spadeful over the side of the ditch sent our feet deeper into the squelching mud of the bottom, moving in our leaden gumboots became harder every minute. In consequence, the six months which it took us to finish that first drainage scheme were the hardest any of us had ever spent.

It was vital that all the pipes were in place and buried in time for us to plough and sow the land by the spring of 1941. Apart from milking the cows, George and I had to carry to them every scrap of the tons of food they required while indoors during the winter months. The remaining pigs and poultry had to be fed and all the stock needed frequent mucking out. Meanwhile, Jack and Fred had to carry the burden of the rest of the work about the farm.

CHAPTER FOURTEEN

Moonlight Revellers

In every available minute we had free from our normal work, we'd run down to the meadow and continue the digging marathon.

Ditching for drainage is an ideal job for early autumn. Without being cold, the air is cool enough to be refreshing. Although moist and yielding, the ground tends to be light; firm but easy to move. We, however, were too late. Soon after we began, the land was saturated and most mornings it was necessary to break through its rock hard frozen surface with a pick before it could be dug. Rapidly sweltering inside the top coats we wore to fend off the cold, we'd begin to shiver immediatley we paused to rest.

Our hands were soon scarred by deep cracks caused by the drying after frequent soaking as we worked to clear the spades of mud. As the weather became colder and the chapping grew worse, the cracks widened into constantly bleeding wounds. Goose grease, cattle embrocation and even Stockholm tar were all remedies we tried in turn.

The work made us ravenous but I found that if I sat at the table immediately I reached the house I was so physically drained that I could hardly face my mother's delicious food. Hours of bending to lift the spade seemed to aggravate my poor digestion. Often only a few mouthfuls would be enough to send me rushing back into the yard overcome by a sudden nausea.

Such a tormented period ought to provide unpleasant recollections, but, as usual, the misery has faded and the sunshine remained. Even in the meadows, life wasn't always glum. From time to time, while digging, we'd stumble upon something interesting and grasp the chance to rest for a minute while it was discussed. Usually it was something commonplace like a piece of corroded chain or a horse's shoe. But early in February, our conjecture became protracted when Fred found what, at first, appeared to be the remains of a dagger with a broken blade.

Some minutes later, another fragment of almost pure rust could, we felt have been its point. Excitement really grew when, from low in a drift of sedge, which had been converted to pure peat, he extracted a scrap of leather which I thought resembled a portion of the Roman sandal I'd seen on a school trip to Chester Museum.

The barely identifiable scrap of mouldering bone not far away instantly suggested to us that we were scavenging in the shallow grave of a man.

We watched for a while, as Fred plodded on, waiting for further finds. But finally we became so cold that we returned to digging our own trenches.

Minutes later, we dropped our spades and ran towards him in response to his excited cry, 'I've got his ribs!'.

Even Jack, always slightly sperior and slower than the rest of us to show any enthusiasm for the finds, moved quickly that time.

So his disgust was the greatest when, as we arrived, Fred stooped and picked up the relics of what was obviously a ladies, 1930's model, metal boned corset.

Achieving middle aged maturity hadn't made Fred any less of a joker. And since he grinned perpetually, it was difficult to be sure when he was plotting. If he had been a dramatist, he would certainly have been a master of timing.

Perhaps his most astonishing effect was achieved when we were hurrying to complete the job. Stronger than George or I and at the height of his powers, he had more stamina than Jack, who was beginning to slow up as he aged. So that he didn't find it difficult to open more yards of trench than any of us each day.

Whenever I surveyed the lines of sticks which marked trenches still to dig and muttered anxiously about 'never finishing in time', he would always joke, 'We'd be all right if only you lot did some work'.

Our strained shoulders, aching thighs and backs provided sound reason for the indignation which this remark always provoked. But, conscious of our need for his prodigious efforts, which I realised helped to pace us all, I always tried to sound cheery when I shouted, 'We can't all be Carneira's', in reply.

He, too, was very conscious of his role as pace maker. He

couldn't help noticing that if he slowed his work rate, we followed suit. This must have prompted his most malicious trick.

Each day, working on parallel trenches, we fell into an established rhythm. When we stopped for lunch, Fred was always a pace or two ahead. But one morning towards the end of March, his rate of progress was depressingly rapid. While we were still many yards from the main drain, he had reached it and begun the trench for another feeder drain. In our efforts to catch him up we worked feverishly. By lunchtime, the too rapid pace had obviously nearly finished us. Fred laughed as we collapsed gasping and exhausted onto a pile of pipes to eat our sandwiches.

'We've put in some work this morning, lads', he commented brightly before taking a giant bite of his potted meat sandwich.

We were all too tired to reply. Looking at our crestfallen faces, he laughed again and nearly choked. Showering us with crumbs, he gestured broadly with the sandwich.

'We'll only need a couple of days to finish at this rate.'

Looking sourly at the yards of trench left to dig, none of us shared his optimism.

The morning's efforts had taken such a toll that we all made excuses to finish the afternoon stint early. George was the first to go, mumbling about the cows. Jack followed after nodding and uttering the single word, ''Orses'.

Shortly afterwards I nodded too and said, 'Calves'.

Fred's farewell grin seemed extra mischievous. But he said nothing and continued to swing away with his spade.

The hill up to the yard seemed interminably long and steep. When I reached the cowshed and collapsed onto a milking stool, my legs were trembling so hard with fatigue that I could barely hold the bucket between them.

It was completely dark and George and I were both wondering how we'd find the energy to complete the milking when Fred came up from the meadows.

Looking towards the door I was surprised to realise that he was surveying us silently while enjoying a private joke. Nodding incredulously, George laughed.

'I don't know how you do it.'

'Getting up early, lad getting up early.'

It was only days later that we realised that he'd been telling the truth.

We had been digging an area of land near a stack of pipes. The surface had become badly puddled by our boots as we'd taken the pipes to lay them in a ditch. As Fred pointed out, you could have used the area as a regimental cemetery without anyone noticing. Realising this, he'd got up before the day light and before even George and I had gone to the shippen to begin milking he'd used a pick axe to loosen the soil completely along the line of the ditch he'd dug with such astonishing speed.

When the land didn't dry out as quickly as we had hoped Jack thought, correctly, that we would have to wait for the spring spate of the river to subside.

Frequently, when we had been digging the trenches, he had pointed out that in places his feet were lower than the surface of the river when it was in flood. Yet the drains we were digging were not, he felt, deep enough to take water from the lowest areas.

His scorn for official advisers became more voluble as each week passed when ploughing was impossible. In his view, the land would never be suitable for arable crops. Because, although drainage might allow the top few inches of the soil to dry earlier and to remain freer of water until later in the autumn, it would always be too damp in the winter and early spring.

'To get over that one, you'll have to deepen the drains and the river. That will cost more cash than you will ever have', he declared bluntly.

He told the man from the War Ag the same thing in an irritatingly superior tone. Jack had never been temperamentally easy, but, after sixty, he allowed his disdain for any form of authority to be expressed unfettered. He made it clear that he considered the War Ag man an ill-experienced desk bound whipper snapper whenever he appeared. This caused me great embarrassment because of the man's powerful position. So I always strove to keep them apart.

However, on this occasion, Jack's goading drove the War Ag man into a trap.

'You are being too impatient. The water has to have time to track its way through — then you'll see the difference', he explained forcefully.

Jack's reply was quick and no less forceful. 'You'll see what you see here now, a meadow full of rushes, in five years time.' I drew the War Ag man into conversation, fearing that Jack

might be taken for my mouthpiece. I couldn't forget that they
had the power to throw me off the farm. 'As soon as this last
bit of filling is complete we would like to make a start on the
ploughing. How deep do you think we should go?' This was
said as we stood looking at an open trench, where three feet of
peat was clear for all to see.

'You must bury all the surface rushes for a start', he said,
'and plough across this line of trenches so that horses do not
push any pipes out of line with their feet. Nine inches should
do it all right.'

We had no idea then how right Jack was about the whole
scheme. It later became patently obvious that the man from
the War Ag had little experience of this type of land.

George was looking forward to moving his two favourite
horses, Prince and Bonny, down on to this meadow. I of
course found it rewarding to see the field change from a marshy
wilderness to rich black peat and George's happy face told its
own story. Only the occasional reed stalk emerged now.
Instead there were long straight rows where the wads of peat
had rolled over and settled against one another, like the pleats
of a scotch skirt.

The peat dried out quickly however, and proved difficult to
break down into a good firm seed bed. When it rained the
water dried off its surface like blotting paper.

Neither Fred, Jack or I were very pleased with the lumpy
loose seed bed. But it was the best that we could produce.

It was during the anxious days while waiting for the first
seeds to sprout that my social life began to develop.

Home Guard and aircraft observation work lead to many
outside contacts. By hiding their aircraft and airmen in our
rural enclave, the authorities provided us with the focus of
many of our activities. R.A.F. Ternhill served not only to beat
Hitler but also as the premises for dances, parties and concerts
to raise funds for the Red Cross to help in treating war
wounded. And, since several hundred young men and woman
were stationed there, it also became an important local foyer
for romance.

The allied forces had been expelled from Western Europe,
the Panzer divisions were plunging into the heart of Russia and
news from North Africa and the Far East was equally depressing. As one major reverse succeeded another, even in rural
Shropshire, we felt that we must increase our efforts. Without

the opportunity to fight physically, the best we could do was raise funds. Our initial informal efforts were not, we felt, sufficient. So a group of us formed a concert party – The Moonlight Revellers – which gave regular performances in pubs, village halls and forces bases in the Drayton region. We even had our own optimistic logo – a red cross badge with the words 'Tauton la titium sparga' (which loosely translated means 'Spread a little happiness') printed across it.

In retrospect, evenings spent with the Revellers remain some of the most comic and joyous of my life. Although initially still rather reserved and playing only minor chorus or bit parts, just being on a stage in front of people did much to foster my self confidence.

Like most rural districts, which in times of peace return to their bucolic calm, during the war, Drayton was blessed by visits by many celebrities. Working alongside them was a thrilling privilege for us amateurs.

Conscious, I suppose, of the worthiness of our meagre efforts, the professionals seemed to consider no engagement to perform, for only incidental expenses, too insignificant to consider. That's how Drayton citizens and forces audiences had the opportunity to be astonished by the thrusting arpeggios and glittering trills of great concert pianists like Eileen Joyce at her peak or to be lulled out of their wartime anxieties by the sonority of Engal Lund accompanied by Ferdinand Reuter as she performed folk songs on the same bill. They provided an unforgettable evening for everyone and a temperamental break-through for me.

In the programme, their items were to surround and buttress a short play I had written. John Justin, the London West End actor who was serving locally, had generously agreed to play the lead. Sadly, he was transferred before the evening of the performance and I was obliged to stand in at the last moment.

The prospect of trying to portray, with conviction, the emotions of a man spiritually committed to a life of integrity but faced with obvious temptations to falter presented by a war, was quite terrifying. I was so taut and struggled so hard to produce the words during the first few minutes that I don't think that I'd have noticed if the player with whom I was conducting the early dialogue had been assassinated. I had no hope that the play would have any dramatic interest. The aim was merely to push the minutes along between the songs and the following recital.

During my first long pause I began to relax a little. Glancing out over the lights I could see that, at least, the audience was respectfully attentive and that the clock had moved on by several minutes without any major breakdowns in the sequence of lines. I reflected briefly that I was quite used both to failure and making a fool of myself so that, at worst, my dismal performance would only be an addition to an already long list. The thought was comforting and, relaxing a little, I think that my performance improved. Towards the end, I became sufficiently vain to gain pleasure from the offering.

The final enthusiastic applause made me smile back happily in acknowledgement of the audience's inevitable kindness to a local boy. While I wasn't besieged with immediate offers by West End managements to star in their productions or write plays for them, the ultimate accolade came with kind congratulations from Eileen Joyce and the other professionals. They provided sufficient encouragement to make me believe in myself. And I am sure today that when I begin lecturing or broadcasting engagements, with little more than an apprehensive tremor, I owe my confidence entirely to their indulgence that evening. There is no doubt that the fillip to my confidence which they provided was of immense value when later I was forced to face a more critical public when trying to sell our produce in local markets.

An inevitable result of that evening was that I gained minor notoriety. Instead of lingering endlessly over a half pint of beer while trying to summon sufficient courage to approach a pretty girl, I found that at charity dances, they would frequently pause, in passing, to mention the play. That made asking them to dance much easier and more pleasurable. It also meant that I arrived home later and later – something which my mother worried about because she still attributed my appalling digestion to fatigue.

Another consequence was that I had even less time available to gobble up her wonderful meals in the evenings before rushing out to participate in one or other of my voluntary activities or to meetings with girls. To make up for my small consumption, she tried to increase the nutritional value of each dish by including even more butter and cream.

I think that my developing social life must have compensated for some of the disappointment I felt when the results of our winter's work in the meadows became clear that summer. Instead of settling down to produce a firm seed-bed for the delicate emerging roots to cling to, the surface soil remained loose and puffy. Nevertheless, the nurse crop of Italian Rye grass developed quite well. Too well, in fact, to allow the slower grasses and clovers to become well established. So that by the time it was necessary to turn cows onto the field to graze it for the first time, their trampling hooves easily broke through the loose surface, dislodging the young perennial plants in the process.

By Autumn, it was clear that the experiment in the meadow was a disaster. Through the Summer, the cows had obtained less grazing that they would have done from the marsh loving plants which normally flourished there. And, after the first heavy autumn rains, Jack's direst predictions came true. 'You wait till them reeds get over the shock of ploughing', he'd said in the Spring. 'You'll see, they'll come back stronger than ever.' Surveying the meadows dolefully in mid October, I could see that he was right.

The flush of the annual Italian Rye grass had been eaten off by the cows. Stapledon's lovely rye grass and clover mixture only occurred as tiny patches crowning the very driest areas. The rest of the field was just a sea of hoof-trampled mud through which the challenging spears of reed were beginning to thrust densely like a fakir's mat.

The man from the War Ag clearly thought that it was all the result of our mismanagement of the grazing and was ungracious enough to say so. He didn't comment when I pointed out that at least the reeds (which needed a lot of water to survive) wouldn't have been there if his drainage officer's scheme had been any good. Instead he insisted that during the coming autumn and winter we provide drains in the remaining portion of the low meadows at the bottom of Banky Field. There was more slope on that land and the drainage would be more effective, more quickly, he claimed.

None of us was anxious to face another winter like the last. But, within a few days the drainage officer came with a further plan developed from the original survey. Soon we were knocking pegs into the ground, lugging drain-pipes on and off carts and before long, Fred was once more pacing us as we thrust our spades into the sticky winter land.

Since the acreage involved was smaller, our task, that

winter, seemed less forbidding. But, in any case, I was so
preoccupied that I hardly noticed the hours spent in the cold
and wet. Whenever a difficult practical task didn't distract
me, I lapsed into that state of divine euphoria which is induced
by love.

Neither Houseman nor Vaughan Williams at their most
lyrical could have conveyed the golden haze through which I'd
viewed rural Shropshire during the previous summer and
autumn. And, ironically, it was a mood which I moved into
literally buttock first while playing charades.

Nowadays, when travelling about and discussing the war
period with people, I am always struck by the way in which
most of them remember the craze for dressing up. Perhaps it
was due to the need for so many to spend so much of their time
in drab uniforms which gave the notion of donning totally
ridiculous garb such an appeal. But, whatever the reason,
throughout the country, at private or public functions, organised for charity or merely as a relief from the sombreness of
wartime life, sooner or later, someone would always seem to
suggest charades or some other game involving a change of
dress. Balloons forced behind army issue underwear transformed harsh parade ground sergeants into bosomy street
corner whores. Flamboyant high crowned feathered fantasies,
which had been mandatory pre-war female head-gear for
church weddings, turned tough tractor drivers into elegant
facsimiles of King Charles. An ignorant observer from another
planet peering into drill halls, dance salons, or drawing rooms
throughout the country at the time would have been bound to
conclude that the British and their allies formed a race of
natural, laughing transvestites.

For the relief offered by laughter was what we most fervently
sought. And what seems naive, stupid or just embarrassing
when attempted now, was capable then of reducing us to
hysterical tears.

Nearly every home in the land seemed to possess its chest of
regalia. In their depths, rubber waterproof pebble pumps and
absurdly coy swimming costumes mingled with chintzes, cot-
tons, lace and flannel — all tailored to the styles of bygone eras.
They concealed other mirth provoking vital props. Bowed
framed tennis rackets with broken strings, scrappily torn
Japanese paper sunshades sent by uncles serving in the east,
handbags with broken clasps and straps or high shoes with

collapsing heels, all provided essential variety to the wardrobe.

Abandoned in public halls, they crammed cupboards to be dragged out and used again when the revellers demanded charades as an interlude between dancing. It was during one of these interludes that I first bumped into May. Plunging into a mound of clothes dumped into the middle of the floor by the organisers of the charades, I grabbed a broken-rimmed, flat straw hat and stepped back with arms outspread shouting to my team, 'How's that?'.

Facing the other direction and making similar spectacular gestures, May stepped back too and our buttocks collided.

Somebody shouted, 'Very good — I bet you couldn't do that again', as I turned in confusion to face the somewhat shocked but radiant, raven haired, dark eyed girl. And he was right. I couldn't, because it is only once in anyone's life that such a trivial event can have such an overwhelming impact.

While I tried to apologise, she raised a forefinger in mock admonition, 'We've been warned that you Revellers are an evil bunch'. Her eyes sparkled almost as brightly as her wonderful even teeth as she ordered me back to my own crowd.

Since she was the secretary of a rival group of young farming fund raisers, I had noticed her before. But that was the first time we'd spoken. Mother had watched the collision and told me later that I blushed almost scarlet. For the rest of the game I was far more interested in her team's performance than our own. I found the usually amusing interval before the music began again long and irksome. So that even before the MC had climbed onto the stage to make his announcement, I had scurried to her side and requested the first dance. She was surrounded by the tall, languid looking, clearly oppulent young men who at that time I found strangely disconcerting.

However, her gracious and immediate acceptance was reassuring. When, clearly as diffident in making conversation as I was myself, she complimented me on my play, my spirits soared. She gave me the confidence to ask her to dance several times more, though, when I saw her leaving with her own group because I hadn't dared to ask her to allow me to see her home, I cursed my lack of courage.

Happily, during dances, I had learned a lot about her. The background sounded to me overwhelmingly sophisticated. For she had been brought up in the vast city of Birmingham which I still hadn't visited. However, our interests obviously overlapped, because she had become passionately concerned by the inadequacy of the diet of townspeople and by everything to do with the production of food from land.

While to me farming was a matter of overcoming the immediate problems of obtaining returns from crops and stock, following the investment of cash and effort, May was intellectually more mature. She could take a philosophical attitude towards man's role and activities on the planet and always strove to understand the way in which natural agencies interact. Even then, she had developed a strong belief that, unless we understood nature profoundly and then tried to work with, rather than against it, man would be doomed.

I found such enthusiasm for the subject in a townsperson strange and exhilarating. But, even more remarkable, I felt, was the fact that someone with an urban background should have volunteered for the land army as soon as the war had broken out.

As we cross-chassied and double-locked our way through quick steps or slid elegantly to the strict tempo of Victor Sylvester's Fox Trots, she slowly revealed that she was now virtually in charge of the cows on Lord Longsdale's farm at nearby Shavington Park.

At least my disappointment at missing the chance of walking her home was mollified by the fact that I knew her address. Shavington lay very close to Uncle Dick Fitton's farm, which became the ostensible destination for most of my rides for months ahead.

I could reach the Fittons by cycling through the Park. I had to make the journey several times before I saw May again.

Cousin John and his family must have wondered why I began to visit so frequently. Disappointed by not having seen May en route, I'd be glum and withdrawn on arrival. Although I muttered about some trivial reason for my visit, I paid scant attention when they replied to my half hearted questions. As soon as was decently possible, I'd explain that 'I must get back' and, feigning regret, cycle off again searching for May.

When I finally saw her, she was returning from driving her herd to an outlying area of the Park and I barely knew what to say.

Her assurance, the angle at which she wore the regulation

felt hat and the scrap of white silk kerchief at her neck, seemed to imbue the drab green breeches and pullover of her Land Army uniform with a surprising elegance. It made me feel inadequate and ill dressed in my most respectable jacket. Breathless and sweating from my determined marathon along all the Park's undulating tracks, I couldn't maintain the attitude of remote astonishment at seeing her which I had planned while pedalling. Instead, I just blurted out the fact that I'd been searching for her for days.

Having said it, I felt terribly exposed and vulnerable.

The low evening sun softly gilded the giant trees and pasture. Making a burnished mirror of the lake, it seemed to emphasise the vast bowl of sky. While an appropriately magnificent setting for such a beautiful girl, it made me feel insignificant. I missed the mischievous, slightly permissive atmosphere which the crowded dance floor had provided for our previous encounter.

Thankfully, the smile with which she banished my discomfort, was as warm as the sunshine and I accepted gleefully when she asked me if I'd like to see the newly weaned calves which she was returning to the farmstead to feed.

Watching them suckle the fingers which she hung in the surface of the milk to encourage them to drink, I couldn't help feeling jealous of the intimate relationship they had with her. But, at least an interest in their progress provided sufficient excuse for further meetings until she admitted that she welcomed my visits as much as I enjoyed making them.

If there was a cloud in the sky, that autumn, I wouldn't have noticed it. Even the War Ag man with his direct threats of having us dispossessed could do little more than provoke a few minutes concern. While the fine weather and light evenings lasted, whenever I could escape from work or voluntary duties, I'd pedal enthusiastically over to Shavington to see May.

I came to know and love the Park as well as she did. Most of the oaks which gave it nobility provided for us bowers of timid intimacy; the deep hedgerows and leafy coverts havens for confidences. Frequently, to extend our contact, she would ride most of the way home with me down the meandering lane to Longford. But often it had become too dark to see the blacked out houses before we arrived. I'd then turn round and declare that I'd see her home. Although the light of our dim lamps only excavated a narrow tunnel in the warm gloom, to me it seemed like an endless glittering path to Elysium.

As the intensity of our feelings grew, the hour at which I guiltily removed my shoes in the kitchen and crept up the stairs trying not to waken my mother, became ever later. Several times I was so late that there was barely time to wash briefly and change into my milking gear before the day's normal activities began. But, despite frequently missing sleep entirely and my continuously deteriorating digestion which cumulatively provided the haunted and gaunt look which upset my mother, I hardly ever felt tired. I suppose I must have been energised by my lyrical happiness.

Forced by the harsher weather and darkness to see less of each other as the winter drew on, we still met whenever we could. We owed a lot of gratitude to George and a cowman at Shavington who both did more than their share of afternoon milking on Sundays so that we were free to be together.

Neither of us could have disguised our love and it wasn't long before Mother suggested that I should stop pretending that my bicycle rides were made to allow me to discuss farming problems with the Fittons and simply bring May home. She looked so pleased and gently encouraging as she said it that I couldn't resent her divining my supposed secret.

'Just because we have been alone and so close for so long, you mustn't feel ashamed because you are courting a nice girl', she reassured. Looking at her attentively as she spoke, I realised that yet again she was preparing to suppress any selfish instincts for the sake of the survival of the family. For the first time, I realised that the effort of sustaining the battle to survive for so long was beginning to show. The formerly smooth skin of her face was becoming furrowed by wrinkles and her hair was turning quite grey. Her intense activity in the dairy kept her looking trim and fit enough. But she seemed habitually very tired.

I recognised in the warmth of the welcome she offered that she shared my hopes that May might one day become mistress of Fordhall. It was as though she was eager to hand over major responsibilities to someone else.

Although she discreetly refrained from mentioning it, I could see that she was clearly even more disturbed than me by the row which had separated May and me shortly after Christmas. In a pique of jealousy, I'd suffered the fate of many who take extraordinarily attractive girls to a dance. The more beautiful they are, the more attention they receive. At first, the partner is inordinately proud. Then, as he sees less and less of her as others claim her attention, he becomes violently resentful. I was foolish enough to complain bitterly before the evening was half over. In consequence, after chastising me for my childishness, May had allowed someone else to take her home. She was the first girl to whom I'd ever been so fully committed and the whole experience was unpleasantly new. My self esteem was tragically sullied and I made no attempt to contact her for three unhappy weeks.

While, before Christmas, I had dug my drainage ditches in silence because I was inwardly ruminating upon my happiness, for a period afterwards I simply choked on the bones of misery and self pity.

At least, the separation taught us how dependent we had become on one another. Because, when she accepted my letter of apology and agreed to a meeting, she generously admitted that the weeks had seemed as long and pointless as any she had lived. Before the row, I'd been too mesmerised by her virtues and too aware of my poverty to suggest marriage. On that sweet day of reconciliation, we both swore we never wanted to suffer such solitude again and I didn't hesitate to ask her to share my uncertain fate.

CHAPTER FIFTEEN

A Wartime Honeymoon

The insistent scrape of hundreds of service boots striking tarmacadam in unison provided the improbable rhythm which seemed to be habitually present during our first few days of marriage. At low tide, the constant sound of marching men even drowned out the surge of the sea. We were woken by it most mornings, dozed through it during afternoon siestas and were often lulled to sleep by it at night.

The whole of Blackpool, the far-off, North Western seaside resort to which we had escaped for a week of snatched honeymoon, seemed to have become a Royal Airforce Camp. Great luxury hotels on the sea front, which before the war must have appeared just as lofty foyers for social life and discreet scandal as any in Deauville or Biarritz, had been commandeered and turned into barracks. Thousands of window boxes, which in past seasons had turned their massive facades into joyous floral cliffs, hung sad and empty; their dry soil a handy hide out for forbidden personal belongings or hastily stubbed out cigarettes.

Instead of the silent glide of the patent leather shod feet of decorous servants, the rooms, corridors and staircases thundered with the sound of shouting men running to obey unintelligibly bawled orders. Just strolling by, the harshness of it all made May and me shudder and move quickly on.

But, no matter where we wandered, along the sea front or in the shopping streets behind, we couldn't escape the military presence. Round every corner we ran into squads of men in blue. Shorn of most of their hair by a brutally unrelenting 'short, back and sides' barber, their cheeks flushed with exertion, most of the ranks looked incredibly young. They were obviously highly embarrassed that their ignominy should be witnessed by a civilian public. While they paused or marched on the spot to allow traffic to pass, sentimental ladies muttering aloud about it being 'a shame' goaded testy, power conscious sergeants and corporals into barking out their commands ever more imperiously.

We made the unfortunate choice for the same reason as the general staff. Blackpool was a long way from the European mainland and a difficult haul for the Heinkel bombers which were making life unpleasant in the South and East. Its hotels, too, which had immediately attracted an Airforce with a billeting problem for new recruits, had been considered a mecca for the more affluent in our region in pre war years. And the person who had urged us to honeymoon there remembered it for its flannelled calm and the wonderful championship course at St. Annes.

We ought to have realised our mistake as we scrambled for seats on the North bound train after a three hour wait at Crewe. So many knapsacked and kit bagged airmen were jostling, drinking tea, swearing and complaining on the platform, that from the crossing bridge it appeared solid blue when we arrived.

Tired after the morning's wedding excitement and feeling unpatriotically civilian in our going away attire, we lacked the thrust essential to board an already packed train. If two airmen behind, desperate to catch the train because they were already late back from leave, hadn't packed like a scrum and pushed us through a door, I doubt if we'd have reached Blackpool at all. All the compartments were full. Men squatted on the floor between the legs of others. Some had even managed to lodge themselves on head high luggage racks. I turned away to try to arrange the cases as a seat in the corridor for May. But, when I'd got them on their ends and looked round she had disappeared. Eager arms had clutched such an attractive and well dressed woman and deposited her firmly on the knee of a gargantuan aircraftman. His puce face leered out at me over her shoulder as I looked into the compartment. In return for my protesting 'I say', all I received was a simian grin. May raised her eyes in resignation. And, while I brooded for nearly four, stifling, hours in the corridor, she made a band of new friends.

By the time we reached Blackpool, she'd seen the dog eared snap shots of girlfriends and wives dragged proudly from the wallets of every man in the compartment. Meanwhile, they had all scribbled down our address on scraps of paper and promised to call on us at Fordhall if ever they were stationed in

Shropshire. Some of them didn't forget. Two called on us during 1944. One bore the sad news that the giant on whose knee May had sat and two others in the compartment that day had been shot down while crewing a Lancaster Bomber over Germany.

We were so late that the other guests had left the dining room by the time we arrived.

'Light in the evening, to allow us to make the most of the rations for a good midday meal, Mr. Hollins.' That was how the proprietress of the small hotel explained away the pitiful offering. She must have seen my alarmed glance at May as the maid had set the tiny scrap of tinned meat loaf and two small tomatoes before us. May found it hard to suppress a guffaw when, in desperation, I held the slice of bread up to the light to try to see the micro layer of magarine with which it had been coated.

'They must have spread it with a blowlamp', I snorted indignantly and was about to protest when the proprietress appeared flourishing a small bottle of mock mayonnaise.

'May I help you, Mr. Hollins?', she offered with the aplomb of a great benefactress offering largesse to the poor. When I thanked her, she daintily patted the bottom of the bottle with her palm and ejected a half penny sized dollop onto the side of my plate. I was looking down waiting for more when I heard the screw cap spun into place as she carried the bottle to a serving table and then left the room. My astonishment made May giggle again. In fact, the way that the contents of the bottle were husbanded, or that irate guests tried to cheat by grabbing it when the maid or the proprietress were absent, became a week long dining room joke.

But, when I complained seriously to May that evening about the meagre fare, she just laughed and said, 'It will probably do you good'. Resigning from her job several weeks before we married, she had split her time between her family in Birmingham and staying at Fordhall. Time spent with us had given her the chance to register our food habits more closely. And she admitted that she was astonished to realise that what she formerly believed to be mini feasts served specially to please her as a guest on occasional visits, were in fact our every day fare.

'I've tried without success to calculate just how much fat you consume in your house', she told me in the dining room that night. 'But it's almost unbelievable — esquimaux gorging on seal blubber to keep out the arctic cold could barely eat more. Even when potatoes and vegetables reach the table soused in butter you both add further gigantic lumps. A dentist could write the complete formula for the dentition of your upper jaw by merely examining the tooth prints in the butter you trowel onto your bread when having a snack. Your mother's cheese is marvellous, but you gobble such enormous wedges I wonder she has any left to sell. Joan's pastry is magnificent, but she couldn't pack in more fat or it would turn to oil in the oven. Yet, when you get it you smother it with cream. There's little wonder your digestion is ruined.'

Laughing sheepishly, I protested that we did live on a dairy farm and then, glancing down at the mess of coarse stewed rhubarb which had been put before me, I grimaced and said, 'I could do with a drop of our cream now'. However, when I had swallowed the first dribbling spoonful, I knew that nothing could save it. Oversweetened with saccharine to the point of nausea, it left a bitter after flavour. May looked pleased as I pushed the plate away in horror.

'At least here there is no chance of your over eating.'

Although the food was so bad, it was so scarce that by the third day we were both eagerly consuming everything in an attempt to satisfy appetites sharpened by long walks in the sea air. While some areas of the coast were forbidden to us because they had been designated military zones and were heavily defended, stretches of beach were still open. They provided fine exercise and training grounds for the forces and much of our time was spent watching squads of gymnasts tumbling dexterously about the sands.

Then, seeking solitude and an escape from the airforce ribaldry, we'd wander slowly out to the sea's edge. Sometimes the water receded so far on the gently sloping shelf that we risked being marooned when the tide changed. But we loved the true marine atmosphere so much that we were drawn back again and again. Plodding through warm shallows, investigating the myriad creatures which they harboured. Stalking great flocks of gulls, sandpipers and seabirds. Or just enjoying the feeling of brine drying on the skin, wide sky, sun, wind and each other, made the time pass too quickly and sent us to bed early and satisfyingly exhausted.

Far out on the shore, the constant putter of piston-engined

training aircraft from Millom, in the North, seemed more diluted, homely and less forbidding than it did when echoing from the walls of buildings in the town. Pilots obviously chose Blackpool's equivalent of the Eiffel Tower as their objective in exercise.

Though, when we bussed north to Fleetwood, to watch the animated preparations for the departure of the Isle of Man boat from its harbour, we could see the mountains of the Lake District across Morecambe Bay, we never made our intended expedition there. Our final evening at the hotel arrived before we had time. Settling to the watery Brown Windsor Soup and holding aloft in the spoon two or three tiny scraps of doubtful mince, I looked at May in triumph, 'Well, my dear, we have managed to survive.'

She nodded, smiling. 'And not only that – we haven't heard a squeak from your stomach for the past two days.'

Posing my spoon back in the plate and gazing round incredulously at poor food being served at different stages of the meal to the other guests, I looked at her feeling guilty.

'By God, you are right.'

Smiling rather shyly, Mother lead the way into the house.

'It's a bit of a mess,' she was explaining apologetically. But I paid little attention because George and Fred were clapping and guffawing as, feeling foolish, I lifted May and gave her a kiss before carrying her through the door.

I nearly dropped her in astonishment when we got inside. The whole working end of the house was like a building site. Although the work was incomplete, Mother's plan was sound and obvious. Her eyes twinkled as she watched our reaction. Despite her limited experience, she knew that we lived in a new epoch. Girls would no longer marry into farming households and play a subservient role to a resident matriarch until either she died or became too old to wield command. What she had already seen of May had made her realise that she was a competent and purposeful woman who would need the freedom to run affairs in her own way if she was to be happy and fulfilled. So while we had been away she'd begun to make the physical arrangements which would make that independence possible. The working end of the ground floor was being carved up to make a small second kitchen/sitting room for Mother from which she was never to stray unless invited.

When she realised how thoughtful she had been and how

cleverly she had disguised her intentions, May hugged Mother and they both began to sob happily. Slightly embarrassed, I went out to pick up our bags. Nudging my way into my bedroom with them, I received another surprise. Instead of my normal squalid jumble of working clothes, books and magazines on farming and even a pick axe handle which I'd somehow absent mindedly dumped in a corner, everything looked prim, tidy and feminine. All my treasured possessions had gone. The aircraft recognition silhouette charts had disappeared from the wall to be replaced by Mother's much loved picture of a rural landscape. Some of Mother's favourite small pieces of furniture were scattered about the room and her dainty counterpane overlay my bed.

'We thought that would come as a bit of a shock.' Margaret, who had come home for the weekend to welcome us back, had crept up behind me unnoticed while I stood trying to understand the transformation.

Moving quickly back along the corridor, she opened the door to the master bedroom with a flourish. 'Enter the bedroom of Mr. and Mrs. Arthur Hollins', she announced dramatically, holding a closed hand to her mouth to mime a fanfare. Following me in, she snatched a roll of paper from the dressing table and handed it to me grinning. 'We didn't think that May would be too fond of these as decoration for her bridal chamber.' I laughed when a flip of the edges revealed the aircraft recognition charts.

Putting her arm round my waist, she squeezed me affectionately and asked me how I liked it. With a wonderful sense of understanding, she and Mother had reorganised the bedroom for its new role. So that I shouldn't feel displaced, some of my favourite books and a selection of scientific publications and magazines were ranged neatly on shelves near the side of the bed. But my rather spartan reading lamp had been given a softer silk shade. Mother's own white appliqued cotton marriage bedspread, crisply laundered and sweet smelling, garnished the family four poster bed. A vase of purple and cream tobacco blossom made a fragrant vertical feature on the chest beside the family bible, which had had its jacket freshly waxed.

Momentarily puzzled by the absence of my working clothes, I was reassured by the sight of them hanging, freshly washed, in my half of the wardrobe as Margaret swung it open. I laughed, too, when I saw that the familiar pick axe handle was leaning in the corner.

'I don't suppose you'll be allowed to keep that there for very long, my lad', Margaret remarked, prodding me playfully in the arm. Before I could reply, May had appeared from behind us and, grabbing the handle and raising it in mock threat, she declared, 'Indeed, he won't'.

Then looking round the room, she was amazed in her turn. As the thoughtful details slowly registered, she began to whimper again. At first, I misunderstood and was upset by the tears. But then I realised that she was smiling happily through them. As I moved to comfort her, she hugged me tightly and gasped out, 'Isn't she being marvellous?'.

When she had ceased sobbing and uttering her gratitude for Mother's understanding, Margaret took her firmly by the arm.

'Come on now, what you need is a cup of tea and Mother has made a tiny batch of clotted cream to have with some fresh raspberry jam.'

Darting a laconic glance in my direction, May allowed herself to be lead downstairs. Following them, I was delighted to see how pleased Margaret seemed about having acquired a sister-in-law who was, at the same time, the new mistress at Fordhall and someone she so obviously liked and admired.

I was happy, too, to notice how self assured and competent the formerly shy Margaret had become. Her career had burgeoned and it was obvious that she loved her work and was being given more responsibility daily.

Despite May's frowns, I deliberately over-compensated with the cream during tea. After the week of short rations in Blackpool, I was so absorbed in eating that it was only when I settled back replete in my chair that I realised that we hadn't seen Joan.

Her departure was another surprise. 'She didn't want to tell you just before the wedding', Mother explained. 'But she knew that May would want to be mistress in her own kitchen and could help me in the dairy. So she accepted a well paid chief cook's job running a canteen.'

There had been understandable tears when Joan left. She had worked hard at Fordhall for nearly thirty years and considered it a second home. We children had always thought of her as an older sister. She was right not to announce her intention of leaving before we were married. I was truly saddened by her absence. Although sometimes the tolerant butt of my ill humour, throughout my life to that point she had been my most frequent partner in jokes. During the blackest period of our pre-war struggle, she had provided constant encouragement and I knew that with plenty of hardship ahead I would miss her cheerful support.

Later that night, I used the shock of Joan's going as my excuse for not sleeping. The strange bed was also having its effect, I said. But, I couldn't hide the truth from May. After a period of restless tossing and turning, she switched on the light and looked at me sternly.

'Too much clotted cream, my man – far too much fat.'

Lying in the darkness again, very aware of my gurgling stomach and the pain round my heart, I remembered the experience of Blackpool. It was obvious that May had diagnosed the reason for much of my past distress. Just before I finally fell asleep, I was comforted by the thought that if my mother had been killing me by years of kindness, the fact that she and May were to have separate kitchens would mercifully avoid the conflict which otherwise would have been inevitable.

CHAPTER SIXTEEN

Under Threat

The hollow slap and hiss as torsos hit water after a racing dive puzzled me as I woke. Disorientated after a week away and a night in a strange room, I climbed out of bed and pulled back the curtains. The alarm on the side table showed that it was still only half past five. Momentarily disturbed by the light and my movements, May muttered slightly and then turned over and settled again.

Raucous voices drew my gaze back through the ivy fringed window to the end of the garden. There, what seemed like a horde of tiny figures had congregated in the darkness beneath the chestnuts, and kept dashing out and leaping into the pool. As they sailed through the air and climbed out shrieking about the cold, their wet naked bodies, picked up by the low sun, had a burnished, Pan like quality.

Waking May gently, I dragged her to the window to watch. At first, as puzzled as I was and still half asleep, she just smiled contently and leaned on the sill fascinated by so much early energy and jubilation.

I feel now that it was something of their demonic energy and impetuous spirits which came to Fordhall with the arrival of May. But, unaware of the omens then, I remember how lovely I thought she looked with her pillow tousled hair, her marvellous Junoesque figure barely hidden by her nightdress and an infectious good humoured light animating her eyes. And I was as happy as she to see the pool providing so much evident delight.

We had only finished it a fortnight before our honeymoon. It was really thanks to the imperious commands of the man from the War Ag that it had been built at all. It was probably one of the few orders he had no right to enforce but it was one from which we ultimately benefitted most.

Just as upset by the slow rate at which the second ten acres of drained land dried out as he was by the failure of the first scheme, he was clearly looking for something else to complain about.

When I came up with the cows one afternoon, May and I found him standing in the middle of the yard slowly spinning on his heels to survey the buildings. Someone had just stoked the coal fire beneath the cast iron copper which, in those days, we used to raise the hot water Mother needed to scald her equipment in the dairy. The brick stack was belching a plume of black smoke, flecked at its exit by an occasional spark where the rapidly heated particle of dust reached richer air and momentarily ignited. I followed his gaze and could see that the sparks clearly fascinated him. When the chimney had been installed we, too, had worried about the sparks. But, twenty years of experience had calmed our anxiety. It was obvious that nothing was emitted that could jeopardise our buildings. For the man from the War Ag, that reassurance wasn't enough.

'I don't like it, Mr. Hollins. I don't like it', he said adopting his most acid look. 'We can't afford stacks of hay and stocks of grain going up or having the animals endangered in times of war. Neither do we want buildings, which we have helped to pay for, burned down', he continued, nodding towards our recently built, heavily subsidised cowshed.

Although I believed that our fire precautions could be no official concern of his, I was afraid to object too strongly. He had plenty to dissatisfy him which could lead me into trouble and I didn't want to increase his grounds for complaint. I always felt that, like the bullying chemistry master he resembled, he was more vindictive with me because I was vulnerable than he would have been if he had been able to dispense more of his venom on my neighbours.

But, happily, in my childhood chum and adult friend and neighbour, Frank Smith, he had met his match. Frank was farming wonderfully well on more productive land and could counter any of the War Ag man's complaints on the committee of our local branch of the farmers' union, which made him a far harder victim to tackle.

It was because of his stronger position that I asked Frank to prepare the newly drained acres of meadow at the foot of Banky Field. Apart from farming, he ran a contracting business and possessed the heavier tractor equipment needed to work stiffer, clayey land, which I felt might do a better job of breaking up the ancient turf than my light horse drawn tools. If, after his attentions, the field was disappointing, I believed that the War Ag man wouldn't be able to blame me and would be reluctant to blame Frank. I was wrong, of course, he did blame me – just as he was preparing to blame me for our thin 1942 arable crops which in May were not very promising.

At that stage, he could do little save seem doubtful but he could insist that we dug a water tank to have a large reserve available at all times for use in fighting fires. 'It's not only your chimney, Mr. Hollins', he explained knowledgeably. 'Up here on the hill you are a prime target for a stick of incendiary bombs.'

I tried hard not laugh out my scorn. While I appreciated that many inland cities had been bombed by Goering's Luftwaffe, I honestly couldn't see the German High Command in some underground bunker pointing determinedly to a mark on its charts labelled Fordhall.

However, I pretended to take the threat seriously and agreed to the wearying prospect of even more digging. After our two winters of draining I felt that we had done our share, but I knew that it would be useless to point that out. It was useless, too, to object, when, after examining the yawning hole which Fred, George, Jack and I had all lost pints of sweat in digging, he decided that it was neither deep nor long enough to satisfy him. May had been at Fordhall delivering a book of recipes to my mother when he came and had wandered out to inspect the hole with us.

Her presence seemed to make him uncomfortable and curter than ever. So, after issuing his verdict, he hurried away. Before he was out of ear shot, Jack had hurled his spade into the hole and shouted loudly, 'Bugger me – it'll be larger nor a swimmin pool afore 'es satisfied'.

'What a marvellous notion', May immediately exclaimed as she trapped the idea with the agility of a great wicket keeper diving for a catch.

I was slower to grasp the implications.

'Can't we, Arthur, can't we? Think of the fun.'

I was still thinking about the tons of extra earth we'd have to dig, but her enthusiasm was infectious. Apart from having distinct notions about the diet, she was passionately devoted to keeping fit.

'Swimming at home – the best of all the exercises – tones

every muscle in the body', she urged. And then more coyly, 'A blessing for children'.

That did it. The thought that we were to be married shortly and would be close enough to have children fired my imagination.

'All right', I said. 'Just for you.'

'Marvellous', she shouted, hugging me.

She could see that it was all too quick for Jack, who was beginning to shuffle in embarrassment at such an open display of affection for his master. Bounding to his side, she hurled her arms round his shoulders and, to his astonishement, hugged him too.

'Say it's a good idea, Jack, say it's a good idea.'

Flustered, he tried to avoid her appealing look but even he found it irresistible. Clearing his throat nervously, he spat decisively into the hole and, lowering his eyes, said timidly, 'We'll see what we can do'.

In the end even the War Ag was amazed as he grudgingly agreed that the pool contained sufficient water to douse even the most destructive blaze. He tried hard to suppress any admiration for the splendid way in which we'd sloped the bottom of the pool to make a diving plunge or that we had clad its smooth cement lining with gay blue waterproof paint. I suspect he considered that with some distaste. It must have hinted at a spirit alien to him. Something reminiscent of the worst excesses of Hollywood for which he could find no justification.

His brief and obviously disapproving dismissal of our effort with a nodded 'I suppose that'll do' rang joyfully in our ears.

I was obvious, on that first morning home, that others shared our satisfaction in the pool's completion. The schools were still on holiday and through Fred some of the local children had asked permission to use it while we were away. My mother had immediately agreed, little realising what a draw it would be. While the warm weather lasted, children seemed to be tumbling in and out of its sparkling water from dawn until dusk — a foretaste of the use to be made of the fine investment in years to come.

Although, to keep it hygenic, I quickly had to learn to test the water for bacteria and dose it accurately with powder liberating sterilising chlorine and frequently I had to clean it after allowing the water to drain away through the drainpipe we had cleverly provided, we have never once had to use its vast reserves of water to fight a fire. For that, at least, we were thankful.

We were thankful, too, for the tomatoes. They were the afterthought which paid for our honeymoon and the pool. They also helped to reduce some of our debts.

Whatever the man from the War Ag said, I was determined not to repeat the errors of 1941. We would wait until the newly drained land had fully dried out, I decided, cultivating it as many times as necessary to kill all evident weeds and provide a good firm seed bed before choosing the crop. But I really favoured vegetables which were in short supply and costly in the district and would, I hoped, bring much needed cash. Surely he couldn't object to vegetables which were beginning to play such a vital role in a low meat, wartime diet.

Well, of course, he tried – hankering after a cereal crop to raise his prestige as an officer coaxing wheat for bread from an essentially dairying region. Vegetables, while generally welcome, did nothing to enhance his reputation. However, thankfully, he was beaten by the season. Despite Frank's best efforts, the land wasn't fit for corn in time. Even to plant vegetables, we were obliged to ridge the land and sow the seed or plant the seedlings into their drier peaks.

Even better than the Italian ryegrass of the previous year, their meteoric growth revealed just how rich was the store of nutrients locked in the decaying turf. An ideal growing season with days of radiant sunshine interpersed by regular and vital showers, greatly hastened their progress. So that, despite the late start, by July and through to the middle of August, all our spare moments were spent harvesting crops of cabbage, cauliflowers and lettuce.

Sadly, we weren't the only bodies interested in their abundance. Rabbits, living in the deep sandy bank of the thick hazel, elder, willow and birch hedge at the South West margin of the field, banqueted copiously on the unexpected flush of lush foliage. Wireworms, too, maturing slowly among the wiry roots of the former turf, feasted greedily on the tender roots of our planted crops. But, despite their depredations, which we countered by replanting or resowing early in the season or with a shotgun vigil and insecticide later on, the crops were very heavy and of excellent quality.

However, it was the tomatoes which surprised us most of all. Even Jack, with all his years of gardening experience, admitted that he had never seen anything like them. Our one thousand plants didn't take up much more than a quarter of an acre at the lowest end of the field. A strip we'd felt was still too wet for the other vegetables, was only planted as the result of a casual suggestion by May. And, despite the fact that I'd never considered them a proper farmer's crop, to please her I had agreed. Her argument was that tomatoes were a crop which always needed lots of water.

When, by July which was hot and very humid, working among them was like being in a tropical garden, I became more enthusiastic. Many of the vines stood nearly six foot high. Just keeping pace with nipping out the side shoots and keeping the main stems tied to stakes demanded hours of work. May came as often as she could to help and when the other men weren't about, we'd chill our burning skins by plunging into the Tern for a swim.

As the first trusses ripened and Mother and Jan found that they could obtain good prices for them at the market, all the effort involved in growing the tomatoes proved worthwhile. The crop from several trusses had been marketed before we married. On our return, many more flowers had set fruit which were developing well. Happily, they didn't need picking then, for we needed all our hands to gather the cereal harvest. This proved difficult because of constant interruption from showers.

Always the farmer's most anxious time, harvesting that year was made more irksome by frequent visits from the War Ag man. Just about every other day he'd call to count and recount the stooks we'd stacked or to regard with his jaundiced eye the crops which remained to be cut. He seemed more than usually impatient for his estimated figures: more than usually keen to please his boss, I wrongly supposed. In fact he was waiting for evidence on which to base his recommendation that I be evicted from the farm and was again being frustrated by the weather. Rather than being pleased, in the national interest, that our vegetables and tomatoes were doing so well, this minor achievement seemed to embitter him further. I suppose he felt it might prejudice the case in my favour and he was obviously determined that I should go.

I will never know why he should have developed such a deep loathing for me. In later years friends and enemies alike have often accused me of being bumptious or over confident about my ideas. But in those days I had little to boast about and was only just learning to overcome my innate timidity. To anyone remotely sensitive, who examined our general plight, it can only have seemed pitiful. But when he presented his case to the committee, he made me seem like a dreadful ogre whose only aim was to pillage the land while sabotaging the war effort by my unwillingness to co-operate in the plans he had for Fordhall. I suppose that ultimately his behaviour can only be explained as a manifestation of the need for men with little power to use it spitefully in goading the weak.

Whatever his motivation, it wasn't long before his objective became clear. Having completed the cereal harvest, we had turned our attention back to the tomatoes. While there were thousands of large, firm fruit, few of them had reddened sufficiently to market. May and I had been packing the ripe fruit into trays when she suggested the answer to the problem.

'We can't plough those in', she announced firmly glancing at the heavy unpicked trusses. 'At home we always finished them in the warmth indoors. I think we had better clear the room above the kitchen and see what we can do.'

Although instantly aware of her fine qualities, in the few weeks we'd lived together I had already learned to trust her judgement and begun to admire her competence. Throughout her life, having made a decision, she would instantly act upon it. Because, unlike many, she was a doer as well as a thinker.

Within an hour of making the suggestion just before lunch, she and Mother had dismantled a bed and stacked its elements against a wall and all the other furniture to one side to leave a large, clear area of floor. Meanwhile, I had found and loaded onto a cart, a huge mound of vegetable crates. Mother went back to the dairy and May, with the rest of the staff, joined me in the tomato patch. By the time we all trooped back to the yard for the afternoon milking, the whole crop was stripped.

Towards the end of the job, there had been a lot of horseplay as, rejecting tiny, half formed fruit we had begun to throw them about. We were still laughing when we saw the group of men approaching the yard from Villa Field. Even at a distance, their demeanour seemed so grave that our laughter died.

I only recognised one of them. Obviously older than the others, he farmed beyond Ternhill and had occasionally played golf with my father. While the others came on into the yard, he walked out into the field again. Pounding his heels into the corn stubble, he squatted down and examined the soil with his hands.

As I approached the group, one of them looked towards me, embarrassed.

'Mr. Hollins?'

The others had turned away and were mumbling earnestly to each other. I was too scared to do more than merely nod. 'Ministry of Agriculture, Mr. Hollins. If you'll excuse us for a few minutes, we'd like to have a word with you later. We couldn't find anybody about and took the liberty of walking some of the land.'

Embarrassed by my presence, the others wandered back out into the field again to move beyond earshot. Feeling too numbed and confused to speak, I just nodded again and joined May in helping to unload the crated tomatoes from the cart and carry them upstairs. From the window, I could see them moving back across the field in starts, like a disturbed covey of partridges. Each time they settled for a minute of two, their discussion seemed to become very animated, with my father's friend gesticulating and frequently pointing at the ground. And then, almost as though escaping from the vehemence of his arguments, the other four would move a few steps on.

Peering out at the distant mime, I felt a raging resentment. It was as though I was being violated. All but one of the group were faceless strangers who were tramping the farm on which I had been born, trying to decide whether I should be evicted and I was powerless to stop them.

When they returned, their spokesman flatly reminded me of the powers of his committee to inspect farms and consider whether the level of husbandry was adequate in view of the nations's wartime need to maximise food production. Our crops, he said, had been consistently below average and that was why the inspection had been made. His committee (part government servant and part co-opted farmer members) would consider all aspects of my case and let me know its findings. With that, he coldly and politely bid me good afternoon.

None of the others spoke to me which was, perhaps, as well. But, as they moved off to their cars with averted eyes, my father's friend momentarily looked in my direction. I thought I could detect both apology and sympathy in his glance. But I was too confused to be sure.

Supper that evening was a glum meal. My pride was dreadfully affronted. Because it was only a few weeks since I had brought a bride to Fordhall to share my life as a farmer. That all our hopes and plans should be so abruptly shattered, after Mother and I had fought so hard to cling onto the farm in the thirties, I found monstrously unjust. I particularly boiled when remembering that our poor crops were the result of a policy which had been imposed upon me. If they had allowed me to carry on grazing the pigs to enrich the soil, I knew the crops from a reduced arable area would have been far more abundant.

Trying to encourage me, May declared, 'They are only trying to scare you'.

Mother was more militant. 'After all we've been through, they will never get us out while I'm alive.'

I wasn't convinced. Sadly, I'd met men in Drayton who had been evicted. A shameful fate, it seemed, in a market town – like expulsion from school. In bravado, they had laughed and boasted that they earned four times as much in a munitions factory that they had by farming. But their eyes betrayed the truth – they felt dishonoured.

My pessimism grew when, next morning, coming in to breakfast, I found a note from the landlord asking me to go to see him. He quickly made it clear that it wasn't our arrears of rent which disturbed him. In fact, our good earnings from the vegetables had enabled us to nearly catch up and he thanked me for my recent cheque.

'It's all this frolicking about that's a bit upsetting', he went on rather abruptly. The children weren't the only beneficiaries of the pool. I'd made it known that anyone from the Air Base would be welcome to come over to Fordhall for a swim. Such a novel diversion from the boredom of life in camp had been welcome to many. Staying late, some of them had taken a short cut through his park on their way back. I supposed that they had been noisy and disturbed him.

But it wasn't that. As he continued, I knew that, as my landlord, he must have had a visit from the committee.

'I can't see how you can pay full attention to the farm when you are home guarding, red crossing, dancing, concert playing, treasure hunting and goodness knows what else for charity, Arthur. I know your heart's in the right place, but maybe you'd grow better crops if you spent more time at home.'

'What about the vegetable that have been helping to pay the rent?' I asked, becoming annoyed.

He made it obvious that he didn't want an argument and was determined to give me a lecture.

'It's not cabbages they want, it's corn.'

As he spoke, I could almost see the War Ag man making the same point. It was clear that what I thought of as patriotism, he had been convinced was frivolity. I don't think that he really appreciated the poor heart of the land he owned and he must have allowed the committee to persuade him that its poor yields were due to my refusing to accept Ministry advice, and use heavy dressings of fertilisers.

I was too grateful for his past generosity to want to row, so I listened in silence as he exhorted me to adopt techniques which the Ministry favoured but I knew wouldn't work.

'If there isn't a great improvement next season, we'll really have to think hard about looking for another tenant', he warned sternly as I mounted my bike and rode away.

Had I been calm enough to reason, I would have realised that there was some hope in his last words. It would have made me less afraid when I saw the Ministry Man's car parked behind the house when I returned. He and the man from the War Ag were in the kitchen drinking coffee which May had provided. The War Ag man looked dismayed and his Ministry boss seemed somewhat overawed. Although still young, May had already developed a strong and authoritative personality. She had clearly manoeuvred both men into a position of disadvantage by insisting that they accept her hospitality. When I arrived, she was just completing a dissertation on the inadequacy of conventional crop husbandry systems on worn out land.

'What is the point in simply ladling on more and more mineral fertiliser if there is no humus to hold it?' she asked rhetorically, staring determinedly at the Ministry man. Ignoring his obvious discomfort, she didn't allow him to reply.

'It's a totally pointless exercise as I'm sure you'll agree. In fact, it is worse than that. It's a criminal waste of vital resources in time of war. That fertiliser should be used on rich and heavy land where it might do a bit of good. I wonder why someone hasn't pointed it out to the Minister so that it can be stopped', she said, as though the idea was worth pursuing.

Worried by his look of alarm, I shuffled my feet and cleared my throat to attract attention. Clearly relieved, the Ministry man greeted me almost joyfully.

'Ah, Mr. Hollins. I promised to let you have an early decision', he said brightly.

I was still too baffled by the rebuke from the landlord to face the verdict with any optimism. Encouraged by my obvious dismay, he resumed his grave ministerial expression.

'The committee view your case as very serious indeed, Mr. Hollins. They are extremely dissatisfied with the results which you have been obtaining and the way in which you have often chosen to ignore this executive officer's advice. I must tell you that a majority of the committee felt that someone else should be allowed to farm this land.'

Believing that a majority decision meant automatic expulsion, I gulped and shouted, 'But. . . . .'

He lifted his hand imperiously and raised his voice.

'No, Mr. Hollins – please – hear me out!'

Acutely conscious of my distress, May nodded towards a chair onto which I sank as he continued.

'One member of the committee argued in your favour. He said he felt that you should be given another season to prove yourself. When we consulted your landlord, he agreed.'

I was so happy I hardly heard the rest of his set speech. He was making it clear that I'd have to accept the executive officer's advice, use a higher level of fertiliser. He glanced sheepishly towards May when he said that and then hurried on.

'And sow as much of the top land and the recently drained lowland as possible with cereals.'

It was a nonsensical prescription but I didn't care. There would be time to try ideas which May and I had been developing – an opportunity to survive. I shook his hand almost too enthusiastically as I saw him into his car. My thoughts were invaded by that same old nagging worry: how to understand and overcome the mysterious lack of fertility in the soil and thereby also increase the market value of Fordhall's land. Perhaps the answer lay in turning over more of the land to grassland or developing social projects related to the farm's facilities, or the farmhouse. My thoughts broke off as Mother, who had been in the dairy and unaware of the visit, met me as I came back towards the door. The recent presence of strangers alarmed her. I replied to her anxious questioning gaze with a laugh. Hugging her shoulder, I pushed her towards the kitchen.

'Thank God', I said, 'that Father played golf.'

CHAPTER SEVENTEEN

Yoghurt and Mushrooms

Although it was still only early autumn, it was very cold when I rose at three next morning, groped my way into my uniform and crept downstairs. Even in my greatcoat, I felt chilly because there seemed to be a hint of frost in the air. Regretting the warmth of the blankets I'd just left, I was grateful for the cumbersome steel helmet as I climbed the hill to the aircraft observation post. The man I was relieving handed me some steaming, well-stewed tea in the cap of his thermos flask.

His duty partner had rushed off early because he was expecting a cow to calve. Since my partner hadn't arrived, he volunteered to keep me company until I had finished the tea and was fully alert.

As I sipped and shivered, I could see that he was watching me more closely than usual.

'You had a near one, Arthur', he said brightly.

Still sleepy, I couldn't understand. At about one o'clock I'd been awakened by the throb of high flying bombers heading north towards Manchester. But I had heard nothing else and gone back to sleep.

'Was there an incendiary bomb or something?'

'No, no, no, — nothing like that. I mean about the eviction', he explained.

A bit startled, I laughed to hide my embarrassment and began to waken quickly. I'd thought my problem was personal and confidential. But it was obviously already common knowledge in the whole district. I concentrated on finishing my tea to give me time to think.

'Somehow our friend from the War Ag and I don't hit it off', I said, trying to sound nonchalant as I handed back the thermos cap.

He laughed as he screwed it onto the flask.

'You are not the only one', he reassured. 'One day the sod will wake up and find himself dead from rat poison.'

Giving me a friendly punch on the shoulder, he stuffed his flask in a knapsack and bade me, 'So long'.

As I watched him walk off into the darkness, I remembered the odd look of curiosity in his eyes. I was obviously the gossip theme of the moment. He wanted to report in detail on my reaction to the threat of eviction. Although clearly sympathetic, his attitude had betrayed just a touch of superiority. It hadn't happened to him. I suppose he must have believed that there must have been something wrong with my farming for things to have reached such a serious stage. Resenting and quickly rejecting the idea, I was forced to face the fact that if my crops didn't improve, his belief would be universal and I would lose Fordhall.

Still disconcerted, I took up the binoculars and began slowly to scan the Northern Sky. If there were going to be aircraft, that was the direction from which they would be flying, scurrying, like nocturnal vampires, back to their hideaways before daylight. I could hear nothing except the distant putter of a motorbike and detect no movement among the bright stars. Peering into that twinkling infinity, my problem seemed insignificant. But, when I posed the glasses back on my chest, I found it hard to forget.

My partner had overslept and before he arrived muttering apologetically about his 'knacky old alarm', I had plenty of time to think. Absent-mindedly peeling a mushroom I'd kicked up on the climb to the post, I slowly began to break pieces from the perimeter of its umbrella and pop them into my mouth. As my teeth cut through the smooth rubbery flesh, they provoked an explosion of flavour. It was like the release of all the dewy freshness of the autumn meadow in which it had grown. My salivary glands almost twinged as my palate memory recalled the smoky bacon which would have been its perfect foil. I was hungry and regretted not having eaten at least a slice of bread before leaving home. Chewing quickly, I had soon swallowed the rest of the mushroom, including its more woody stalk.

I had eaten it too quickly and a minute or two later I hiccupped. Searching my pockets urgently for an indigestion tablet, I was disappointed. After our return to Fordhall, I hadn't needed them since the excesses of the first night. I was starting to rummage through all my pockets again, when I realised that after the single hiccup of protest, my stomach had

settled down and I felt fine. In fact, it occurred to me, as I
stared out into the darkness again, I was feeling better every
day.

Quite subtly and without talking about it, in the few weeks
since our honeymoon, May had radically changed my diet and
it was having an effect. The flour she used for baking bread was
less refined and the additional flavour and texture it imparted
to the loaf compensated for the reduction in my butter consumption on which she insisted. It also helped to soak up the
fat from the home cured bacon of which I refused to be deprived. However she gradually altered the way I ate most of
that. Instead of always having it fried, I consumed more of it
boiled and eaten hot with beans or cold with salad.

I thought I'd soon be bored by that. While always happy to
cut up a firm and sweet tomato, crunch a crisp radish or spring
onion or munch the heart of a lettuce, I'd never been a salad
fanatic. But May changed all that. In preparing salads, she
displayed an imagination which almost amounted to wizardry.
Her principle was that nothing which was fruit or vegetable,
flavoursome, fresh and wholesome need be excluded. 'The
trick', she said when shrugging off any suggestion of special
knowledge, 'is simple – just bite the ingredients and concentrate hard. Try to remember the flavours and that will tell you
which can be mixed to provide harmony and variety.'

Her interest in preparing these dishes had been stimulated
before the war when she had started to think about ways in
which the diets of the world's poor could be improved nutri-
tionally and made more exciting. Since meat was an expensive
product, and, even then, she was leaning towards vegetarian
foods on compassionate grounds – eggs and diary products
provided the other major ingredients of her cuisine.

Her great joy in coming out to Shropshire, she told me, was
to be able to obtain so easily supplies of rich, full cream milk
which hadn't been pasturised.

'A miraculous living medium,' she called it, 'in which the
bacteria it contains can be managed just like a crop. Encouraged to develop or remain quiescent by merely changing the
temperature or conditions under which the milk is kept. It's a
system which can also be used to multiply other organisms
which will process it for you as they grow.'

As I stood stamping to warm my feet and peeping eastwards
in the hope of glimpsing the first freckle of welcome light, I

chuckled. I was remembering how quickly May had won over my mother to her ways of thinking. We'd always deliberately soured milk at Fordhall and then strained the curds through muslin to produce cheese as a change from our Farmhouse Cheshire or the rarer Blue Cheshires which Mother made. But May amazed her by the variety of cream cheeses she prepared. Apart from the inclusion of chopped, fresh cucumber or chives which were old country standbys, Mother considered May's inclusions exciting and audacious. Other herbs like mint, thyme or chervil were commonplaces. But chopped celery, grated apple, shredded pineapple, chopped walnuts, raisins, thinly sliced green peppers from a friend's Birmingham glasshouse or rare powdered red paprika from a continental warehouse in Shrewsbury all joyfully assailed our unsophisticated palates. As one exciting recipe followed another, Mother's admiration for May's talent became almost embarrassing. Repeatedly, when we were alone, she'd clutch my hand and squeeze it conspiratorially and murmur 'That's a wonderful girl that you have married'.

May was the happiest about our instant liking for yoghurt. To avoid intimidating us, she had smuggled back from Birmingham a small culture of Lactobacillus bulgaricus and used it to prepare several pots of yoghurt which she initially flavoured with vanilla. While we were expressing delight at the new sweet, she told the fascinating story about the reputed longevity of Balkan mountain peoples which was attributed to a high consumption of yoghurt.

We had never seen her so enthusiastic or heard her expound these theories before. Whether her belief in yoghurt's near miraculous properties was fully justified or not, we found its smooth yet tantalisingly fugitive granular nature exciting and its tangy flavour delicious. We were equally impressed by the depth of May's study into the natural fermentation of milk. It reinforced, she explained, her belief in the wisdom of always trying to work with nature. 'Minimal disturbance' was a doctrine she always preached. That's why she preferred to work with milk that hadn't been processed by heat or chemical sterilisation.

'Milk in which teeming millions of organisms have established a natural balance which only changes gradually in an orderly and predictable way.' Her contention was that what she called, 'milk just filtered and cooled from the cow' contained a population of bacteria which would resist the accidental or deliberate invasion of other bacteria. So that change only took place slowly. Whereas milk that had been sterilised, while a fertile medium for bacterial, yeast and fungus growth, possessed no natural inhibitors. If it became contaminated with the wrong organisms, it wouldn't ferment to produce wholesome products; it would merely putrify rapidly, she claimed.

While an avowed minimal disturber, happily she never shrank away from what she called, 'natural interference'.

Mother was fascinated by the cyclic rhythm involved in maintaining the culture of the yoghurt bacteria and its introduction to ferment further milk. She found it totally acceptable since it so resembled her own procedures with the starter culture she used before adding the rennet when making her own cheese. We were both enchanted when, just as she had 'interfered' with the cream cheese by adding different natural products, May used yoghurt as a vehicle for so many savoury and sweet flavours. That autumn we were regaled with yoghurts enriched with blackberries, late raspberries and even a small batch of second crop strawberries which Mother had found at the market.

We'd eaten them in yoghurt on the previous evening as part of what became a celebratory supper after the Ministry and War Ag men had left. Remembering them with pleasure as I stood on duty, I realised that it was the first time I had discovered that strawberries could be served at a table without cream and sugar. Initially, I had been resentful that there would be no strawberry perfumed cream to scrape up with the pink stained sugar in the bottom of the dish. But I'd been obliged to admit that May's strawberry yoghurt was equally good.

'Not only good, but probably better for you', she admonished. 'Because there is something in straight cream, milk and even butter which you are not very good at digesting. It is probably the fat but it could be milk, sugar or something else.'

Whatever it was, I reflected, she seemed to be right. She thought that perhaps the lactic acid in the cream cheese and yoghurt must have made the fat more digestible. Or possibly, by fermenting the lactose milk sugar into lactic acid, the bacteria had made it more acceptable to my system. All I knew was that I was eating copiously with great pleasure, feeling much fitter and sleeping as profoundly as a badger in winter.

I understood and endorsed Mother's respect for May's sound views. That is probably why, reminded by the after flavour of the mushroom I'd just eaten, I started to think hard about something she had mentioned on our honeymoon. I'd been complaining about the Ministry's insisting that I cut back the stock, thus depriving our fields of the valuable pig manure. None of my neighbours would, I explained, be foolish enough to part with their own cow manure. Even if I could buy it, the transport costs would be crippling.

May remembered a market gardener on very sandy land near Birmingham with a similar problem. He had built up his soil with spent mushroom compost which had originally been stable manure when it had been discarded by a producer.

Since we had no mushroom growers nearby, the market gardener's experience didn't seem very relevant to the Fordhall situation as we plodged on the edge of Blackpool sands.

But suddenly, just as my duty partner started to explain his delay, I realised what I had to do.

My exclamation confused him.

'That's it!' I shouted, beaming at him.

He looked understandably puzzled. Feeling, I suppose, that I had been deranged by my affair with the eviction committee.

'It?'

'Yes – it! I'm going to grow mushrooms.'

'Really,' he said very patiently, swinging his haversack onto a chair and rummaging for his flask, 'Very good'.

At first, it was just a visual irritant. A tiny speck on the whitening of the ceiling, it resembled the carcase of a midge. But that was only the wraith of an idea, momentarily blurring the mind when the eye lit upon it when thinking about something else.

As days passed, it commanded more attention. More obviously a stain, it quickly became too large to be just the product of a minute decomposing body spread by the condensing kitchen steam. Perhaps a mouse above the ceiling which had met a sad end, I wondered? But, when the pale brown mark reached three inches in diameter, I knew that wouldn't do. Water? I speculated. There had been more heavy autumn showers. A slate could have been disturbed by wind or some mortar pointing could have fallen out of the ancient walls. Once it enters a house, water can track anywhere and emerge in the most unlikely places, I knew. One of our creaking, cast iron waterpipes could have corroded and begun to seep.

No one either mentioned or connected the patch with the smell. For days, the crushed herb fragrance of the ripening tomatoes had dominated everything. When entering the house from the fields, it seemed to lurk everywhere – in the corridors and cupboards, between the sheets, under the pillows and even in the folds of laundered linen stacked in drawers. It almost obliterated the good aroma of cooking and the mixed bouquet of other faint odours which always linger in a house inhabited by people who work with livestock.

But each of us began to notice the elusive scent of something different; less wholesome, but, at first, faint enough to dismiss. The dog, as usual defying the strict instruction to remain in its kennel in the yard and flopped in ecstasy by the stove, could, we imagined, be responsible.

It was the splash that infuriated May. Several times she had urged me to climb up and examine the stain. 'It could be dangerous. It's spreading towards the light cable', she warned. And I had it well in mind. But somehow my obsession with mushrooms prevented me from pushing aside the table and dragging in a pair of steps.

She always assumed additional dignity when writing. It was as though the act of putting pen to paper changed her status from farmer's wife to business manager – a metamorphosis which demanded a particular set of circumstances. The table had to be cleared and the dishes washed, so that one end could be laid out neatly with paper, envelopes, pen, ink and blotter – like a real executive's desk. Then, with apron removed and hair tidied, she'd settle to work.

That evening as I lolled in a chair, lost in a text on mushroom production, I was startled by her anguished shriek. The essential order had been desecrated. She had just addressed the paper in her bold and elegant hand to Darlingtons, the established supplier of specialities to mushroom growers in distant Sussex, when the drop of putrid liquid bounced off her forehead and onto the page. There it rapidly fused with and smudged the still wet ink.

Before I'd leapt to my feet, its pervasive rotteness had filled the air. Urgently wiping the splash from her forehead, May was gasping and grimacing her distaste. For a moment, we both peered at the patch, mesmerised as another drop began to form at its centre. And then, arriving at the same conclusion almost simultaneously, we dashed for the door.

'It must be those damned tomatoes', May shouted as she ran ahead of me up the stairs.

She was right. Her indoor ripening plan had worked well. Within a few days of bringing them into the house, hundreds of the green tomatoes had reddened and sold well in the market. The boxes were piled three deep. Since there wasn't room or time to move them about, we simply sold the fruit from the top boxes as they ripened, planning to work our way down and jettison anything which was too shrivelled to sell from the bottom layer.

This had been satisfactory until we had started to light the kitchen fire before supper in the evenings. That additional heat, rising through the floor and radiating from the chimney breast which formed part of the bedroom wall, had initially hastened ripening spectacularly. But, sadly, it had also provided perfect conditions for fungus development.

Spores of blight disease, which must have contaminated the fruit during the warm, humid, latter days they hung in the field, developed quickly. Once activated, their filaments of mycelium had rapidly probed their way into the flesh and making prodigious growth, transformed it into a liquid rotting pulp.

The situation was worse in the full, lower crates where the ventilation was least good and, crushed by their own weight, the liquified fruit were beginning to drain out and flow away through the cracks in the floorboards. It took us until nearly midnight to clear the bedroom of crates. May and I carried them downstairs while I barrowed them to the midden. Our clothes had been soused in the nauseating fluid. So, after my last trip, I stripped in the kitchen doorway and hurled everything I'd been wearing out into the night. Although I was still hot from the hectic activity, as soon as I felt the bite of the air, I ran for the warmth of the bathroom, grabbing my book on mushrooms en route.

I must have become completely absorbed very quickly because the water was quite chilly when I realised that May hadn't appeared. I was all clean and relaxed in my pyjamas and heading for our bedroom when I caught sight of her head over the top of the stairs.

'It's all right for some', she said sternly.

I felt ashamed. She was on her knees, beginning to scrub down the contaminated stair carpet with a bucket of steaming, sweetly disinfected water. This, after having retrieved my clothes and put them to soak and mopping the kitchen floor. I must have looked so crestfallen that, exhausted as she was, she overcame her resentment and beaming me her most seductive smile she ordered me to our room.

'Go on – go and read about your mushrooms. Though I'd have thought you would have had enough to do with fungi for one night.'

It was nearly two in the morning when she had finished drenching the tomato store room floor with disinfectant and bathed. I had finished the book and covered several sheets of paper with calculations on and sketch plans of the proposed mushroom operation. Stimulated by the work, I was anxious to discuss it with her. While she was settling into bed, I collected the papers together and put them into the correct order for presentation. Without turning towards her, I proffered her the first sheet. 'Have a look at that.'

Then I realised that she hadn't taken it from my hand. Still sitting up leaning against her pillow, her head had fallen forward and she was deeply asleep.

Although I darted behind a pile of compost boxes as soon as I heard the latch click and saw the crack of daylight, I knew they must have seen my buttocks. The old shippen door creaked closed again while I hastily pulled on my bathing trunks. But there was still someone there. I could hear them breathing.

Stepping out and peering through the thick steam, I saw May's amused face. Wagging her forefinger in school ma'amly admonition, she tried to look severe when saying 'Naughty boy'. But any doubts she had about my sanity must have disappeared after five minutes in that torrid heat. Because, she, too, was soon down to her bra and pants. And sweat was beginning to channel its way down her compost blemished skin.

I'd only been a quarter of an hour in the steam before I'd

gone back to the house to fetch my trunks. After a while, even they had been too irksome and when May arrived I was naked except for my sodden plimsols. I had little fear of being disturbed because, when I proposed the mushroom idea to Jack, he told me, frankly, that he thought I was mad. There was too much precise science and mystery about culturing mushrooms for him.

'That's a job for experts', he said. 'We could use the spent compost but that way I reckon you'll go bust getting it', he went on, wiping the drop from the end of his nose on his sleeve to make it clear that he was instantly dismissing the idea.

'Perhaps it's as well', May commented. 'The War Ag man won't understand either. So we better do the work ourselves. And then he won't be able to accuse us of diverting our labour from jobs he will consider more important.'

While agreeing, we hadn't been able to do without all of them on the three contract lorry expeditions to the stables near Whitchurch to collect the thirty tons of vital horse manure. Their muscles, too, had powered the forks we used to build and turn the heavy heap we created when we got it home and wetted it with a hose. Because, before it could be filled into the cropping boxes, the manure had to be partially decomposed by encouraging the bacteria it contained to multiply and feed on its cellulose. Nature had to helped by turning the heap three times to incorporate oxygen and then compressing it by treading to prevent too much drying out. A messy process which took more than a fortnight and gave our exposed skin, which caught the splashes, an almost perpetual dark brown tan.

Though drier and pleasanter to handle when mature, the compost still had to be filled into thousands of wooden fish boxes and topped with a thick layer of clayey soil before it could be sterilised and used. Loam and fragments of compost seemed to get everywhere as we prepared the boxes and stacked them in the shippen. I remember making Mother and May laugh when I came down from the bathroom and showed them a tuft of the compost which had secreted itself in my navel.

We were inevitably slow and inexpert when preparing for that first mushroom cycle. But I was pleased by the early progress. The system I had devised seemed to have worked and we were ready to sow our first spawn by the end of October. A frenzied fortnight of building had converted the now unused shippen into a mushroom house. After blocking out all but one door and the windows, I insulated the interior with glass wool and tarred paper. A second hand, oil-fired boiler was installed to feed hot water, through pipes round the walls, to provide general heat. Nine inch vent pipes from the roof of the new cowshed were used to draw their warm air into the shippen, as well.

Really peak, wet heat, needed to sterilise the compost at 180°F before sowing the spawn, was provided by the old cast iron copper in which Betty and Joan had formerly heated the water for our Monday wash. Placed inside a corner of the shippen, it was heated from a stick and coal furnace outside the wall. During the previous week, I'd fed the furnace night and day at four hourly intervals. And, although very tired, I was pleased. Because whenever I'd peeped at the dozen thermometers I had placed in the compost, they always read above the critical temperature.

After a week without the copper boiling, the heat had steadied down to between 90° and 100°F – a nice midday temperature in sizzling Khartoum. May and I, by shuffling the boxes from pile to pile, seeded them with walnut sized pieces of spawn set at six inch intervals. That evening, before half the task was over, we had long ceased joking and were beginning to wonder just why we had begun. May vowed that she had never sweated so much since she had been with her sister to a turkish bath in London.

Closing the shippen door on the second evening, I trudged into the cowshed to help with the milking. The dim light and drier warmth there, coupled with the soft pillow of the cows flank, quickly made me doze. George had to wake me twice to prevent me falling into the half filled bucket and then finally chased me into the house.

The kitchen was in darkness and when I switched on the light, May was sitting at the table with her head slumped onto her folded arms, snoring loudly. I almost had to drag her up the stairs, supperless, to bed. The first marathon was over.

It was four anxious weeks before we knew whether the effort had been worthwhile. During that time, the spawn had 'run' to produce a thick web of white, felt-like, mycelium which completely enrobed the compost. Then, by allowing the temperature to fall to just above 60°F and increasing the moisture by spraying with a hose, we prompted the mycelium to put up its first, shy, button mushrooms.

They say that the olympians fed on a fungus with magic properties. But, no god ever tasted mushrooms more delicious than the first handful I brought back to the kitchen to have for our breakfast on that bright mid November morning. Making everything seem more festive, the low sun, shooting across the yard from behind the stable, was collected into a thick golden curtain by the hazy air. Its warm gaiety matched George's bright smile as I gave him a hatful to take home too.

Mother, particularly after she'd seen how sapping the work had been, was dubious about the project. She, like Jack, somehow felt that mushrooms should be born in a field. But, she, too, shared our joy. And it was she who, when we'd pushed back our plates and were happily buttering our toast, gave a tremendous boost to our confidence. Her rancour over the injustice of our near eviction had lasted longest. So that she looked quite triumphant when she stumbled on the idea.

'Well, now it doesn't matter what he thinks.'

Neither of us understood and she began to look annoyed.

'Well does it?' she asked with mounting irritation.

'Who, Mother, who?' I implored.

'The man for the War Ag, of course. It doesn't matter what he thinks because it looks as though you've discovered another way of earning your living.'

We both jumped up and hugged her.

'She's right,' we cried. 'She's right.'

Despite Mother's reassurance and the confidence it gave us, the 1943 season with the man from the War Ag started badly.

We were more affluent than ever I had remembered. A third cycle of mushrooms was just beginning. The first two had yielded three fine flushes of mushrooms each. An unrationed luxury, they had provided welcome variety in the diets of hundreds of well paid war workers and the cash had been flowing in. Ironically, despite our beautiful broad acres, all our arrears of rent and previously unpaid bills had been settled by earnings from these strange and demanding organisms which flourished in a dank and musty building when kept in perpetual darkness.

The respite from habitual financial worries they provided, allowed me time in the winter evenings to plan. Talking seri-

ously with my landlord and the friend on the committee who
had saved us from eviction, I'd persuaded them to make the
committee agree that I should be allowed to use my season of
grace for an experiment.

I wanted to prove to them that our land would yield best
when provided with heavy dressings of organic matter. Own-
ing up to the mushroom project, I made them understand
that its main aim was to provide spent compost for the land.
When each mushroom cycle was complete, the remaining
compost and the residue of the mushroom spawn would, I
explained, be added to the surface of the soil on a small area of
land carrying early potatoes. To be of any use, I pointed out, I
would have to apply at least ten tons of compost per acre. So
that only about six acres could be properly treated that year.
But, I was sure that those acres would yield well. And there
was plenty of room to plant more untreated potatoes to act as a
comparison.

In making my plea, I asked for (and received) a promise that
if my contention proved correct, I'd be allowed in future to
manage my land as I best thought fit.

The man from the War Ag had been most unhappy about
the committee's agreement and clearly hoped the experiment
would fail. Certainly when he turned up in April to inspect the
crop, things looked bad. His already jaundiced vision was
probably further marred by the nasty incident when he arrived.

It was all the fault of the Flight Lieutenant's children. A
lively socialite, he'd become a collaborator in many of my
charity enterprises. More than anyone else, I suppose that he is
responsible for a business which we have continued at Fordhall
until today. After being stationed at Ternhill for a few
months, his wife had let their house in the beleaguered home
counties and joined him in the previous autumn. Their four
children were away at school in North Wales. Worried about
where to lodge them over the Christmas holidays, he'd
approached me suspecting that we had free bedrooms. Both
Mother and May liked the children and their parents and
enjoyed the added gaiety they provided on Christmas day. The
arrangement proved so successful that there has hardly been a
weekend since when someone, either a friend of the family, or
a paying guest, hasn't been helping to animate the old house.

That Easter, the children returned for their holidays to
Fordhall. When the man from the War Ag drew up, they were

playing rounders. Hearing his car, I just entered the yard in time to witness the disaster. One of the Flight Lieutenant's boys had connected beautifully. The whack as he swung the wicket through the damp and mud blackened tennis ball echoed like gunshot from the tall lime trees behind and the ball rocketed. He was jubilantly shouting, 'Rounder . . . rounder' when first his sister, trying to field the ball, crashed into the War Ag man, treading painfully on his foot. And then, the ball itself, spinning like a gyroscope and centrifuging off the last of its load of dank, wet mud, hit him squarely on the bridge of the nose. Only the War Ag man really heard my screamed, 'do be careful'. The children had disappeared as quickly as mist on a hot morning.

Even May's gentle clucking solicitude when bathing away the mud with a warm flannel did little to appease his wrath. 'I could have lost an eye', he kept muttering reproachfully. Meanwhile, I was certain he thought our having paying guests in the house was yet another distraction from the serious business of farming. Something else to record in the long list of complaints he would make against us.

I could only share his opinion that there seemed nothing to chose between the composted and uncomposted potatoes and that the progess of both was disappointing. I pointed out that it had been slow growing weather, that all my neighbours were complaining, that even Frank Smith, our district's top grower, wasn't happy and that I still had one more top dressing of compost to make. But, nothing reassured him.

'Not very good, Mr. Hollins, not very good', was all he seemed to say as he walked further and further into the crop.

'You'll have to do a lot better than that', he warned as he climbed back into his car. 'A very great deal better indeed.'

I don't know if it was the distorting effect of the bruise which was beginning to develop on his forehead or just undisguised malice, but he looked quite triumphant as he drove away.

Long days of hot haymaking in Cottage and Drayton Fields at the far end of the farm had kept us away from the top of Banky Field where the potatoes were growing for most of May. That's why they had been ignored. Depressed by their progress at the time of the War Ag man's visit, I'd only returned once, shortly afterwards, to spread the final load of mushroom compost along the edge of the newly earthed ridges. So it was Jack who brought the news. Rising early, he'd cycled to a farm near Ternhill to borrow a couple of mower blade teeth to replace a pair broken late on the previous evening. On his way back he'd peered at the potatoes.

I'd rarely seen him so flushed and excited. "Tis unbelievable they are nearly up to your thigh.' He demonstrated with his hand while describing the composted crop. 'While the others', he paused wondering how to belittle them. 'Well, them arn't even as high as your knee.'

Leaving the field, I dashed off to see, collecting May and a fork on my way. If anything, Jack had been cautious. The composted crop seemed weeks ahead. Plunging my fork beneath one of the stems, I quickly tugged it upwards and almost buried May's feet in a mound of fine potatoes. Hugging each other, because our first fully combined exercise was being so successful, we took the potatoes home for lunch.

Three weeks later, we were harvesting hard. Only the crop in the composted area had really bulked up so it was tackled first. While weighing and recording everything before it went away, I insisted that both the War Ag man and the committee came to see the difference in both quantity and quality of the crop in each area for themselves. Despite the War Ag man's sour and ungenerous suggestion that one swallow didn't make a summer, the committee was satisfied.

Happily, I didn't see that War Ag man again. He was transferred to another region and replaced by a much milder and more reasonable man. News of his departure simply capped what had otherwise been a wonderfully happy day. It began with a worry for me. When I came into breakfast, May had looked pale and unwell. Halfway through the meal she rushed out of the kitchen in obvious distress. When I realised what had happened and was starting to follow, I ran into mother in the corridor. She pushed me back into the kitchen. I was surprised that she was smiling and seemed pleased.

'Finish your breakfast, she'll be all right', she said firmly, pointing to my chair. Upset by her callousness, I unwillingly obeyed. Taking away the pan she'd come to borrow, she left me alone. When May reappeared, she was smiling and looked much brighter. Apologising for what she called 'feebleness' she admitted that she was pregnant.

Throughout the day I couldn't help thinging about it. And each time the thought recurred, I became more lyrical. It was becoming a wonderfully fruitful summer. We had found two ways of increasing our income — the mushrooms and the visitors. It looked as though we might gradually restore the fertility of the land.

That word again! Now I was applying it to us. Like the plant that sets seed, we had created life. Life that is generated . . . how? Do we transfer the essential seed to the soil? Is the secret of fertility in the plant's abilitiy to make living cells from the earth's chemicals, chemicals which the animal perpetually returns to the soil, linking the whole mass of created life?

CHAPTER EIGHTEEN

From Country Club to Market Stall

It was the insolent snapping of his fingers which made me realise we had to stop. Trying to create an impression of commanding worldliness, to provoke the admiration of a mocking teenaged girl, he had merely raised his arm, snapped his fingers and shouted in a lordly voice, 'More cream'.

For a moment the hubbub of conversation at the dozen tables round the swimming pool subsided. And, everyone, including people in the water, looked in his direction. He clearly enjoyed the attention. Because he greeted my annoyed glare with a charming but arrogant smile.

I have got to admit that it was the right smile for the face. It fully exploited flawless teeth which contrasted sharply with eyes, so dark and sparkling that it was hard to distinguish the iris from the pupils. It seemed to ennoble further an already fine patrician nose and hung well on a head carrying such a mane of slightly tousled, black and curly hair; hair which would have embellished a greek shepherd and which seemed to flaunt his good fortune and his difference in a short back and sides austerity post-war Britain.

Trying to remain professional, I curtly nodded my acknowledgment and continued to lay plates of buttered scones and dishes of clotted cream and raspberry jam before the guests at the table I was serving. As I did it, I could hear girls at surrounding tables beginning to talk about him admiringly. Their enthusiasm made it even harder to stifle my anger.

My ill humour had been roused an hour earlier when he raced into the car park in his immaculate vintage red label Bentley open tourer and failed to apologise to some new guests who had been forced to scatter to avoid being injured. Watching the incident from the bathroom window while washing before my afternoon as a waiter, I stood amazed and dripping, wondering how he had the effrontery to arrive at all.

He had been present on the previous Saturday when I had

the unpleasant task of asking his parents if they would resign
from the Fordhall Country Club. They were understandably
resentful. Members since the Club was founded, they believed
that their four year loyalty entitled them to special privileges.
That's what caused most of the problems. A whole group of
early members had begun to think of the Club as their own
private domain. Over the years they had acquired proprietorial
attitudes. New members or guests were made to feel unwel-
come. Particular seats in the clubroom, it was made clear by
offensively loud remarks, were the rightful cradles for founding posteriors. First claim on the new issues of *Country Life,
The Tatler, Field, The Illustrated London News* or the other glossy
magazines ought, they felt, to rest with people most likely to
feature in their pages – the socially minded who had early
become the Club's patrons in an attempt to re-establish some
aspects of pre-war 'county' life.

The elect obviously resented the fact that the people from
nearby towns who didn't derive their incomes from the land
(but simply enjoyed the fine food we served, the facilities for
fun like the tennis and swimming which we had created or
merely the agreeable surroundings and pleasing landscape)
were every bit as welcome, even though they had joined later.

In the past year, it had also become annoyingly clear that
the early members who had used all their charm and tact when
persuading us to allow them to join the club, now considered
May and me as their servants. They forgot that the club rooms
were still part of our home; that we had created everything –
most of it with our own hands.

Once we had conceived the idea, in early 1946, we had torn
down walls and remodelled the house to make it suitable for
club activities. Running cables and lamp holders out of doors,
we had ignored the frost in March and often worked by electric
light until midnight. When, with torn hands and lungs full of
powdered, age-old, lime mortar we had stumbled coughing
into bed.

Before Easter, we had cleared the wilderness of scrub and
trees, creating and planting the herbaceous borders, the
shrubberies and the lawn. Without the Tern Valley and Shropshire beyond the hedge, it would have been nothing. But May
knew intuitively that if we produced a flowery and fragrant
viewing platform we would be able to offer an environment of
matchless appeal which would help us to capitalise on the

landscape asset and profit more directly from the produce of the land we farmed.

We didn't want the dream ruined by milling crowds, so the Country Club formula had seemed best at the time. We had, we believed, to keep it exclusive.

But, by 1950, the very exclusivity which we had previously sought had become its undoing. I had tried to explain this to the boy's parents. I had waited for days to have an opportunity to talk to them alone. Because, I was sure that they wouldn't understand and I didn't want to inflict their likely unpleasantness on newer members.

As I predicted, they reacted very badly. While I tried calmly to tell them why I would be grateful if they would resign, the father, whose bumptiousness May had always detested, looked increasingly as though he might become violent. His wife, a self important committee lady, kept shaking her head in emphatic denial of every point I made.

Happily, they said less than I expected. When I had finished, he was shaking with indignation but he maintained admirable control. As though dismissing my criticism with contempt, he tilted back his head and rather deliberately brushed the underside of each wing of his exaggerated moustache with the top of the forefinger of each hand in turn and then cleared his throat. 'Righto, Hollins', he barked in the tone which I expect he used to his batman during the war. 'If that's the way you want it, that's the way you shall have it. But, I warn you – if we go you will hardly have a club left by the end of the month.' With that threat, he beckoned to his wife and son and they left.

In the week that elapsed, we had seen nothing of the family or a large batch of their friends. And the Club had seemed a happier place. Now, surprisingly, the boy had returned.

Scampering down from the bathroom, I was just in time to see the back of his pale pink Oxford Club blazer with white edging as he paused for a moment to pick up a magazine from a side table and then went out onto the lawn with his partner trailing languidly behind. When I reached the door, they were already drawing their chairs up to a table. The girl was the obvious accoutrement to the sports car. When caught by the wind, her long blonde hair would obviously billow becomingly while her imperturbable features remained haughtily indifferent. They made a well-matched pair – striking but unpleasant.

At first I was going to ask them to leave. But, I couldn't think of any way of doing it without upsetting the other members. So, instead, I wished them good afternoon, took their orders and served them tea with scrupulous politeness. His cry for more cream was just a further outrage to be tolerated. For, as anyone who has served the public in any menial role will confirm, you frequently have to choke back justified resentment at the intolerable behaviour of a few, in order not to destroy the pleasure of the essentially considerate and easy going majority.

When all the members had left at the end of that trying but radiant day, I pondered the fate of the majority. They were very late in leaving, induced to linger by the musky softness of the evening. As I slowly moved from table to table removing glasses and wiping off their surfaces, I could still faintly feel some of the remaining midday heat eddying from the ground. Overhead, among the barely distinct, but heavy, summer foliage of the chestnuts and limes, I could hear birds fidgeting as they settled to roost. When I stopped to listen more carefully to their amusing chuckle, my ears detected the damp evening nip in the air which had finally driven everyone home.

Shivering slightly, I hurried back to the kitchen with the rest of the glasses. Mother and May both looked slightly weary as they finished washing the night's massive mounds of crockery. Although we weren't serving full dinners, farm sausages, egg and cheese savouries proved so popular that there was always a mountain of work at the sink. Taking a towel from Mother, I sent them both to bed.

Before I'd completed the drying, I realised that I, too, was exhausted. Apart from the strain of appearing habitually bright and cheerful even if your head is pounding, hustling about carrying loaded trays between crowded tables makes the calves twinge with cramp. When the load was heaviest, at weekends, I was beginning to find it unsupportable. Because, when I wasn't acting as a waiter, I still had to complete my normal farm work.

Alone in the kitchen, I began to brood over the rationality of the whole enterprise. Life, I realised, was becoming grimmer rather than better. That was something only we could change. When I'd finally rinsed through the sodden towel and hung it to dry, I continued ruminating as I walked slowly down to the river in an attempt to ease off the tension of the day.

Just beyond the garden, I tripped on the flapping remains of a punctured rubber ball. 'The cows', I thought, picking up the relic of a hot afternoon game, 'could strangle on that'. I felt resentful because, despite a hundred requests, members made little attempt to supervise their children's games. It was just another rather annoying reminder that Fordhall was no longer our own.

I grunted as I realised that I was reacting just like Jack who, at seventy-two, could be more cantankerous than ever and had always loathed the members. He was so antagonistic that I used the excuse of his age, saying repeatedly, 'You've done more than your share, take it easy, have the weekend off, to discourage him from working and avoid embarrassment when the Club was busiest. But he was hard to stop if he knew jobs needed doing and I could never understand why some members treated him with such disdain just because he wore rough clothes and had simple, country ways. Had they watched the patient way he tolerated the teasing, or responded to the questioning of our inquisitive lively youngsters Robert and baby Barbara, our children, they might have shown more respect. For although impatient with adults, as he aged, he became much more forthcoming with children.

Watching him even going to the bother of catching and haltering a horse to be able to lead them for joyful rides across the fields, when I remembered our own constrained, early relationship, made me aware of just how much he had mellowed. It was a process which began on that stunning Christmas Eve in 1947 when he staggered to our door to declare, through rheumy, incomprehending eyes, that his wife was dead. Fred and Betty, who moved into his cottage to look after him, said that he had never ceased to grieve.

I was thinking about this again when, having reached the low meadow, I was stalking through the reeds and sank up to my ankle in mud. For, even after weeks of dry weather, there were still very wet patches. It was a challenging reminder that down by the river the drainage problem remained and at least half our potential prosperity was locked up in that puddingy land.

I saw again Jack's exasperated expression when growth began in the spring of 1944. By that time, any minor improvements due to our 1942 and 1943 digging marathon had become insignificant. Most of the grass plants which we had sown had disappeared – crowded out by the original swamp vegetation. The crush of head-high reeds which hovered above exquisite knee-high water irises seemed indeed to have prospered from the disturbance caused by the plough. It was as though, instead of producing pasture, we had deliberately set out to lay a marsh.

The best that could be said of our achievment was that it provided pretty vases of irises for sister Margaret's wedding to her Air Ministry husband a few weeks later. She remembered them often later when, working in searing climates abroad, she began to think of England. But, while a beautiful lesson in plant associations and the environment, it was depressing.

In the autumn of 1945 a more benign Ministry of Agriculture agreed to pay us a drainage grant if we tried again. While, owing to silting and the high level of water in the river in winter, neither Jack nor I believed that the meadows would ever be very dry between September and March, we did hope that a deeper drainage system might provide more fruitful grazing in the Spring and Summer.

More good grazing was what we needed most. By that time, we were allowed much more control over our own farming policy. Although spent mushroom compost had greatly improved the yields from our higher ploughed land, it really only acted as a temporary palliative. It had taken millenia for nature to build up the fertility of our light sandy soil which my father had demolished in a decade of abuse. Obviously it would take years of very careful husbandry to recapture even some of the former productive potential. The only answer, we realised, was to return as much of the farm as possible to grassland and avoid ploughing again for a long time. Dung from grazing animals and the beneficial compacting action of the hooves was, we realised, what our land needed most.

Had it been available, more spent mushroom compost laid onto the surface and dragged to the soil by the feverish worm activity it encouraged would also have been beneficial. But mushroom production, which had done so much to allow us to carry on at Fordhall, was no longer worthwhile.

A new generation of really professional specialist producers had been spawned by the war. In dugouts in Tobruk or gun emplacements in Italy and Germany, men had ignored the scream and chaos while thumbing through dog-eared texts on scientific mushroom production. Many of them decided that, instead of returning to infant careers abandoned in 1939, they would invest their gratuities in becoming their own bosses and rearing mushrooms for a living after the war.

Starting in new, specially built premises, they began to produce mushrooms cheaper and better than ever before. Meanwhile, our improvised building at Fordhall was producing an ever dwindling crop. The ageing masonry had become deeply infected by other fungi which revelled in the hot, damp conditions. Despite intensive treatments with disinfectants we found no way of killing them out and as soon as we put a new batch of compost in the spawning trays, they hastily invaded and contaminated it. So that by the end of the war, we ceased production. It was a decision we took with regrets. Because cash from mushrooms had helped a lot in paying the weekly bills.

With far fewer acres producing cash crops and no mushroom money, it was vital that our grazing land yielded maximum crops of grass to support increased livestock from whose products alone we would have to live. Urged on by the fact that, apart from Mother and May, I now had a two year old son Robert and a two month old daughter Barbara to support, once again, together with Jack, Fred and George, I began the task of trenching the low meadows.

This time we went much deeper and discovered something which was initially very encouraging. When Jack first struck it, he seemed to know immediately what he had discovered. 'God damn it – look at that,' he cried with unusual vehemence. 'Some bugger has been here before us.'

He'd been digging with noticeably increased vigour and muttering hard for the previous five minutes. So when he shouted, we all dropped our spades and ran to his trench. Allowing the blade of his spade to hang limp, he gradually drew it along the top of a line of flattish stones which he had exposed in the floor of his trench.

'Now, just watch this', he exhorted as, bending down and puffing, he managed to get his fingers between two of the stones to lift the end of one of them an inch or two. 'See', he proclaimed as we peered into the mud. 'It's edges are sitting on top of two other stones to leave a channel below for the water to run. So we aren't the first to have had drainage troubles down here.'

Jack had uncovered the relics of a defunct drainage scheme which could well have been laid down by some of Fordhall's earliest farmers. And it was clear that they had discovered that to dry out their pastures in summer, drains of that depth were necessary. A sequence of later farmers had obviously arrived at the same conclusion in their turn. Because as we continued to trench at that depth, we found plenty of evidence of their activity. Crude, inverted, horse-shoe shaped channels or narrow, obviously homemade and baked, clay pipes, even relics of hollow wooden piping, choked with silt, were revealed. There was great excitement when, in deep peat forty yards from the river, Fred found a well preserved wooden sluice riddle. A perforated board, our ancestors must have used it to collect pebble from the river on which to set drains or merely to make a permeable underground line to conduct water. The daily likelihood of unearthing something of interest did much to make us forget the burden of the digging. And it encouraged us to believe that our new drainage scheme would work.

But it hadn't, I thought bitterly, as I dragged my foot loose from the sucking mud on that balmy summer night in 1950. It had been the best scheme yet. Quite large patches of ground dried out much quicker than formerly and decent grass had replaced the reeds on them. But still more than sixty per cent of the meadow was habitually wet and unproductive.

Roughly mapping the drier areas and then examining them on site, yielded no satisfactory explanation for the failure elsewhere. At least, I thought, as I puzzled over it again, the throng of club members and the income they brought had protected us from the worst effects of the failure.

May had realised that, with a reducing mushroom income, we would need another source of cash. She knew enough about dairy farming to be sure that our pastures wouldn't support sufficient livestock to allow us to live from them alone. The club idea had been one obvious answer. But, while so attractive on paper, when evolved during the dark winter evenings in the kitchen, it had proved burdensome, if profitable in practice.

Mother, always in the van of the fight for survival, had thrown herself vigorously into helping in every moment she could spare from the dairy. While still wonderfully active, the strain of her early battles was producing its marks. Although only sixty-four, she was beginning to look older and the additional work in the kitchen at weekends was depriving her of the rest she needed.

If May and I were wilting under the strain, our children were flourishing. Instead of just parents or a grandma, they always had dozens of members' children with whom to play and every month seemed to bring a new crop of aunts and uncles to spoil them. However, May and I habitually complained that we saw too little of them. Even Barbara had started school and May particularly felt that we might one day regret not providing time to give her and Robert more attention. Standing watching the listless summer river distort the light from a rising moon, I worried again about that prospect.

It would be hateful, I thought, if, one day, Robert or Barbara should have as much cause to regret my neglect of paternal duty as I had resented my father's long absences from home with his golf club friends. I could imagine no way in which catering for the whims of the obnoxious youth who had demanded the cream that afternoon would compensate for my becoming estranged from my children.

That's what I explained through the steam to May when I reached the house again and found her still easing tired muscles in the bath.

'Then why don't we simply close the club at the end of the summer and merely take a few selected guests for weekends instead. If we chose carefully, it will be just like having friends and they will continue to provide extra income.'

Although we still needed more money than our cows could earn, five years of almost exclusively grassland farming with very careful grazing control was slowly beginning to pay. More grass was growing and each year we found that we could keep a few more stock.

So, the decision to close the Club, while it lead to some tightening of our belts initially, proved to be a good one. We had much more time for real family life. And our family seemed to swell tremendously because our holiday guests, as May predicted, became genuine long term friends who return to Fordhall still.

Despite its fascinations, Sir Albert Howard's *Agricultural*

Testament was too weighty a book to keep me awake on that night early in 1955. Having read articles by his disciple, Eve Balfour (whose *Living Soil* had created such a stir among conventional farmers), I was determined to read the words of the man himself. They might contain, I hoped, the key to our persistent Fordhall fertility problem. Howard had, I knew, done wonderful early work in plant breeding in India. He sought and produced much more abundant wheat selections for Indian conditions.

But as his familiarity with Indian peasant farming grew, he realised that it wasn't only the quality of the seed which was restricting crops in that frequently famine-stricken continent. To make the most of any variety, it must be properly nourished. Although the chemical fertilisers which were becoming available in India at the time were cheap in European terms, their purchase or even an understanding of their correct use was beyond most of the peasantry.

However they did have one source of plant nutrients which, in Howard's opinion, was being wasted. That was the vast quantity of vegetable matter casually discarded from other crops and allowed to merely disappear in the burning sun. He knew that the inedible leaves and stalks from the vegetable and salad crops of an essentially vegetarian people could, if they were properly fermented and preserved, make a wonderfully enriching compost to incorporate in their soil. So he laid down hundreds of demonstrations and trials to prove it.

I was wading through some of the more spectacular results, peeping from time to time at the clock and wondering what had happened to May, when I fell into a profound sleep.

I can't have been long admiring the gracious Sari clad maidens of Bengal shuffling round their villages when May's flushed and excited face broke into my dreams. But she was impatient that I should understand the dimension of her triumph. Plonking her admirable buttocks beside me in the bed, she shook my shoulders and then laughed and kissed me when she realised that I was barely awake.

'A sell out I said — a total sell out. And they were clamouring for more!', she crooned joyfully. 'They were right, Arthur, they were right.'

The 'they' which she referred to were our holiday guests. For at the end of their stays with us they frequently said that the hardest thing about returning home was leaving behind the

Fordhall dairy produce. They insisted that our Cheshire cheese, cream, clotted cream, butter, cream cheese, yoghurt sweet and savoury, had a unique flavour – something which they couldn't obtain from the shops in their local towns.

'Why', they kept saying, 'don't you sell it to us deprived townsfolk?'

At first we thought that they were just being kind. But as we heard the same cry so frequently, it gathered credibility.

The enthusiasm seemed to grow stronger in the 1950s and we wondered whether if it had anything to do with our introduction of Jersey cows.

One year we made the astonishing resolution that, no matter whether we could afford it or not, we were going to have a holiday. The pinched childhood of both May and me had never even permitted the contemplation of anything as profligate as a holiday.

And, we were determined that our family should be protected from a similar regret. So duly, in August, all five of us which included baby Marianne (then only five months old) set out for the Channel Islands.

Secretly, both May and I knew that, despite the alternatives in the travel brochures, Jersey was the obvious and inevitable destination. For we had become fascinated by its native cows.

Our dear, docile and familiar shorthorns had such big bodies. Although an advantage when we wanted to fatten their calves for beef, they consumed such large quantities of feed in just supporting their large frames before they even produced a drop of milk. We were trying desperately to expand dairy production while buying in a minimum of expensive feeding stuffs and the seemingly unappeasable appetite of our herd wasn't helping. Jerseys, we had read, being much smaller, required much lower maintenance rations. They also had a characteristic which fitted our requirements perfectly. Their milk was much richer and contained more butter fat than our shorthorns provided. Also, despite their size, their yield of milk was much higher. Since we were processing much of the milk ourselves, these would, we believed, be tremendous advantages. They were coupled with a more golden, attractive-looking, cream which hinted at the sunny maritime climate in which the Jerseys had first been bred. Since appearance plays such a vital role in marketing farm produce, Fordhall products made from Jersey cream would, we suspected, be more attractive and have a distinct commercial advantage.

While we enjoyed the almost infinite sweep of Jersey's white beaches and its magnificent warm bathing, we also spent intoxicating hours exploring inland. There we met couples with tiny farms which made our one hundred and sixty acres seem as vast as the prairies.

But sometimes on as little as seven acres they were milking as many as twelve cows and making a good living. We were astonished by what we considered this near miracle. Of course, thanks to their mild Channel Island climate, their grass started growing far earlier and grew much longer into the autumn than ours. But it was soon obvious that the thriftiness and extraordinary productivity of their tiny native cows was responsible for much of their success.

It was a formula we were determined to try ourselves on our return to Shropshire.

Although the sale of our forty stalwart shorthorns only yielded sufficient cash to buy twenty costly Jerseys to found our herd, it was obvious from the beginning that we had made the correct decision. They had soon generated enough income to allow us to buy more in-calf heifers and to be able to hold onto the best of our own female calves to swell the herd.

Apart from their superior cream and increased productivity, their appearance, we found, was a wonderful asset. As though chosen as part of an Arts Council project, their reddish coats and Bambiesque heads seemed to meld perfectly with our park-like landscape. They always provoked gasping, 'Ah, aren't they lovely' comments from even the most cynical and hardened of our visitors, when they first caught sight of a grazing crop clustered by a copse of trees.

I understood Mother's early reservations about the Jerseys. They were unfamiliar and she was ageing. She felt comfortable with the brindle and white, frequently crumple horned cows she had been brought up with and had known all her life. She couldn't believe that the new strawberry roan miniatures would ever provide sufficient milk for her dairy. But it took only a few weeks to convince her that we had made a wise change. The additional gallons of frothy golden liquid (which was now being pumped instead of carried in buckets) in her cheese vats, once she had got used to coping with its extra cream content, she quickly realised, allowed her to produce even more magnificent crumbly Cheshire cheeses. They were cheeses which she was so proud of, that despite her age and developing rheumatism, she was reluctant to allow anyone else to handle as she accomplished her mystical rites of shifting them about the shelves in the maturing room.

With May's return from Wolverhampton, it was now obvious that the Jersey products were appealing to townsfolk as well.

Despite her hard day, she was so flushed and animated by her success that she was reluctant to sleep.

I, too, had been up extra early that morning. Once I had cranked, sworn, cranked again and finally started the ageing Fordson tractor, its crackling exhaust roar must have shocked everyone else into consciousness as I hitched it to a trailer and drove them thundering round to the dairy door for loading.

During the previous week, we had all worked late into the night to prepare for May's expedition. Mother's best cheeses had been carefully selected. Dozens of extra cartons of May's dairy products had been prepared and stacked in crates. Twenty of the plumpest of May's ducklings had been chosen, slaughtered, plucked and dressed for market.

They were now a firm favourite with guests at Fordhall. Initially, May had begun to breed them because she felt that no farm felt quite right without them. But, while the guests agreed that they were picturesque, they also developed a passion for their succulent dark flesh and crisp bronzed skin, so that inevitably the breeding flock had to be greatly expanded.

When I had helped May to climb onto the trailer beside her great mound of crates and cartons, I felt a leap of pride. Everything which surrounded her had been produced at Fordhall. In taking it to a great city, where she would attempt to sell it direct to the urban public for the first time, it was as thought she was carrying the dewy freshness of our pastures and the innate bounty of rural Shropshire right into the brick and concrete heart of Industrial Britain; returning in a positive and practical manner a bonus due to the masses upon whom our national prosperity depended.

I watched reflectively as George drove the tractor away along our track to the road. As it bumped along I hoped he was driving carefully enough to keep the load on the trailer.

Although we had only had the tractor (which we bought second hand in 1953) for two years, George had become a driver maniac. He was the only one with a licence to drive it on the road and welcomed any task involving tarmac travelling. We were all proud when, newly licenced, he had diffidently driven it snarling into our yard from the dealer where I had bought it. It seemed to denote progress. But, that morning when he drove May off with the produce to catch the early train to Wolverhampton, I felt doubtful whether they would ever reach the station. In previous weeks he had developed many obviously nasty driving habits. Stopping always involved arriving in top gear at speed and then braking hard to produce a dramatic, dust swirling, ground scarring squeal. Turns were accomplished at a dizzy pace with nonchalant spins of the wheel using only one hand.

Whenever I looked, he seemd to be standing on the pedals and peering backwards as he urged the rattling chassis across the fields. When I clung on beside him or tried not to be bounced out of the trailer, he seemed to treat sloping meadows like the Cresta run.

Although I shouted frequently and tried to make him realise that if he wasn't more careful he would kill one of our valuable cows, he always pretended that he hadn't heard through the roar of the engine and simply grinned, nodded and pressed the accelerator even harder.

His antics, while worrying me, roused hostility in Jack and Fred. Despite the fact that they needed catching, grooming, watering and feeding daily, Jack would never believe that the work of his horses could be surpassed in quality. The noise and power of the tractor, too, clearly made him nervous.

While less derisive, Fred was obviously much more jealous. As George spent more time driving and less in the cowshed it was inevitable that they worked together more frequently. But the difference between managing a team of horses and driving a tractor lead to an increasing coolness between them.

I could only spare George for tractor work because I had new help with the cows.

Mary Barnet was another town girl who became an invaluable resident at Fordhall. A niece of May's from Birmingham, she had spent many holidays with us. While many of the other children simply used the farm as an adventure playground, she had quite early insisted on being allowed to help with farm work, particulary in the shippen.

At first the men had been dubious about her ability, but, as she developed strength, they began to treat her with growing respect.

Physically, she was a robust girl like her aunt and as she grew older the resemblance increased. A tremendously jovial person, with unlimited energy, in many respects she also reminded me of my own Aunt Edith.

When she left school and pleaded to be allowed to become one of the staff, I couldn't refuse, despite Jack's muttered doubts.

'It's all right in the fine weather, but she'll be back in Brum after the first mucky winter', he predicted with a face like Job.

Mary had proved him wrong. The harsher the weather, the brighter she seemed and slowly, as he realised her capacity for work, his admiration for her grew.

By the time May had made the first of her weekly visits to a stall in the Wolverhampton market, Mary and Jack were the closest of friends; always involved in conspiratorial discussions from which the rest of us were excluded.

Better than any of us, she could find ways of helping Jack with work which was becoming too heavy for him, without offending his dignity. That's perhaps why, once she had become a permanent part of our team, she was the only one he would allow to help him with building the sheaves on top of the stack at harvest time.

Despite my obvious yawns, May wouldn't allow me to sleep. Her buzzing enthusiasm made it clear how important Mary's help would become.

'It's going to be bigger than you think,' she said emphatically over her shoulder when she returned from the bathroom and began vigorously brushing her hair.

Waiting for her to reach the bed and put the light out, I had tried to get into the Howard book again.

'Well, I mean, it is', she insisted. 'And it stikes me that we are going to need a van.'

Since just running the tractor and paying the children's school fees was still a big enough problem, that was a very startling idea. She could see that I was still not really following.

'No, darling, you don't understand!'

I knew then that I had better pay attention. Because that statement from May always heralded a long and carefully argued thesis to which she had devoted much thought and on which she was certian to expect action. Since her schemes were unusually so successful, I listened respectfully as she told me more about her remarkable day.

By three o'clock, her stall was virtually empty. She was wondering whether to pack up and return early when a woman who had bought lots of products in the morning came back to the stall. May remembered her because of her enthusiasm when buying and the intelligence she had shown during their brief discussion. Her family, she explained, had sampled some of the Fordhall products for lunch and sent her back for more. As the remaining stock was packed in a cardboard carton, they began to talk again. May felt more relaxed and had more time to expound some of her ideas about a rational diet and was encouraged by a receptive listener.

I grinned when May explained that the discussion continued for over an hour and culminanted in an invitation to address a branch of the Women's Institute at a meeting due to be held later that evening. The main speaker, it transpired, had been forced to cancel his engagement owing to illness and May was delighted by her reception as his substitute. Though conscious of her need to catch her train back to Drayton, the question time had gone on so long that she missed it. Ultimately, she had been driven the thirty miles home by the grateful W.I. secretary.

'You can't believe the demand for old time authenticity — they want pure and uncontaminated products. A whole new generation of housewives is thirsting for information about sane diets. We should fill that demand', she declared forcefully as she finally switched off the light and sighed contentedly.

Her recital had generated such excitement in me that I began to plan ways in which the dream could be realised. We'd have to extend the premises, produce more milk to provide the raw material for the products, even if it meant buying in more concentrates and even more forage for the cows. A more advanced milking parlour would be necessary to handle greater herd members. Our present dairy wasn't remotely large enough to provide space for greater clotted cream, yoghurt or soft cheese production. That seemed to me the most difficult of the snags.

'How on earth are we going to cope?', I said out loud as I sat up, frustrated by the difficulty of the problem.

All I received in reply was a comforting grunt as May turned over and wriggled her way further down in the bed. She was already sleeping the sleep of the triumphant hero. But the ideas which she had generated kept me restless and awake for hours.

CHAPTER NINETEEN

The Decade Which Changed
Our Lives

More than half a century of incorporating rich animal manure
had built up the rectangular bed until it was inches higher
than the surrounding land. It had become a peat brown, fluffy
eiderdown of high organic fertility. Despite the heavy frosts
of the previous few days the double rows of peas and beans
which made emerald ribbons across its surface looked robust
and thriving. It clearly wouldn't be long before they began to
climb the precisely marshalled line of man-high, hazel rod
arcs set above them. And, when they did, there was no likelihood of the arches collapsing no matter how heavy or abundant
the foliage. For they betrayed the work of a master rural
craftsman. In girth each component pole seemed identical.
Swift strokes with a keen edged axe had removed branches so
cleanly that the remaining scars of freshly cut wood stood out
like white eyes against the dark bark. Their oval form provided
decorative contrast to the tight, almost identical, cross lashing
of bright yellow raffia which held poles together at the apex of
the arches they formed.

Staring along the line through her tears on that day in
March 1958, Betty began to smile.

'Doesn't matter what they put in the church yard — they'd
be as good a memorial as any.'

Until that moment, almost numbed by the event, I managed to restrain my emotion. But, looking back across the
garden which Jack had tended with such an absorbing passion
I, too, began to weep.

For although the sun shone brightly, making the frosted
relics of old man's beard in the hedge sparkle, for us at Fordhall it was a very drab day.

Jack had died but we still felt close to him. On the bed, in
the cottage behind us, his body was still almost as warm as
when we had laid it there a few minutes earlier to await the
official visit of the doctor.

He had finished tying up the poles less than a week previously.

'I told him that with his chest at eighty, he was mad to do it', Betty explained. 'But he was so damn stubborn he wouldn't hear of Fred going off to cut them. So off he went, all the way to Dandy Hollow. It was blowing hard and the air was like a knife but he took no notice. Even when he'd stumbled back with his great bundle, looking like a snowman, he wouldn't come in till he'd stuck them in the ground and tied them up. "Only a minute, woman", he shouted, everytime I stuck my head out and called him in. When he finally reached his chair, he was sweating like a bullock and breathing as heavy as wind through reeds. He never got out of the chair again. Delirious, he was, half the time. But just before he went, when I was tidying his blanket, he looked up and said quite clearly, "Mind you watch them beans".'

Jack's death, after sixty-six years of continuous work at Fordhall, broke a chain which stretched right back to my grandfather's days. For Jack's father had worked on our land before him and my mother told me that my grandfather, with only daughters of his own, had treated Jack like a son.

Jack was as dexterous in dying as he had been in all his farming operations. He went early in a decade of extraordinary change at Fordhall; leaping clear before he needed to make radical adjustments which he would have found difficult at his age.

He had outlived all his generation of companions at the pub and had been one of the coffin bearers when we had buried my mother in the previous year.

Perhaps that grim occasion, more than any other, made him conscious of his gradually loosening ties with a life of service to Fordhall. She was the only connection which he had left with his childhood on the farm. For, as a boy of nine, he had been aware of the excitement surrounding her birth.

For several days after her funeral, he was barely approachable; silent and resentful. And then, with no objection at all, like a meek child he accepted my suggestion. Instead of working full time, I said he should merely turn out when the weather was good and the fancy took him to lend a hand with whatever needed doing. Such ready acceptance from such a stalwart soul I found strangely affecting. Deeply saddened, I realised that his wonderful belligerent spirit was waning.

Reflecting upon both their deaths as I walked back to the house, I was pleased that at least all my children (even Marianne who was only four) had been privileged to know them. Happy, too, that they had known a much more approachable Jack than I had known as a child.

My mother had survived long enough to spoil them as all grandmothers should. Then, when we least expected it, she slipped away with the discretion which governed all her actions, happy in the impression that our future at Fordhall seemed assured.

She had lived long enough to see her optimism well founded. For May had been right. There was an enormous unfilled market for dairy products of our type in the big towns. Her success in Wolverhampton began the decade which changed our lives. To confirm that it hadn't been just a propitious moment which had lead to the exceptional sales at Wolverhampton, for two years she and I personally visited and sold Fordhall products at every market which we could reasonably reach in a day.

For a few months we continued to use tractor and trailers to carry our stock to the railway or bus stations. When attending small markets, I would often set off on an old grocer's bicycle. I'd have so many cardboard boxes strapped about the bike and on my shoulders that the station master, on seeing me approaching, would rush out and catch me as I stopped to prevent me falling off. But, it soon became clear that we needed more sophisticated and less bothersome transport. That's when we bought the second hand van which widened George's horizon.

Although somewhat battered, it was fairly reliable and it enabled us to reach much remoter markets more quickly. Since George did most of the driving until May and I had plucked up the courage to learn, he naturally began to help with selling from the stalls.

One day, while pausing to drink tea, I watched the splendidly deft way in which he handed out products, coped with cash and kept customers amused and interested by his bright talk. On returning to Fordhall, I suggested to May that we could trust him to sell at markets on his own. This gave him an independence and a taste for travel which he has never lost.

It also allowed at least one of us to spend more time at home. Because, while the hectic days of eyeball to eyeball confrontation with sceptical customers, by regular attendance at markets, taught us vital lessons about marketing, they created increasing work at Fordhall in organising the production of extra supplies.

Repeated contact with the same customers taught us the products and pack sizes likely to be the most acceptable. At the same time, they made us realise that we had something special on which to capitalise. With almost monotonous frequency, we were told that our products had a unique flavour. Customer after customer commented that they didn't taste like the packed products available in their supermarkets. They were, the majority of them declared, 'better'.

I wasn't really sure why this should be. I knew the quality of the milk we used was excellent. But the great national dairy companies certainly were no novices when it came to production. I was aware that our formulae were well tried and offered perhaps a greater variety of flavours than the products of the large dairies. However, that seemed insufficient reason for the praise we received.

I was mumbling about my lack of understanding one evening, just after Jack's death, while May was trying to concentrate on the accounts.

Clearly irritated by my constant interruptions, she looked at me with the resigned incredulity one might use when conducting a dialogue with a cretin.

'It's obviously because we are an all organic unit', she growled, lightly tapping her forehead with a finger. 'We've hardly used a gramme of synthetic fertiliser since we were married — everything we grow is a product of truly natural processes. That goes for the dairy products too. We use no real factory techniques. The milk we use is unpasteurised, carrying the bacteria it brings from the cow. We don't transform it with laboratory chemicals — we only use natural ferments. Even the rennet we use to make the hard cheese comes from a cow's stomach. Surely that's why our products are better. We produce them as nature intended.'

Slightly peeved by the way she dismissed my question and plunged back into her column of figures, I was about to argue. After all, I thought, I don't suppose that nature designed the cow so that we should steal the milk destined for her calf. But, I had to admit that it was organic manure which was increasing the productivity of our high fields, and there was no doubt that our products did seem to be extra appealing. Any inclination to contradict disappeared when I had the idea.

'Then why the devil don't we tell people?'

Tutting impatiently, she looked up again. 'Tell them what?'

'Tell them how we do it, why we think the products are more delicious — let them into the secret for a change. Don't just treat them like morons who are expected to buy whatever they are offered, wooed by advertising, blind and unquestioning.'

She began to bite her lips absentmindedly, trying to decide whether I was an idiot or a man with a good idea.

'You mean . . .'

'Yes, yes, yes', I shouted, pre-empting her. 'Come clean, take them into our confidence — give them the recipes.'

She began to beam as she fully understood. 'Wait, wait', she said, standing up as excited as I was. 'What about telling them exactly how to do it and even . . . even . . . invite them here to see how it's done. Show them the fields, the cows, the diary. Give them the chance to sample everything before it even reaches the carton or wrapping.'

What an amazing five minutes of mutual perception. To celebrate the revelation of what remains our best, but in some respects our most time-consuming and fatiguing idea, we went mad. We opened a small bottle of locally brewed ale. But the ideas for executing our plan crowded in so fast and we discussed them so urgently that the beer was long flat before we had emptied our glasses.

We soon began to trade as Fordhall Organic Farm and there is no doubt that we were lucky in our timing. Our decision came at the beginning of an epoch when discerning people were beginning to ask questions about the origins of the food they ate. The small but more discriminating sector of the public were no longer enthralled by the truly amazing success of the food technologists whose wizardry in preservation had blurred the seasons and lead the ignorant to overlook the fact that food had anything to do with activities on rural land. So they began to react — seeking supplies whose authenticity and natural origin and whose more pronounced flavours were more apparent. They sought caponised chickens whose flesh had become firm and savoury by four months pecking about the fields instead of the forty-nine day broiler house wonders the were offered. Rather than accept insipid, fat-free beef from barley-fed nine month old animals, they preferred to locate butchers buying from farmers who really fattened their animals for slaughter in more than twice that time on grass. They wanted to extract peas crisp from the pod and eat fruit and vegetables fresh from the orchard and field in place of less blemished and more uniform, preserved products.

Food departments in some of our most prestigious stores, always quick to sense changes in customer preferences, began to cater for these requirements. Since our products obviously fell into the same category, it wasn't long before we began to approach them. But we were rather diffident at first. On reaching towns like Liverpool, Birmingham, Manchester and London, we couldn't help but be conscious that we dressed and spoke like country people. We were worried about our bucolic allure – afraid that we wouldn't be taken seriously by the sophisticated buyers from stores whose names were nationally known as synonyms for quality. Would they believe, we wondered, that small Shropshire farmers could be relied upon for adequate supplies of products of continuing excellence as they expanded the market for them. Happily we found them much less over-awing than we had expected.

It takes a great salesman to make a sound buyer and they detected in us potential we hadn't expected. 'Yes', the products were first class, they said after sampling. 'Yes, we would like to offer them on our shelves.' 'But we need your help initially', they all said without exception.

Our presence in their departments when our products were being launched was quite essential, they all insisted. We, as the people who had farmed the land, milked the cows, developed the recipes and done the work, were vital, they explained. We would add genuine authenticity to the promotion, be there to touch and talk to; to expound and explain. And, 'No', they shouted when we muttered about more appropriate clothes in which to talk to townspeople. 'Whatever you do, don't do that. Come as you are, or better still, come as you are with your tweed suits covered by the white aprons you wear in the dairy.'

And go we did. For whole weeks, one or other of us would be away, attending stands of Fordhall products in the initial launching period and then returning to the same stores to help to promote new lines. It was exhausting work because it meant

standing most of the day. And, often, from the moment that the store opened and the first early shoppers drifted in to the time when the doors were finally closed we talked and answered questions non-stop.

We were amazed by the thirst for knowledge, particularly as the interrogation usually began so gently.

'How is milk turned into cream cheese?,' they would ask innocently.

'By encouraging the development of the bacteria which are in it when it is drawn from the cow', we'd reply with bright finality, turning to someone else.

'What bacteria?' the first sweet voice would enquire.

'Mostly members of the Lactobacilli', with a quick jerk of the head.

'But bacteria can be responsible for disease', sharply this time, with much more acid in the voice.

'Ah, well, that's a long story.' Invariably they wanted to hear it.

Partially mollified by a description of the whole process and armed with technical literature on the products, we imagined they would buy and move on. But no.

'What happens when the bacteria are swallowed?'

In the end, some of the discussion became very basic. At times we were worried. On the fringe of the crowd, black jacketed, pinstripe trousered, hard white collared food department managers hovered. They were men reputed to offer the most exquisite truffled pate de foie gras, Beluga caviar or smoked larks' tongues in Europe. So much mention of the alimentary tract and bowels made them cringe. But they knew too much about their business to interfere. Because instead of being repelled, they realised that when we reached the human intestine, the crowds grew. As we entered awkward areas, we'd notice a fidgety adjustment of spectacles, or a heavenward glance of horror and a quick removal of the managerial presence.

Certainly customers seemed to welcome our rustic attendance and, despite the fatigue, we enjoyed it too. As farmers, it gave us an intimate contact with our town dwelling consumer customers which very few of our breed obtain.

Frequently appalled by their ignorance, we were happy that it was a situation most of them wished to remedy.

As the result of having to think about and answer their

questions, we also learnt a lot. It gave both of us the poise, fluency and self confidence to address audiences. For as the popularity and reputation of our products grew and our ideas became known, we received an increasing number of invitations to address societies and associations on farming in general and sane diets and our production system in particular.

In any case, we couldn't have resented the reactions of people upon whom our gathering prosperity depended. And we profited greatly from both the travel and the social intercourse. For people so static that we had formerly considered a journey to nearby Market Drayton as an adventure, we became almost too familiar with railway time-tables and metropolitan hotels.

Often, passing under the Longford Road bridge when, slumped into the corner of a compartment and still very tired I was setting off for yet another journey, I remembered with irony the days I had envied travellers while leaning over the parapet with Frank and Harry when we were on our way to school as children in the 1920s.

Inevitably, such a packed schedule became irksome. We began to regret that business was both separating us and keeping us away from home so often. A car, May felt, would free us from such a total reliance on trains and buses and enable us to spend nights at home more frequently.

It seems surprising now that we should have taken so long to reach that decision. Despite the fact that every twenty year old representative who visited our farm on a sales mission was driving a shiny modern vehicle, to us it represented undreamed of luxury. We had been desperately poor for so long and our old van still seemed appropriate transport for people who lived at the end of a farm track.

However, after hours of anxious discussion, we decided to buy a car. Once the decision was made, something strange happened. Faced with a bewildering choice at the showroom, I had more or less decided on something quite modest when I received a shock. I was naive enough to imagine that I could take it away.

'Not a chance, sir', the polished young salesman announced while gently prodding the unblemished tyres with the shining point of his shoe. I have since discovered that it's a habit which many of them have and betokens mild disdain and boredom.

'At least four weeks delivery on that one and a good deal longer if you are fussy about the colour.'

I felt dreadfully affronted. There was I, about to spend more money than I had ever spent in my life on an object which wasn't strictly utilitarian and he seemed almost pleased that I had been thwarted.

'What can I take then?', I demanded with irritation.

He had clearly decided that I was a penniless peasant and worth little to him in sales commission.

'Well, I'm afraid there's nothing really . . . except . . .'

Smiling superciliously, he made a languid gesture towards a gleaming monster marked at several hundred pounds more than my original choice.

It was then that I seemed to hear the voice.

'Go on — have it — just to take the wind out of the blighter's sails.'

I'll swear it was my father in his most flamboyant mood.

'That will do', I said offhandedly. 'Get it licenced and I'll call back at two.'

It was worth the money just to see his flabbergasted face.

'Don't you want to try it?' he asked weakly.

'Not really', I replied rather haughtily. 'I'm only looking for a run about.'

That turned out to be a gross deception. The car did allow us to reach home more frequently. But to do it, we regularly drove 45,000 miles per year. So, for a period, changing cars every two years was essential.

While nerve fraying, driving so incessantly and travelling so extensively provided us with a wonderful chance to discover all the shorts cuts which helped us to avoid the congestion of towns and inevitably made us familiar with an extraordinary variety of farms. We saw them in all seasons and could follow their progress and visually evaluate the systems which were being practised. To strangers our dialogue must have seemed bizarre.

'Those oats have collapsed completely now', May would announce, bustling into the kitchen on returning from a journey.

Robert, doing his homework, would look up puzzled. He knew we grew no oats and was unaware of a conversation May and I had had three evenings earlier.

'How did the sugar beet look?' I'd ask.

'Not too bad, but it's bolting a bit', May might reply.

At the age when he was nearly adult and felt that he should

be included in all discussion, Robert would become really angry.

'What are you talking about?'

Looking at him mischievously, May would pretend to be impatient.

'You know well enough. The piece of land near the Dutch barn on the corner.'

Of course, there was no way in which he could have understood. We would be talking about a farm near Peterborough over a hundred miles away. But, to us, towns like Peterborough had become as familiar as Market Drayton.

Sometimes we loathed them. Because success anywhere meant even more work.

Gallons more cream would have to be steam scalded in vats to clot it after the evening milking. Then, after packing in pots, it would be transferred to the fridges to cool overnight. A five o'clock start was necessary to ensure that it was packed ready to ship away on early buses and trains to reach the shops in time for that day's trade. That, after frequently returning after midnight, provided a hectic life.

I, even more than May, regretted that it left me little time for farm work at home. If I had been present more often I might have been able to prevent the tension which lead to Fred's sad departure.

Although pretending to be uninterested, he obviously resented George's frequent absence at distant markets. My allowing him to occasionally look after stands in more local markets clearly didn't do much to help. When they were both working at Fordhall together, George's highly developed skill with the tractor always came between them. If Fred was carting with a horse assisted by George with the tractor and trailer, the speed of the tractor bewteen the field and the yard always made it seem as though George was doing more work. Although he was a much older man, Fred tried to reduce George's advantage by loading much faster. This unnecessary extra effort left him looking gaunt and exhausted. But when, towards the end of the task, George, in sympathy, tried to help, he would be rudely rebuffed.

While often Fred's resentment simply made him a bit offhand and awkward with the rest of the staff, at times he upset them so much that they came to me to complain. When ultimately I had to ask him to leave, it was a decision which caused me great pain. He had been so kind to me when I was a boy and provided such loyal and fine support through the anguished Thirties. But he seemed to welcome the decision. At the end of our interview, he pointed to three sturdy teen-aged boys who were just coming out of the milking parlour.

'Any roads', he said rather bitterly. 'You won't need me now that you've got they.'

The boys were our latest student arrivals. I suppose that they only helped to exaggerate Fred's discontent. In a way they symbolised farming changes which made his dwindling job as waggoner and horseman seem less important.

To carry the extra cows needed to supply the raw material for an expanding business, we had abandoned ploughing and the only crop we produced was grass. Much of it we preserved as silage and the grass machinery we used was tractor hauled. We still needed some help from Fred's horses at hay time and could use his carts to help spread the dung. But after he left, both jobs were equally well done with a tractor and trailer and a mechanical muck spreader. Since he hated working with cows, apart from general help in mending gates and fences and cutting hedges, he was becoming superfluous and felt it. The youths whose presence he resented were, on the contrary, quite vital to our operations.

With George so frequently away, Mary Barnet had taken charge of the herd. Unbelievably efficient, she kept scrupulous records which she referred to constantly. When asked a question, she could instantly cite the number of gallons each cow had given on the previous day or in each week right back to the moment it had calved and begun its new lactation. She controlled all the breeding, putting the heifers to the bull, recording conception and anticipating and supervising calving. Better than most herdsmen, she was aware of the feeding stuffs situation down to the last bag of calf nuts.

She monitored milk production in relation to cow feed consumption so carefully so that she could withhold expensive concentrates from the needlessly greedy, lower milk producers and use the surplus to encourage the high producers to consume more and do even better.

Her winter evenings seemed filled with calculations which always culminated in the announcement of the status quo – so many hundred weights left – so many days to go. Like an aircraft navigator habitually rechecking progress and fuel con-

sumption against pre-departure estimates, Mary, having prog-
rammed the winter rations before the cows came off the grass
in late autumn, constantly checked her remaining stocks of
feed against the stage of wintering the herd had reached.

Since she had some second sense about the welfare of livestock which neither I nor George had ever possessed, she
spotted abnormalities more quickly and the general health
level of the herd rose remarkably in consequence.

With such competence at out disposal, I soon felt that our
absence from the shippens would hardly be missed.

However, the willing horse does tend to be put upon. And,
as the work grew, I began to worry about Mary becoming
overloaded.

One morning, before driving off to Birmingham, I'd
noticed how tired she looked. A difficult calving had kept her
awake much of the night and she had been too kind to waken
me.

I was still wondering what to about it as I helped to fill the
shelves to provide the background for a launch of a new fruit
yoghurt which we were introducing. So I didn't realise that
someone was waiting to speak to me.

I normally have a terrible memory for names and since I was
seeing so many new faces every week I had become quite bad at
them as well. Nearly treading on her toes as I turned round, I
was greeted by the sort of smile which expected instant recognition.

'Hello', I said breezily, trying desperately to remember who
she was.

'Morning, Mr. Hollins — he was sixteen yesterday', she
announced with baffling pride.

'Good, good', I said, rubbing my hands together gleefully,
wondering what sinister turn the dialogue might take.

She was nodding her fur hat in such violent excitement at
the event, that for a moment I feared it might fly off and land
in a splendid pyramid of soft cheese I had just fashioned with a
spatula. In order avoid the disaster, I placed both hands on her
shoulders and, laughing loudly, I gently backed her away as
though the manoevre was just a conversational gambit.

'And what's he going to do now?' I positively trilled.

She seemed slightly pained and set aback for a second and
then, smiling broadly again, she tapped me coquettishly on
the arm and said, 'that, Mr. Hollins, depends on you.'

'Lord', I thought. 'Now I'm in a mess.' When happily I remembered. It was the nodding hat that provided the reminder. Some months previously she had approached me after a lecture. Impressed by what I had told the audience about our farm, she wondered if I would consider taking her son as a pupil. I'd said then that he was a little young, but if he looked robust enough and sounded keen enough, at sixteen I would consider it then.

Remembering Mary's face that morning, I asked her to bring the boy to see me during the following weekend.

He was keen on cows and too bad a scholar to gain entry to college. But his parents had promised that if he spent five years working on other dairy farms and satisfied his managers they would help him to buy a farm of his own.

He became the first pupil I had ever taken and proved to be a wonderful help to Mary with the herd. His eagerness to learn and willingness to smile made up for his initial ignorance. Best of all, if he did something wrong he never blamed anyone else and did his best to repair the damage himself. That's a quality I have always looked for in the host of pupils who have subsequently served an apprenticeship at Fordhall.

Coming from all sorts of homes and backgrounds – from tiny Pennine farms to a soft luxury life in South Kensington flats – those characteristics have always been evident within a week of a new pupil beginning a trial period. And I have been surprised just how many town-bred people can quickly develop a feel for agriculture if they are given some initial encouragement. Certainly many of those I would have formerly called Townees have proved to be wonderful assistants with the livestock at Fordhall and have allowed me the possibility of developing other aspects of the farm.

While it is likely that, at the time, an apprenticeship on other larger scaled dairying units might have provided a sounder background to the economics of cow keeping, it is certain that they could not have offered more fun.

For by 1960 our need for help in dairy production had grown so astonishingly that we had over thirty girls working daily at Fordhall. No matter how shy a boy pupil may have been on arrival, having been the butt of their humour for a few days, he soon learned to retaliate. This frequently led to more earnest entanglements.

As Robert remarked when he sat down to supper one evening during the time he was acting as assistant herdsman before going off to college.

'Young Trevor has become engaged to Sally. Blimey, he has only been here three weeks. This place is developing into a marriage mart.'

When George announced his intention of leaving, we all jokingly said that he too was being hounded out by the women who found him so attractive.

Over the past five years he had been as responsible as anyone for the development of our retail business. But five years selling the same lines to the public had understandably wearied him. The bit he liked best was the driving, but the need to erect and man stalls, frequently outdoors in all weathers, had become weekly more irksome.

Meanwhile his vast experience as a traveller was just the qualification being sought by a firm looking for a reliable and proven driver. So that when the job was offered, George accepted with our blessing.

It was his departure which most of all made me realise how life at Fordhall had changed. He had been with us before our engagement, while our existence as farmers was still in grave doubt. When he left, Fordhall had become a well established business based almost entirely on grass and cows. And until his Fangio tendencies had begun to dominate, grass and cows at Fordhall were what George's working life was about. Latterly, I have often wondered whether it was certain factory-like aspects of the production area at Fordhall which subconsciously drove him away.

For, before he left, our extended premises were certainly starting to resemble a factory. Even in the shippen it was hard to escape from the thump and hiss of hydraulic machinery as it vaccuum formed packs for our products from wafer thin sheet plastic. Counterpoint was provided by throbbing sealers which rendered leakproof our waxed cartons of clotted cream and milk which carried our insignia – the image of a Jersey cow in gold.

I was worried often about the way in which so much machinery might erode the impression of rural tranquillity which our increasing numbers of visitors sought. But I could think of no way of continuing to supply the growing demand for the products which they favoured without it.

CHAPTER TWENTY

The Soil Never Sleeps

Feeling the same excited anticipation as a boy about to spring from hiding to surprise his mother, I wished May would hurry.

Sitting high on the tractor at the top of Villa Field, I could see all the farm. At least in its general configuration it couldn't have changed much in the eighteen centuries which had passed since the retired Roman centurion had sited his villa a little further down the hill. What would he have thought about the strange apparatus behind the tractor, I wondered. A novel mining or seige instrument perhaps? Or a revolutionary ballista — a quick firing, primitive artillery piece for hurling rock at his enemies, the Welsh tribesmen to the west which his settlement had been planned to subdue. That made me chuckle aloud — something which farmers, who spend much time alone, do frequently if they are in a light hearted mood.

Certainly, on that morning, I felt very gay. That good humour seemed to brighten my perception of the whole scene. It was as though it had been coloured with glossy enamel. Patches of scudding white clouds streaked an otherwise clear sky like festive bunting.

May, with her hair held in a scarf and her loose, lambsfleece coat flapping in the strong breeze, was just leaving the buildings and beginning to climb towards me.

Beyond her I could see our cars nuzzling, cold snouted and dormant beside the house. What a delight, I thought, that the worst of the driving was over. By reorganising our lives we could share experiences again. By rationalising the business, we now even had money and time for the irrational as well, I realised, glancing down at my prototype pulvo seeder.

It ought to work I knew. I had tried its components individually so many times. But I hadn't yet had the courage to lower it into the earth and apply the power to spin it as an assembly.

It did look very primitive. However, the idea, I felt was

beautiful. Not only a collection of slightly rusted and crudely fused together parts, it was also the embodiment of a whole theory. The logic seemed as clear to me as the dark brown carpet of cow dung laid across the meadow by the muck spreader on the previous day. I believed that, at last, I had discovered the best way to repair the damage which my father had done to our land half a century earlier. The good sense of building up fertility while at the same time improving the soil structure, had been demonstrated long ago. That was the main lesson derived from the experiments with the grazing pigs just before the war. Without subscribing to any dubious muck and mystery theories, it was evident that we just had to be organic farmers.

Nevertheless before we became an all pasture farm, the arable crops we grew in post war years taught us that there was much which was mysterious that we had to try to understand.

As our cow herd grew, we had more and more of their vital manure available to use on our crops. But still results were extremely variable. We were frequently disappointed when we had anticipated bumper yields or agreeably surprised by the production from areas of land we had been unable to manure in a particular crop year. It gradually became obvious that our salvation depended on the way we actually used our manure. It wasn't sufficient, we realised, merely to scatter it over the land in the summer and then bury it when ploughing in the autumn. That was common farm practice which I had naturally followed. But I began to doubt its wisdom when I was ploughing a field and found the dung seemingly unchanged in the place where it had been initially buried in the previous year.

Climbing down from the tractor, I discovered great clods of it in which I could still easily see the straw of the original animals' bedding. It seemed no more decomposed than it had been when dug out of the dung heap. Apart from providing some reserve of moisture during very dry weather, what possible value could it have in feeding my crops or improving my soil structure, I wondered?

I had been attending an evening course in microbiology at a Polytechnic in the Potteries so that I could understand activity beneath the soil surface better. And it was obvious that conditions hadn't been right for the soil dwellers to do their work.

I knew that, contrary to the belief of most laymen, fertile soil was not merely the lifeless mineral relics of the effects of the elements on geology. Although they represented its bulk, soil, to support crops, had to be a violent cauldron of physical, chemical and biological activity — the battleground of a complex fight for survival between literally thousands of species of animals and plants, most of which it would be difficult to imagine why they were significant if their numbers were not so astounding. A teaspoonful of the richest soils with an abundance of organic matter could, I now knew, contain more than a thousand million bacteria.

They could be sharing a home with a million Actino mycetes (lying in the classification between microscopic fungi and bacteria), a hundred thousand minute fungi and innumerable virus, protozoa (single celled animals which move in films of water by wagging whip-like tails or vibrating their coating of hairs) or tiny algae. Lumbering about among them, with the relative scale of dinosaurs, ants, millipedes, spring tails and a host of earth dwelling insect larvae fight their own skirmishes. Coupled with the passive and ceaseless writhing of worms, this turbulence ensures the primary mechanical breakdown of organic material and assists the movement of air and water, essential to most life processes.

Absentmindedly breaking up a lump of the undecomposed dung between my fingers that day, I knew that somehow, when burying it in deep furrows, I hadn't played a useful role as sponsor for all this activity. My studies of microbiology had made it obvious that, in the last analysis, to be a successful arable and dairy farmer, I would first have to become a good husbandman of the much smaller subterranean soil animals. Unless their nutritional and evironemental needs were catered for, the seed I sowed or the livestock I grazed would fare badly.

Organic matter reached my soil via complex paths. Grazing livestock frequently laid it on the surface as dung. Within days, the fly and beetle larvae with which it quickly became infested provided birds with an irresistible banquet. In beak clashing squabbles over the tastiest living morsels, the pats were broken into widely scattered fragments; pieces small enough to be ingested by worms or carried into the soil by other hoarding insects. A similar fate awaited the relics of the thousands of insects, plants or small mammals which annually died on the land.

I contributed directly by ploughing in manure collected in the midden. Once beneath the surface, it fuelled an even more complicated cycle. Cool temperature loving micro-organisms – bacteria like Enterobacter aerogenes or Anthrobacter terregens – with actinomycetes like Streptomyces or Micromonspora and fungi such a Mucor pusillus and Aspergillus fumigatus aided by the protozoa Euglenida or Spirotrichs would first attack it. Their microgluttony lead to a vast increase in their numbers and rapidly altered the microclimate. Locally the temperature would rocket to over 70°F.

Since that was hotter than most of them could tolerate, they would begin to die, leaving the arena clear for the real heat lovers. The bacteria Subtilis or cerous, Thermoactinomyces and tough fungi like Humicola insolens took over the attack on the organic matter and even devoured the corpses of the cool temperature lovers. But even their success was transitory, for as their numbers grew, the supply of organic matter began to run out. When it became really inadequate, reproduction dwindled and with less biological activity, the temperature would drop allowing most of them to perish. Cool temperature lovers, which had survived in fringe regions, would prey on their remains and break down what was left of the original organic particles.

As food supplies ran out, cannibalism would become rampant and then more mobile protozoans would feed indiscriminately upon both living and dead bacteria. They in their turn provided further sustenance for the worms and small insects which had initially been responsible for burying and breaking up the organic remains.

While I realised that no microscope was powerful enough or laboratory techniques sophisticated enough for anyone ever to be able to understand the whole process fully, it was clearly an affair of balance. And if I wanted to intervene, the best thing I could do was to try to ensure that the balance fostered and tipped gently in my direction by ensuring that sufficient organic matter in the right condition was always available at the right time and in the right place to fuel the whole process. Ultimately I'd only be harvesting the surplus from the cycle.

When fully decomposed, what was left of the organic matter became the turbid colloidal and slightly sticky humus which both helped very fine inert soil particles to adhere and become crumbs while at the same time it forced them apart to allow air and water to percolate freely. After the worst of the predation was over, other bacteria thrived on the remains of the major spoilers and in the process, converted the protein of their corpses into nitrates which could be absorbed by the roots of plants. Apart from improving the soil structure, the humus held onto these valuable plant nutrients preventing them from being washed away by rain and yielding them slowly to the roots as they were required. Byproducts of the activity in the complicated underground factory lead to the production of mild organic acids which gradually attacked the mineral rock particles of the soil to liberate the potassium, phosphates and other micro-elements which plants need.

My discovery of the undecomposed manure led me to doubting the value of the plough on my light land. I didn't need it to begin the preparation of a seed bed and obviously it was responsible for an inefficient use of our valuable manure. Farmers on deep, rich and heavy clay soils, who needed the plough to break the soil up initially, could afford the inefficiency. I couldn't.

My forebears had been obliged to use the plough. It was the only primary tillage implement available which they had sufficient power to draw behind their oxen and horses. I had greater traction available. There was sufficient horsepower beneath the bonnet of my tractor not only to draw heavy equipment but to activate it with power as well. By connecting a shaft to a power take-off behind the seat, I could drive one of the rotary cultivator machines which were becoming popular. Instead of merely hauling a plough share through the soil to cut and turn over a slice, the rapidly rotating blades projecting from a horizontal shaft placed just above the ground would mill and pulverise the soil as it was drawn past. And I realised that that was the action which I required to fragment manure scattered on the surface and mix it intimately with the soil to provide the best possible conditions for micro-organisms to act upon it.

Later that day. I bought a rotary cultivator and I have hardly used a plough since.

Before May had got halfway to me, she was called back to the buildings to take a telephone call. Infuriated by the delay and chilled by the spring wind, I climbed down from the tractor and began retightening nuts on my machine with a spanner.

The activity warmed me slightly, but I was pleased when I saw May emerge from the buildings again.

'There is no doubt', I ruminated, 'My theory may be correct but by retarding all tillage activities until as later in spring as possible, I have let myself in for chillier work than the traditional ploughing which often takes place on quite warm days in the autumn.'

Sadly, I had concluded that it was necessary to coddle the mirco-organisms and small animals by leaving them safely beneath a cosy blanket of vegetation through the autumn and winter. It was a conclusion which I had arrived at gradually after many different experiments. They stemmed from an observation made orginally in 1945. I had been obliged to leave a patch of potatoes in the ground. During the summer, they had received a thick top dressing of mushroom compost, As the autumn progressed, all the stems and foliage had died back and fallen to the ground. Meanwhile, there had been plenty of warm autumn rain and weed growth had been prolific.

Walking over the patch in the spring, I noticed that much of the softer autumn weed growth had also died as the result of heavy frosts. But, when I scraped beneath the remains of the compost, I was surprised by the feverish earthworm and soil insect activity I revealed. The land elsewhere hadn't warmed up and animal activity in the top soil was minimal. Whereas beneath the layer of rotting compost vegetation, the soil must have stayed much warmer and encouraged the soil fauna to work.

When that land was eventually ploughed, it again had a strong flush of weed growth but it worked much more easily and provided a much better seed bed. The spring barley sown upon it was also markedly superior to that in the rest of the field.

With greater knowledge later, I supposed that we also benefitted by protecting the naked soil surface from the effects of strong early autumn sun. Direct sunlight can quickly raise temperatures in the first few inches of bare soil. If we had ploughed in the autumn and incorporated the well decomposed compost at that time, the higher temparatures might have stimulated the micro-organisms to finish its decomposition quickly. The nutrients released by that work would have been lost in the winter rains before either autumn or spring sown crops were really capable of benefitting from them.

I had concluded ultimately that the best seed beds and the optimum crops would be obtained on my light land if I always ensured that it was covered in the winter; even if this meant sowing a crop such as rape or mixed forage in late summer to provide that cover. That would always, I knew, provide some valuable additional feed for the stock. By shielding the ground, I ensured larger earthworm and insect populations in the top soil. So that when I ultimately mixed the organic residues and spring growth of vegetation they would start to break it down quickly, providing a wonderfully rich medium for the activity of micro-organisms which accelerated as the weather became warmer.

My aim was to have all the new organic material well broken down so that by the time seeds had germinated and established feeder roots of their own, they could benefit to the maximum.

It was a notion which took nearly twenty years to fully formulate. Perhaps my understanding of why it worked was far from complete. But I have no doubt that under my conditions, it lead to greatly improved crops.

And it became one element in the composite growing theory which led to the development of the pulvo-seeder.

Once I had begun to speculate with more curiosity on the activities in the ground which I trod daily, other ideas began to sprout.

I was constantly reducing our area of arable land and ultimately the crops I grew were either feed barley for the cows or grass.

The grass was sown in mixtures of species which included clovers to replace pastures which had been damaged by overgrazing. But, both the cereal and herbage crops were very shallow rooted. Most of their feeder roots spread widely within the first inch or two of top soil. My aim had become stabilising and building up the structure of very light soil. It needed no deep cultivation to ensure drainage. Therefore, there seemed no point in disturbing anything below about three inches by deeper cultivation.

'After all', I repeatedly argued to myself 'any decaying organic matter releasing nutrients below that level is hardly likely to benefit my shallow rooted crops because they won't be able to reach it.'

Even to me, brought up in the era of deep ploughing ('Make sure you go down deep and do a proper job, Lad,' Old Jack had always admonished.), the idea seemed like heresy. However, it nagged so hard that I tried it and it seemed to work.

It took a lot of experiment with the rotary cultivator to be able to prepare such a shallow seed bed and to make me realise that what seemed to be the greatest snag about the technique looked as though it was one of its major advantages.

Such shallow cultivation, while beheading and subduing most of the shallow rooted annual weeds, did little to suppress the deeper rooted perennial plants which most men consider as weeds in pasture (and kill with chemicals), but I now prefer to call simply herbs.

For although pastures, reseeded in my new way, rapidly contained a much broader spectrum of plants than those prepared by other methods, the cows seemed to thrive better on them. With such a relatively small herd on a commercial farm, where statistical experimentation is difficult, it is hard to be dogmatic about such conclusions. But, it is encouraging today, that many animal nutritionists throughout the world are beginning to believe that many plants we have been conditioned to call weeds do seem to be beneficial.

The yarrow and the dandelions which we used to scorn certainly seem to remain green longest in times of drought, presumably because they have deep tap roots and can reach what water is available. My cows looked grateful for them in arid years. Since they differ physiologically so markedly from the grasses, they also seem to extract a different spectrum of micro-elements from the soil. And since one obviously important factor in the productivity of grazing stock is what they eat, there are now even strong hints that the plants we formerly dismissed may be able to provide cattle and sheep with more of the dietary ingredients they require.

Early in my experiments with shallow seeding, I'd scrape beneath the loose soil disturbed by the rotary cultivator several hours after it had passed. Baring the cut crown and tap root of a well established perennial weed, I'd be amazed to see the quantity of sap still pumping from the sliced surface. It was still too early for the wound to have healed and osmosis — the chemical pumping processes by which much liquid is moved up the plant — was still very active. When I first saw it, I thought it startlingly reminiscent of the way in which blood continues to spurt from the severed neck of a chicken, under the reflex pulse of the heart, for some minutes after a crude execution. It is one of my most nightmarish, childhood memories. I had watched Fred take a chopper to a plump cockerel in our yard and was shocked by the splash of warm blood on my bare leg.

Happily, sap welling up from the tap roots was less gruesome and watching it I thought that it might help to solve one of the farmer's perennial problems.

He can't prepare his seed bed until the land is dry enough to permit the passage of heavy implements without causing permanent damage to soil structure or before it will easily break down into the nice, fine tilth he needs for sowing. However, it is vital that he conserves in the seed bed sufficient moisture to encourage the seed to germinate and furnish it with water as it begins to grow. Cultivating the soil to produce the tilth unfortunately lets in air and encourages evaporation and drying that is almost too rapid.

Ideally, of course, he prays for nice, gentle showers when sowing is completed. But, the great controller doesn't always oblige.

Would my natural pumps, working hard to draw up moisture from well below the seed bed and liberating it into the close atmosphere beneath my layer of cultivated soil, be useful, I wondered?

Well, it is certain that they couldn't do any harm. So although I must say that in truth, I don't really know how beneficial they are, I believe they do a lot of good because the germination and subsequent growth of the seeds I sow seems to be excellent even in very dry springs. It is hard to believe that sufficient moisture is rising to make a significant difference to the humidity of the microclimate beneath the soil. However, as I grow older, I become less willing to disregard factors which I might previously have considered insignificant.

There was certainly nothing insignificant about the din the pulvo-seeder made when I let it whirr into the ground as May finally joined me on top of the hill.

I wanted her to see it particularly because it was while watching her using an electric blender in the kitchen that I had first conceived the machine.

I was astonished by the speed with which the rapidly revolving blades quickly reduced chunks of apple and other fruit into the smooth drinks which May and the children so enjoyed.

Although my rotary cultivator was good, I longed for a machine which would break up the mixture of top soil, live vegetation, organic residues and the manure I applied, much more finely and intimately. No matter how many times I rotovated, there seemed little chance of accomplishing this while all the products remained on or in the ground.

Ideally, I would have liked to dig up the soil and sod, a spoonful at a time, pop it into May's blender along with the manure, spin it into a kind of coarse earth flour and put it back.

The fuss, when I was tempted to try the mechanics of the mixing in the kitchen, was terrible. May caught me washing out her blender after I had tipped the blend into one of her best soup tureens to be able to examine it more closely.

'God knows, no one is keener on research than me, Arthur', she exploded. 'But this is too much. The last thing I want is your bacteria from the field and midden in my kitchen. Just imagine how you would feel if your children died of some dreadful livestock disease?'

Chastened, I slunk away with the tureen and peered at its contents in the garden. The mixture looked as fine and fertile as the best John Innes potting compost sold by the garden suppliers. It had the texture and richness of the soil I had so envied in old Jack's vegetable patch. I felt certain that if I could clad my land with a similar mixture, most of our problems would be solved.

If I couldn't achieve it on the ground, it slowly dawned on me that I would have to detach the top two inches of the soil with the live and dead vegetation upon it, mix it with manure and then mill everything together. It seemed a ludicrous notion at first, but gradually I began to believe that it could be realised. The prototype pulvo-seeder was my first attempt to produce at least part of what has subsequently become a complete system.

As the tractor progressed across the field, what May saw was the cutter blade removing the first two inches of soil with all the vegetation and the manure which had previously been applied. This was all passed into a tough drum inside which blades and chains revolved at high speed to pulverise and mix everything. While that was happening, a grass seeds mixture was sown onto the exposed soil surface through rollers mounted just behind the earth cutter. From the rear of the pulverising drum, the mixed compost was fed back out onto the land to cover the seed.

The horrendous noise the apparatus made was due to the large stones being hurled against the inside of the pulveriser housing. And, although I was so thrilled by the final effect of the machine's work that I tended to ignore it, May, as an observer, was perceptive enough to realise that they would greatly reduce the life of the components and would have to be removed.

The strips of meadow which have developed from that pioneering pulvo-seeding effort turned out to be everything which had I hoped for and my cows enjoyed it. But, it has taken a whole decade of further research and development to produce a system truly worthy of factory production.

Apart from overcoming the problem of shrieking stones, which made May clap her hands over her ears as soon as I began to work, it has also been necessary to devise a satisfactory way of carrying a bulk of seed and metering it to the sowing head. To eliminate the need to drive twice across the same field, it has also been necessary to learn how to feed bulky manure from a separate trailer into the pulverizer while it is spinning.

Now that these problems have been solved, I can create new meadows as easily as the men from the council re-surface the road outside my gate.

What pleases me most about the system is that it has become the subject of serious University research. Hopefully, the research teams' findings will help to reduce a scandalous waste in this energy-short epoch.

Even before I built the prototype pulvo-seeder, I had begun to use sewage sludge – one of the most ignored and valuable byproducts in Britain.

Purified by the aeration and separation processes at the local sewage works, I could obtain the sludge cheaply if I paid for the cost of transport. As soon as I became aware of its availability, I realised that it could help in the solution of our fertility problem. No matter how many cows I kept, I could never produce enough manure to feed our hungry soil. Yet here, at a give-away price, I could obtain almost unlimited supplies of a material high in organic matter and rich in plant nutrients. I couldn't understand why so many other farmers seemed to ignore it or why the nation allowed so much of it to be polluted and become useless for land improvement by permitting residues of dangerous, heavy metals in the effluent from industrial processes to enter the sewers. That was (and still remains) a profligacy which we, as a country with limited land resources, simply couldn't afford. We were spurning fertility sent to us from abroad.

Instead of returning all this surplus, tropical energy and plant food to the land or recycling the waste from our own temperate crops, we simply pour most of it away in the sea.

Even today, plans are being finalised for the construction of a vast new sewage pipeline to carry more Greater London sewage far out into the sea off the point of Kent. That is a tragedy when a pipe of similar length could convey it into the heart of Britain's East Anglian corn belt, so that it could be used to enrich the land.

When we first tested the prototype pulvo-seeder on that day in 1968, it had been suggested that the local authorities might like to locate processed sewage tanks on the edge of Fordhall land. It was an idea I found exciting. Because, I believed that ultimately I might be allowed to mix that sewage with dung from my own animals and, using the pulvo-seeder, incorporate it with my soil. If sewage disposal was a growing problem for the authorities, their quandary could be my solution. The problem of rapidly increasing the microbe family would be solved almost overnight, and I optimistically imagined a permanent increase in the energy output of my soil.

My knowledge of these massive processes of interaction was as yet very scanty, and learning soil management would be slow indeed with only one chance per year to test it in relation to cropping, using the evolving pulvo-seeder. It was however obvious that the valuable microbes would have to be protected from the sunlight that would destroy them and the only practical material was the trash from each crop; and that must also apply to my permanent pasture which would have to be carefully managed for winter grazing by developing suitable species of grasses for a good foggage.

Barbara, now equipped to study bacteriology, was ready to complement my observations by work in the laboratory. I was becoming impatient, but I knew I was getting ever closer to an understanding of my obsession: fertility.

CHAPTER TWENTY-ONE

Pell Wall

May's discontent was bound to surface eventually. For a woman who had been an intensely active partner in all my activities for twenty eight years, she found decreasing demands upon her energy irksome. By 1970, our business was running so smoothly that it required little more than occasional attention from either of us.

I was fully absorbed in developing my farming system. Revelling in the additional time and capital available, I found nothing to prevent me from experimenting. If, on a whim, I desired to see what effect deliberately including wild herb seeds in cultivated grass and clover seed mixtures would have on the grazing and production of my cows, I had only to try it.

But May, while always encouraging me, was clearly becoming bored by idleness. The competence with which she had imbued all our family was partially responsible. Robert, having graduated from Wallford Agricultural College and Nottingham University had learned to market dairy products in the depot of one of our large London distributors. He was now in charge of the sales of Fordhall products in the remoter South Western region from Worcester down to Torquay.

As production had grown, it became vital that we should produce large supplies of bacterial ferments ourselves. Each of our production batches had to undergo stringent quality tests. Barbara, our eldest daughter, was studying microbiology, and took a great interest in all the activity in the Bacteriological Laboratory. Marianne, the youngest, while understudying Barbara, was busily learning the arts of dairy production. She had already become a valuable trouble shooter. Mary Barnet, assisted by students, continued to provide the increasing quantities of milk which they all worked with.

I saw my role as trying to make the land support more of Mary's cows.

If circumstances had been different, May might still have

had to control production – seeing what quantities of our range of fifty products had been ordered, ensuring their manufacture and dispatch, sending out the invoices and keeping the books. But this job had been usurped and it was May's fault. Because when he first turned up at Fordhall, in response to our call for someone to help with the books, May had spotted potential in Jim Brown which I had failed to notice.

I liked the big boned, round faced, fair haired, jolly boy who was only twenty when we interviewed him. After he left, I said I thought that he would fit in well with the team and that his clerical experience should be adequate. May was much more thoughtful and perceptive. 'He is still young and rather shy. But when he has learned how to manage all those women, he will be capable of running the whole dairy by himself', she finally announced with what turned out to be justifiable conviction.

Books and invoices alone were not sufficient for Jim. That's why he had opted for a job on the farm. The practicalities of dairying had a great appeal for him and it wasn't long before he began to master them and take more and more work off May's hands. Delighted that her intuition had been proved correct, she persuaded me to allow him to attend the management course which further increased his value to us. Ultimately, May found that she could leave him totally in charge of the operation.

Initially, she used some of the spare time which Jim's appointment generated, in trying to foster increased sales. But, apart from occasional lecturing and demonstrating engagements, there was little she could do. By that time, our products had become very well known. In each region, we had distributors with their own sales force and we found it hard enough to match our production to the orders which they booked. The stands in major stores which featured Fordhall products were manned by our own full time professional demonstrators.

One day, when watching the skill with which our favourite London demonstrator (a reformed cat burglar) manipulated the attention of his audience and ultimately sent them home laden down with our products, I realised that we had come a long way since George used to set up his stall in the rural markets. In fact, we had moved too far from those pioneering days for May's extraordinary fund of energy to be usefully employed.

As she realised it, she became rather introverted. Whenever I asked her what she was thinking about, I knew that it was more than the triviality which she offered in reply. I ought to have realised that she was once more incubating one of her grand plans. Because, if I had, I would have been less surprised by her look of embarrassed guilt when she thrust the estate agent's sheet into my hand.

Pell Wall Manor was a spacious, Victorian, neo-Tudor house, with a splendid garden, only a few miles away. It was a property which we had always coveted because we had had discovered that the land on which it stood had been linked with my family in the past. For a period, it had been a school, which Robert had attended.

In the early years of our marriage, when we were still struggling to pay the Fordhall rent, we had often jokingly said, 'That's what we'll buy when we're rich'.

'What do you think?' she asked enthusiastically before I'd read enough of the paper to arrive at the price. The fact that Pell Wall was up for sale seemed to me an irrelevance. She knew we weren't rich. True, we were earning more money than ever before, but we were also spending heavily on equipment and facilities to support the business. We hadn't reached the stage when we could adopt the pretensions of gentry and settle down in a mansion to live in luxury. We were still as interested in package holidays abroad as anybody.

'It's the chance we've been waiting for', she almost shouted impatiently.

Remembering our old vow to buy the place, I merely laughed. But, when I realised that she wasn't even smiling, I knew she was serious.

'But – but, what's wrong with Fordhall?' I asked, beginning to feel a sense of panic. She was clearly exasperated by my lack of comprehension.

'Nothing's wrong with Fordhall, you dim wit.'

'We can't afford Pell Wall as well.'

'Not Pell Wall, you fool. Not Pell Wall. We can't afford to buy another home. But – Fordhall Way – we can afford.'

Suddenly I understood. Years earlier, stimulated by the fine reception of our pure products, we had idly discussed what a nice idea it would be to embody our ideas about a saner life and diet into a very special kind of hotel and restaurant run, we coined, The Fordhall Way. Since it would have needed more

accommodation and a calmer setting than the bustle of a
student-packed Fordhall provided and we had little money at
the time, it was only one of many splendid ideas which had
been allowed to drift away.

But I realised that it was onto the life raft of that idea that
May had clambered during her recent thoughtful moods.
Before I had fully adjusted to seeing Pell Wall in this new
perspective, she was developing her well-rehearsed theme.
'Good heavens, Arthur, you have often said it yourself — too
much money is immoral — we are as comfortable now as ever
we need to be. The children are educated and could look after
themselves tomorrow if we failed. Now's that chance to spend
what little surplus we make in doing what is worthwhile.
What is the point of money if it can't be used to develop
ideas?'

It was an appealing notion. For a moment, I felt myself
expanding into the role of Rockefeller, Gulbenkian or a Car-
negie: a founder of worthy institutions. I must have looked
pleased because just as reality was returning, she plunged
exuberantly on.

'We'll do it as it has never been done before. It will be the
perfect haven. Nothing will be allowed to destroy the calm —
no television, no radio, no personal telephones calls or contact
by messengers with frenzied offices. A complete insulation
from the nervous worries of town life. No motoring, no traffic
jams, no noise — rattling typewriters, ringing bells, chattering
telexes, hooting horns. No exciting diversions at all except
good books, lots of sleep, and long walks in pure air to revive
jaded appetites. No spurious theories either, just wonderful
pure food, as much as they can eat of things which won't harm
them if they over indulge; wholemeal bread freshly baked and
full of fibre, honey, dairy products, fresh fruit and vegetables —
only a little light meat for variety if they insist, poultry and
fish for preference — a few eggs. In a couple of days, they will
be so amazed by the change they won't even notice that they
aren't allowed to smoke or drink alcohol indoors!'

As she declaimed, she became more enthusiastic and began
to emanate the infectious radiance which I always found irresistible. Once she saw I was smiling, she adopted a quieter and
more contrite tone as she put her arm around my waist. 'I
knew you'd agree', she said quietly. 'So I immediately wrote

out a cheque for the deposit to prevent anyone getting in before us.'

I was a bit startled by the admission, but had sufficient faith in her judgement to disguise my initial fears. I knew that it would require more than our reserves just to acquire the property, let alone to convert it into the paradise May envisaged. But, on the other hand, most of my life had been spent trying to accomplish the seemingly impossible, so I began to savour the thought of a new challenge. And, of course, she was right. Money didn't really matter. It was the idea which counted.

With the exchange of contracts for the purchase of Pell Wall Manor, May rediscovered all her past verve and enthusiasm for life. She worked as hard in the preparation for its new role as she had worked on Fordhall in 1946 when we were opening the Country Club.

Night after night, I had to drive over and force her to come home because, stranded at the top of a ladder, she refused to answer the telephone. When I got there, her inevitable 'just wait a few minutes until I finish doing this' frequently meant a wait of over an hour. This gave me plenty of time to witness and appreciate developments as they took place.

I was almost flabbergasted by the disciplined way in which she adhered to her theme of complete calm. Although the house was in fine condition when we took it and required little structural alteration, simply furnishing it was not enough. Absolutely everything had to be extremely comfortable but cool and harmonious. Muted pastel shades and rather simple unfussy cretonnes dominated. She resolutely fought off any suggestion from any of us that she should use any paint or fabric that was remotely strident.

This fine attention to detail and insistence on the non-irritant extended even to such features as towel rails next to wash basins in bedrooms.

'Many of our guests will be old and some of them partially disabled. The last thing we want is them bending their backs as they grope around for towels', she explained if I casually suggested that an ill-placed rail looked all right.

Tired myself and frequently a bit exasperated by such perfectionism, I'd retire to wait in the newly appointed Physiotherapy and Exercise Room. Sitting on a static cycling unit, slowly turning the pedals, I'd gaze about wondering what figures from my past would think about it all. My father, I felt, might have approved; it had a sense of style and that was his strongest instinct. Old Jack, however, would have been totally baffled. Any man who caught pneumonia while cutting bean poles in a blizzard while over eighty could hardly have understood why stagnant townsfolk should have needed to bother with such expensive energy consuming paraphernalia. But May was prouder of that room than any other which she created.

'It will be a marvellous place for Barbara to practise once she has trained and gained some experience in hospitals', she proclaimed. May's sister was a senior physiotherapist and had been helpful in arranging that an eminent consultant physician should visit Fordhall Way once a week to offer advice to anyone who needed it. May's sister too, would visit to carry out any physiotherapy he prescribed.

Now that Marianne was so competent in the Bacteriology Laboratory at Fordhall, Barbara had decided to try to become accepted for a training in Physiotherapy. May clearly hoped that one day she would become a regular member of the staff of Fordhall Way.

By the time the house opened for its first guests that summer, it had been completely transformed. And, as May had predicted, it was an almost instant success. Contacts gained during years of speaking engagements throughout the country soon became regular residential clients of Fordhall Way. Others arranged parties to make a meal there the high point of a day's outing.

Unlike our former Country Club members, both types seemed to appreciate the light but rather authoritarian way in which the house was run. May was determined never to lapse from her founding principles and this purity of purpose was accepted gladly, even by people who, at first, found it restrictive. They soon realised that without it Fordhall Way would have become a country hotel like any other.

Once the house was completed and working to capacity, May set about the garden. It had many fine features, but had suffered from neglect. She aimed to make it sufficiently beautiful that older guests would be happy in obtaining all the exercise they required without stepping beyond its gate.

Although she had help indoors and in the garden, she was so meticulous that she never stopped working physically herself.

Planning and supervising everything, she did most of the outside marketing, compensated for everyone else's minor defici-
encies and when everything necessary had been done to look
after guests indoors, she would carry on with her gardening.
The results were worth it. But, despite help from Barbara and
Marianne when they had time, so much work was exhausting.
The room we arranged for her, so that she wasn't always
obliged to return to Fordhall when working very late or planning an extra early start, wasn't as helpful as we had hoped. It
just meant that she spent even more time looking after and
worrying about improving Fordhall Way. But, whatever anxiety we had about the way in which she over-tired herself was
always diminished by the fact that she was so fulfilled by the
success of her idea and that she was clearly so blissfully happy.

Hurling my narrow bladed ditching spade towards the
ground, as a boy might throw his sheath knife, I was pleased
when, instead of biting deep, it bounced from the hard soil
beneath the turf and toppled over. Prostrate, it looked as
foolish as a dog on its back. Three days before, following a
heavy local thundershower, that patch of land had been very
wet. But now that the·drains were working, its surface had
rapidly dried out and been cooked hard by the August sun.

I had thrown the spade as a gesture of delight. Because when
I reached the series of pipe drain outlets which fed the open
ditch which I called the Grand Canal, water was gushing from
several of them. Set in an impressive wall of concrete, the
protruding pipes resembled some strange version of a multi-
barrelled field mortar. But the jetting water, curving prettily
down to froth the surface of the ditch, softened the original
impression of belligerence. To me, it became the most beautiful fountain in the world. For it looked, at last, as though I
had accomplished something which my recent ancestors had
striven for but failed to achieve. I had finally found a way to
dry out the low meadows in summer.

One of the plumes of water, still stained with the suspended
earth disturbed by my upstream digging, seemed to confirm
that the final wet spot would soon dry out. The moist soil it
carried had probably never been dry for centuries, I speculated
excitedly. But now, in 1975, it seemed as though at last I had
succeeded in turning our swampy bottom meadows into fine
pasture.

Hurrying back to the spot where I had made my final underground drainage connection, I picked up my shirt and began to run uphill towards the house to phone May.

I'd hardly seen her for days as it was the high season for activities at Fordhall Way. I had been digging from first light to last on the long summer evenings, determined to try to complete my five year task. Now I had something very important to tell her.

Slowing down as I approached the buildings, I realised that the effort I had made had taken its toll. My back ached. In fact, there hardly seemed to be a muscle or ligament attached to any part of my frame which was not throbbing. But the pain was strangely comforting – a reminder of the accomplishment. It travelled down tracks as complex as the underground crochet work which had been all absorbing for so long.

From Spring 1946, when Jack and I had realised that our second attempt to drain the meadow had failed, until early 1971, I had never ceased to brood over the problem. Each winter, when the worst areas became saturated, I'd drag out the master drainage plan and try to understand why it hadn't worked. But there seemed no logic about the pattern of failure. In places, the whole strip of turf between the feeder drains remained dry much of the time. There the large reeds had disappeared and the grazing had greatly improved. But that didn't help very much because, tempted by tastier offerings, the cows ignored the swampy areas and spent more time on the dry places. In consequence, they became badly over-grazed and the quality of the turf deteriorated. Between other drains, patches of dry land stood out like the islands of an archipelago from tracts of swamp which varied in size from a dining table to a tennis court. Frequent close inspection revealed no abrupt changes in land surface which could account for the phenomenon.

It seemed obvious that the problem lay underground. But no sufficiently detailed geological survey was available to display the bare anatomy of my land. Clearly, if it was to be dissected, I would have to be the surgeon. Once Fordhall Way was successfully launched, I was free to carry out the investigative probing which ultimately lead to such a major, sub-soil operation.

Despite the analogy, there was nothing very clinical about the proceedings. On that first day of digging, in Spring 1971,

I realised that I was becoming involved in a long, solitary and extremely messy enterprise.

Wet earth must be the densest and heaviest substance known to man. I needed no reminder of the fact when trying to extract my first spadeful from the centre of the small undrained patch I tackled initially. It was only prised loose from the surrounding soil with great difficulty and, once raised, it was so sticky that it seemed reluctant ever to be discarded from the blade of the spade. Grabbing a piece of stick, I broke it while trying to scrape off the clay. I ultimately learned to overcome that irritation by tying a bar of iron onto a piece of binder twine and allowing it to dangle from my waist. I could use this to clean the spade after every clinging spadeful was removed from the trench which I dug from the centre of the patch to the nearest feeder drain.

It was tedious, laborious work made more difficult by the water which quickly filled the holes as I created them. I have never attempted to calculate how many times I thrust the spade into the ground during the ensuing five years. But, I estimate that at least one thrust in every five brought up soil which needed urging from the blade. So progress was very slow.

That's why it took nearly a week to dig the few yards of that first trench which revealed the reason why we had such drainage problems. Just beyond the margin of the marshy area, I discovered that I was working in almost pure clay which reached the ground surface. It turned out to be the rim of an underground clay basin which was holding back the water. Once I had cut a deep trench through it, water began to flow out of the basin and into the feeder drain even before I had installed the clay pipes. My feeling of triumph, when I announced this discovery to May, was short lived.

Within a few days, an area of the wet patch had dried out well, and having installed the pipes, I optimistically refilled the trench. However, my daily visits to the site became increasingly disappointing. One area remained wet.

Believing that in replacing the soil in the trench I may have disrupted the system, I dug it all out again. But when I reached the pipes, everything seemed perfect. Without bothering to replace the soil, I dug outwards from the centre of the basin to the centre of the patch which remained wet. This brought a troubling revelation. For I soonfound myself digging through yet another thick clay basin wall. Once the breach had been made, water began to drain out of the remaining wet patch as well. To ensure that it continued to flow, I laid clay pipes in that trench and joined them with those in the first.

It took a month of observation before I could be sure that the whole patch had drained and I dared to replace all the soil. My pride when that tiny job was completed was indescribable. It only began to wane when I carefully marked my two new drainage lines on the master plan. When held at arms length, the two insigificant ball-point pen marks could barely be seen. Surveying the whole plan of the meadows and mentally shading in the wet areas, I realised that I had accomplished nothing.

For, if each damp area comprised not one, but several, clay basins, I was facing years of agonising work. And that is just what it turned out to be. In the worst areas, I even found that I was trying to drain basins within basins within basins. So that it was necessary to cut through several clay rims before achieving very much at all.

It was thus that I slowly became aware that I was repairing the disruption caused by the meandering of the river across our valley bottom over thousands of years. The basins had been formed from the finest silt deposited and built up by its turbulent currents before melting snows or violent storms had provided such a thrust of water that it had burst its banks and changed its course, leaving the former river bottom stranded.

My task was to repair the damage caused by all that haphazard deposition. I suppose that once I realised the immensity of the problem, I only found the courage to solve it because I was aware of the obvious improvements in each tiny area when I had made the water flow.

There is no doubt that the sight of withering reeds and the first flush of new grasses rising to replace them, stimulated me to even greater exertions and working on the drains became obsessive. At times it was obvious that even May began to find my preoccupation an embarrassment. Frequently, after a minor success, I'd drive over to Fordhall Way to have supper and tell her about it.

Given the least encouragement, I'd even bore her most faithful clients with details of my mole-like underground grovelling. Most of them showed charitable indulgence. A few became as intrigued as I was and frequently walked down to the meadow to inspect progress. But other, more urban souls, found it too confusing to follow. Instead of sharing the joy of my achievements their eyes either began to glaze or they would glance curiously at May after noticing the black stains of peat beneath my finger nails or the streaks of dried mud, which I had overlooked, in my hair.

A life at Fordhall had made me intimately familiar with its landscape. But it was the constant re-examination of the large scale ordnance survey maps and the drainage plans which heightened my appreciation of its topographical excitement and the surprising variation in its vegetation.

Although many of the finest trees in Long Covert and Castle Wood had been sinfully pillaged by a thoughtless wartime administration, the scars of their vandalism were healing. In the twenty five years of regrowth, some fine sycamores, beeches and chestnuts had developed.

Since I was only needed for major business decisions, I could work year round on drainage. All areas of the meadows needed attention, so I used virtually all tracks to them and became even more infatuated with the land I loved in all seasons.

Sometimes, when obliged to be away from my digging and wandering about our fields and woods for several days, I'd become desperately homesick for them. With friends in London I found it hard to describe the joy which I missed so much. How could anyone in Chelsea fully understand my guilt when I realised that my drainage operations were reducing the habitat for the formidable but beautiful reeds? If I admitted that, in compensation, I bought narcissus bulbs and wild flower seeds and planted or sowed them in other less disturbed corners, they would probably considered me mad.

Even May's guests, who were disposed to sympathy, were clearly bewildered by my enthusiasm until I'd had a chance to show them round. Then, having walked the woodland paths along the bank of the river and caught my enthusiasm for the wild life there and on the pond, they would begin to share my pleasure.

In five years of lonely digging, there was plenty of time for contemplation. Remembering visitors' delighted reactions, I mentally planned walks over Fordhall which would reveal all its most cherished features. Sometimes I'd complete whole stretches of trench working like an automaton, unaware of my effort while I picked my way along a particular route in my mind. Often, I'd discover that I had stopped work completely, simply puzzled by the problem of suggesting to an aging hypothetical visitor how he could negotiate an awkward ditch.

'Of course', I'd say aloud 'it needs a little bridge'.

And then, staring across the meadow to the tricky place, I'd imagine it erected.

In the first years of digging, these ideas were infrequent and I accepted them merely as a random distraction from my task. But gradually they became more dominant because I realised that they were in harmony with other notions which both May and I had been developing.

The success of Fordhall Way had made us aware that we were filling a genuine need. Townspeople really wanted what we had to offer. More importantly, we realised that we enjoyed providing them with an opportunity to live simply and calmly in a rural situation, nourished by food we believed to be the most wholesome available. Judged against pure commercial criteria, Fordhall Way yielded a poor return on our investment in cash and effort. But, it provided a wonderful sense of fulfilment. As an enterprise, we were happy with it because it seemed to suit us so well.

Whether we liked it or not, the merchanting side of our business kept demanding time we were increasingly reluctant to give. So we began to look for ways of changing direction to centre our activities more on Fordhall where they are firmly based today.

It was while draining the meadows that the idea of inviting townspeople to ramble over Fordhall along a nature trail fully germinated. If I couldn't convey to them my reasons for loving the place, it seemed logical to let them flirt with it a little themselves.

In short moments, pausing to rest between bouts of digging, I began to make small plans and sketches of the tracks I would create. It revived all my intense youthful interest in wildlife. I'd provide them with hours of enchantment. Catalogues, maps and charts and information boards would locate for them the rarest wild flowers and birds. Initially dubious about the wisdom of this idea, I decided that people put on their trust frequently behaved their best. I'd tell them too where to lurk to spot the fattest trout or watch the herons fishing.

In the woods, everyone would be taught to be his own Romany. The way in which beech mast, chestnuts and acorns were nibbled and jettisoned betrayed the activities of mice, voles, squirrels and hedgehogs in a clear language which I would teach them. Those who wished could stay late in a hide which I'd build to observe the badger sets on Castle Hill. Perhaps while waiting for the shuffling, mid-summer night's ballet, they might gingerly chew exotic forest fungi which I would help them to identify. Depending upon the season, they'd be able to return home with full baskets of brambles, sloes, or tiny crab apples and wild cherries for jam. There were more at Fordhall than anyone could ever eat and I'd rather they took them openly than leave them for more furtive marauders.

While with us, our nature trekkers would also be encouraged to discover something more about the fundamental business of producing food from land. That might, I hoped, make them into broader people with a greater sympathy for rural life and farming problems. By helping to feed and milk the cows or shear the sheep, they might, I believed, gain insights into the discipline which looking after animals imposes. It could prompt deeper understanding of farmers' disappointments when, after all their efforts, disease or weather robs them of their crops and stock or collapsing markets minimise their profits. At least, I hoped, they would feel that a farmer's resentment was justified when townsfolk complained about paying 60p per pound for butter — less than half the price of a seat in many of the City cinemas which they frequented. I planned that we'd say little about that — just hope that the total Fordhall experience made them more conscious.

May was as anxious as I was to see the nature trail established. But I had resisted the tempatation to build the bridges and styles or erect the discreet direction signs and notice boards which would be essential, until I had finally completed the draining.

Meticulously, before going to bed every Friday night, on more than two hundred and fifty occasions, I had traced the previous week's ditching activities on the drainage map.

Now that I only had one more tiny entry to make, the whole sheet resembled a web of the finest lace. I'd tie the final knot, I decided, before ringing May.

I laughed as I thought about it, heading towards my study to make that last mark. What a water diviner's nightmare, I thought, his rod would gyrate and dither like an angry snake.

I was too anxious to make the addition to the plan to bother about answering the telephone. But nobody else seemed to hear it and the ring became insistent. Irritably tossing down my biro, I picked up the receiver.

Barbara's voice was wonderfully calm and reassuring. But she was clearly badly affected and struggling to maintain control.

She and Marianne had been helping to look after Fordhall Way. May and the small daughter of one of the guests had been taking some of the staff home.

They both heard the violent crash and the tormented cries. Simultaneously, they raced to different windows to peer towards the gate. Within seconds, they were both at May's side. Her car was upside down and she and the little girl had been hurled clear. Another car was canted crazily against the hedge with its driver slumped over the wheel.

By the time the ambulance arrived, May had recovered from the worst of the shock, was fully conscious and appeared to be miraculously undamaged. Apart from minor bruises, both the little girl and the other driver seemed equally unscathed.

After phoning me, Barbara went in the ambulance to the hospital in Shrewsbury.

On the way, May was talking normally and happy about her escape but mentioned that she had a bit of a pain in her side. Meanwhile I drove quickly in pursuit.

When I reached the waiting room, Barbara explained that the casualty department merely wanted to examine May thoroughly before we went in to see her. So we waited optimistically. The news that the little girl and the other driver would be fine, when they had slept off their shock, provided additional encouragement.

We were even bright enough for Barbara to tease me a little about my habitual dishevelled appearance because I was still unwashed and in my dirty ditching clothes. They weren't really hospital visiting attire she felt, not quite suited to the clinical allure of the building.

On reflection, perhaps that little injection of intimate family bonhomie helped. Because when the clearly troubled nurse arrived with her dreadful announcement, we needed all the mutual support we could summon.

May's bit of pain in the side had been a broken rib puncturing a vital organ and nothing that the doctors had been able to do could prevent her from dying.

It was all such a sudden reversal of fate and so completely obliterating that we returned home quite numbed.

With the reassuring competence which they have inherited from their mother, the girls dried their tears and forbade me to worry about Fordhall Way. They would attend to everything there they insisted when I dropped them back there late that night.

Before making the painful duty calls, I picked up the ball-point pen, leaned over the drainage plan and angrily scratched in the last short line. The gesture made me feel frustrated and deprived. What dreadful luck, I felt, that May, who had been aware of every major change at Fordhall, hadn't been beside me at what would have been such a significant and rewarding moment.

Later, when staring out from the window of this master bedroom into the musky night, I cried silently. I knew that I was going to have to face loneliness. I thought of May and the family that she had given Fordhall, and so of the past generations of my own family, who lived on in our river valley, in our slopes and woods, and in this lovely old farmhouse. Perhaps they too had stood in thought at this window, faced by problems, sadness or joy. They had not known what lay ahead; and now I must lead Fordhall into the future, in a world where man is gradually destroying nature's natural balance and variety to satisfy his own greed.

I pray God teaches us to find true harmony with nature, and that all of us, white, black and yellow, can help rebuild the rich fertility of the Earth, and together enjoy the life that it offers us all.

EPILOGUE

In the days, and especially the nights which followed, I began to understand how Mother must have felt when Father died all those years ago. The tortured, anxious expression I had caught on her face was now my own. I felt I had been selfish and that I had failed to show May how much I loved her.

May and I had pushed ourselves to the limit to make something of our lives and of Fordhall, which really amounted to the same thing. We had been almost too busy. Just when we had both virtually achieved what we had set out to do, she was gone and Fordhall seemed empty.

But of course the days went on passing and I began to adjust my continuing love for May to a more spiritual level. I had tried to prepare myself for the ordeal of the funeral, but when the tears came, as I stood there with Barbara, Marianne and Robert, listening to the inspired words of the vicar, they were in a way tears of joy. For May had it seemed, been an inspiration not only to all who had come into contact with Fordhall or Fordhall Way, but to absolutely everyone whose life she had touched.

On the way back to Fordhall I made it very clear to the three children that they were to continue the lives and careers exactly as planned; only in that way could they express to the world all that Fordhall had tried to teach them. I was surprised that these words flowed so freely from me; May's influence was certainly still there.

After a short break in the Dovedale Valley with Barbara and Marianne, which taught us that things would never be the same again, we returned to Fordhall and some very important decisions. Now, more than ever, I felt the urge to bring my farming into harmony with nature: I didn't want to fight it. To me that meant putting all my energies into finding out how to improve the soil, and so in practical terms it meant further development on my pulvoseeder.

Fordhall had never been a factory; if it were not to become one I knew that without May I would have to close the yoghurt dairy. We had been among the first to pioneer this product; now it was popular everywhere. I felt that phasing out production would in a way be more difficult than getting it going had been, and so it proved.

May's gift of bringing food alive had taught me to love cooking. Though Fordhall Way could not continue with Barbara training in hospital and Marianne back at college, there was a way in which I could carry on the tradition which May had started, and so in a way say thank you to May. So the restaurant was moved back to Fordhall, and I have been cooking meals for apparently satisfied customers, who are also my friends, ever since.

My greatest ambition was to see Fordhall become the research, development and marketing centre for the pulvoseeder. My years of experiment had absolutely convinced me that this was an important invention and one that needed to be brought to working perfection. I took heart from the good heart of my land, now after forty years of struggle restored to health. I had learned how to work with and not against the massive and often unsuspected life in the soil. My vision of how I could convey this to others in a practical way began to grow and my appetite for life to return with this renewed sense of purpose.

So the dairy business was run down – it could not be sold for the Hollins have always been tenant farmers – and the dairy herd changed into a beef suckling herd, with the aid of E.E.C. grants which encouraged farmers to come out of the over-supplied dairy industry.

Finding a manufacturer to take up and develop the pulvoseeder was not an easy task, for of course the machine is not in line with mainstream current agricultural thinking; rather, it is the machine of the future.

So I set out on the road to realising my dreams, to completing my pledge to myself as a boy that I would not only put the heart back into Fordhall but teach others to do the same. I did not realise how hard a road it would be, but now, as I near the end of my sixties, I know we are on the verge of a breakthrough. Recent trials of the pulvoseeder have attracted great interest from academics and those concerned with farming in the third world. I feel that it has all been worthwhile.

I hope I will be able to continue the story in another book, but for now I wish you goodbye and hope that you have enjoyed the Fordhall story.

Hand to the Plough
Old farm tools and machinery in pictures
DOUGLAS LAWSON
Text by Henry Jackson
Foreword by Bernard Price

A beautifully produced, award-winning collection of 150 black and white photographs tracing the development of farm machinery from the 1880's to the 1940's. It shows clearly the increasing sophistication of agricultural machines, and the growing reliance of farmers on them, as cheap, plentiful labour vanished. The accompanying text by Henry Jackson sets each machine into the context of the farming year.

£6.95 paperback

Ploughing by Steam
JOHN HAINING & COLIN TYLER

This book is a comprehensive account of the use of steam in agriculture; starting at the troublesome birth of steam ploughing machinery, through the heyday of steam from 1862 which saw the production of the 1st commercially successful ploughing engine; to its decline and replacement by petrol and paraffin powered tractors.
The authors use documents and 250 photographs to revive the atmosphere of this age. They describe the various machines and the implements and how they were tested and rated; the men and companies, whose

ideas and actions played a key role in steam powered cultivation; the technical and financial aspects of steam ploughing and miniature models that can still be seen today.

£7.95 paperback

The Additive Checklist

A Shopper's Guide to the additives in food produced by leading manufacturers and supermarkets

STEPHANIE LASHFORD

Food additives and their possible link with allergic reactions and with hyperactivity in children have been much in the news, making shoppers more aware of hidden ingredients in food.

This easy-to-use pocket guide lists over 4,000 foods from major supermarkets and manufacturers, in 22 categories ranging from Baby Products to Ready Prepared Meals, showing if they are or are not
Artificial colour free
Preservative free
Monosodium glutamate free
Totally additive free
so helping shoppers make a more informed choice for themselves.

£1.75 paperback

Overcoming Food Allergies

You don't have to 'live with it'

GWYNNE H. DAVIES

This book explains how to identify and then overcome food allergy. The points covered include testing for allergy, the foods at fault, suggested specific diets and the relationship between food allergy and conditions such as arthritis, migraine, skin problems and asthma.

£3.95 paperback

The Allergy Cookbook

STEPHANIE LASHFORD

A comprehensive wholefood cookery book using 'alternative' ingredients to enable those allergic to *eggs, cow's milk, white flour* or *corn* to enjoy interesting and varied meals. This new, revised edition includes an *additive free* section, more vegetarian recipes and symbols defining each recipe's characteristics, such as whether they are low-fat, high-fibre, or gluten-free. *The Allergy Cookbook* brings a whole new concept to eating and food preparation, providing simple quick recipes for everyday use and exotic recipes for special occasions.

£4.95 paperback

These books can be obtained from your local bookshop or direct from Ashgrove Press, 19 Circus Place, Bath BA1 2PW. If ordering direct from Ashgrove Press, please add 50 pence postage and packing per book. A catalogue featuring these and other books can also be obtained from Ashgrove Press.